18 17

18 17

18 17

18 17

18 17

18 17

18 17

18 17

18 17

18 17

18 17

TEACHING HEALTH IN ELEMENTARY SCHOOLS

HARPER'S SERIES IN SCHOOL AND PUBLIC HEALTH EDUCATION, PHYSICAL EDUCATION, AND RECREATION

Under the Editorship of Delbert Oberteuffer

TEACHING HEALTH IN ELEMENTARY SCHOOLS

MARYHELEN VANNIER, 1915-

Professor and Director, Women's Division
Department of Health and Physical Education
Southern Methodist University

HARPER & ROW, PUBLISHERS
New York and Evanston

TEACHING HEALTH IN ELEMENTARY SCHOOLS

 For information address Harper & Row, Publishers, Incorporated, 49 East 33rd Street, New York 16, N.Y.

A–N

LIBRARY OF CONGRESS CATALOG CARD NUMBER: 63–7292

THIS BOOK IS DEDICATED TO MY SISTERS:

MARGARET CHAMBERS

MILDRED BUSENHART

MAXINE HARDING

IN REMEMBRANCE OF OUR WONDER-FILLED CHILDHOOD
THAT WE SHARED WITH MOTHER AND DAD

CONTENTS

PREFACE

This book contains recommended methods and suggested activities for teaching health to elementary school pupils successfully through many new kinds of enriched educational experiences. It has been written mainly for four groups: (1) the college student who is preparing to be an elementary school teacher; (2) those studying to become health education specialists; (3) the beginning and experienced teacher searching for more productive ways to teach health to children; and (4) administrators and school health service personnel seeking new suggestions for helping teachers and parents so that they, in turn, can assist children to develop better health standards and improved health habits.

The author is aware that there are many ways of teaching any subject area in the school curriculum, and that superior teachers will find their own successful methods by the slow process of carefully blending the ingredients of what is known about learning, the techniques used by former admired instructors, and their own trial-and-error attempts. It is hoped that they can profit from the many suggested activities and teaching methods presented in this book and tailor them to fit their own and their pupils' needs and their unique teaching situation.

Part One contains materials showing the nature, purpose, and scope of the total school health program. Part Two presents many new methods for teaching health to children, guiding factors in curriculum planning, and a wide variety of teaching aids. Sample graded programs containing many suggestions for integrated studies for Grades 1 through 6 are given in Part Three in the areas of Nutrition, Safety Education, Dental Health, Mental Health, Family Life Education, and Body Care, Structure, and Function. Each of these sample units contains materials under the headings of Desirable Outcomes in Terms of Knowledge, Attitudes, and Practice, Suggested Activities, Techniques for Evaluating the Results, Learning Aids (including recommended pamphlets and storybooks for children, health readers, films, and other types of visual aids), and Teaching Aids (basic references, films, and a wide variety of supplementary teaching materials). Part Four contains recommended ways in which school health education programs can be improved. The Appendixes include sources of free and inexpensive teaching aids, health reader series and textbooks for elementary grades, recommended forms for the evaluation of the school health program, sample letters to parents, physical and dental examination record cards, and other types of helpful information.

It is imperative that teachers join with parents to develop healthy, happy, vigorous children with initiative, resourcefulness, imagination, and courage. Like Diogenes, the author contends that the foundation and real wealth of every nation lies in the education of its youth.

It has been said, in truth, that the final appraisal of any life must be based upon what causes have used it, what powers have surged through it, and what ideas have mastered it. May this book help teachers to discover, strengthen, and increase a dedicated desire to lead all children to the discovery of the beauty, joy, and miracle of life.

MARYHELEN VANNIER

Dallas, Texas
July, 1962

ACKNOWLEDGMENTS

The author is indebted to many persons who have made this book possible. Appreciation is due to my family, professional colleagues, and students for their encouragement and assistance during its creation.

Gratitude is expressed to all who gave permission to reproduce photographs, record forms, or other materials which appear in the book, especially to Mrs. Ora Wakefield, Health Coordinator and Director of Safety for the Nashville Public Schools; Blanche Bobbitt, Supervisor of Health Education and Health Services for the Los Angeles Public Schools; Vivian Weedon, Curriculum Consultant for the National Safety Council; Frances Mayes, Health Specialist in the Virginia State Department of Education; Robert Yoho of the Indiana Bureau of Public Health Education; Walter Graves, Assistant Editor of the *Journal of the National Education Association;* George Wheatley, Vice-President of the Metropolitan Life Insurance Company; Ella Wright and Nancy Kane Rosenberg of the AAHPER; Mary Ellis and Helena Hunt of the American Institute of Baking; Mildred Srnensky of the Wheat Flour Institute; and M. M. McDonald and H. D. Carmichael of the Dallas Health and Science Museum.

The author thanks the various publishers of Health Textbook Series who sent sample copies of various health readers along with a Teacher's Edition for each book.

The manuscript was typed by Mrs. Dorothy Jane Good, assisted by Mrs. Wanda Joyner and Bill Starr.

ACKNOWLEDGMENTS

ONE

BACKGROUND

THE EDUCATED PERSON

—UNDERSTANDS THE BASIC FACTS CONCERNING HEALTH AND DISEASE.

—PROTECTS HIS OWN HEALTH AND THAT OF HIS DEPENDENTS.

—WORKS TO IMPROVE THE HEALTH OF THE COMMUNITY.

PURPOSES OF EDUCATION IN AMERICAN DEMOCRACY

1 THE TOTAL SCHOOL HEALTH PROGRAM

Health education is a comparative newcomer to the American school, in spite of the fact that man's chief concern has always been self-preservation. Although the problem of survival pitted our primitive ancestors against ferocious beasts, today man faces his greatest foe among other human beings. He faces a highly competitive society wherein merely staying alive is a major struggle in an age of ever-increasing speed and scientific discoveries capable of mass destruction.

School administrators, teachers, and the general public are giving increasingly more attention to the concept that the "whole child" goes to school and that it is the task of the educator to develop each student to his highest potential physically, emotionally, and socially, as well as intellectually. Increasingly too, the layman and the professionally prepared teacher realize that the main task of education is leading students to a happier, healthier, and more productive life for the present as well as for the future, for boys and girls both during and after the school years.

Before 1900, the first concerns for school health centered around protective programs of controlling communicable diseases, providing medical inspection, classroom ventilation, and suitable room temperatures. Although by 1880 most states had passed laws requiring that schools give lessons stressing the evils of narcotics, tobacco, and alcohol, it was not until after World War I that health instruction gained a secure enough foothold to stay in the rapidly changing school curriculum. In 1918 the *Cardinal Principles of Education* stated that the development and protection of health should be one of the primary objectives of American schools. It was also during this period that school physical education programs developed rapidly, largely because of the alarming statistical findings of the draft which disclosed that far too many young men were unfit physically for military service. Although school health services expanded during this period, there was little cooperative action between teachers and parents, the school, or the community. Health classes became large dumping grounds arranged to meet at any available free period in the pupil's daily class schedule. Frequently unprepared and uninterested teachers were responsible for teaching the class, or else it was conducted by a local physician or nurse who stressed human physiology, anatomy, or the control, symptoms, and prevention of communicable diseases. Physical education and health education often became one in the eyes of school administrators and general public. The physical educator, who was assigned to conduct physical activity classes, coach winning athletic teams, as well as teach health classes, usually neglected the latter.

When draft rejection figures of World War II and the Korean War showed that the physical, mental, and emotional health of young men of military age had not improved over the years, regardless of an exposure to school health education and physical education programs, public criticism of these two fields became extensive. Experts in both areas, however, have convinced most of the general public by now that the vast majority of American schools did not have even minimum program requirements in either area; all too often makeshift programs were directed by teachers unprepared in either field, and physical education programs consisted mainly of athletic programs for the few highly skilled players. Then, too, people are becoming increasingly aware that many of the draft rejections were due to faulty vision, hearing, illiteracy, malnutrition, and other factors more directly connected with the school health service program than with either physical or health education.

Americans are fast awakening to the fact that we are far from being as physically strong or as healthy as we must be to survive as the leading nation in a changing world. Consequently, it is now the educator's task, whether he be the chief school administrator, the classroom or the specialized teacher, to lead the way by providing adequate health education and physical education programs in all schools; he must also convince the people that every student has the right to attend school in a safe, hygienic environment, receive periodic physical check-ups, and partake of educational experiences which will enable him to learn how to live a productive life. Although most parents want the best for their children, they are often confused as to what is the best or how to obtain it. Americans have always bought what they wanted, and supported the causes in which they believed. To convince them now of the need for a superior total school health program conducted in a safe, hygienic school environment by competent teachers is the duty of every educator, regardless of whether he is teaching children or older students. The development of a "sound mind in a sound body" in every student is a major goal of American education.

THE MEANING OF HEALTH

Children with health problems are found in every classroom of every school in every state of the U.S.A. Yet medical authorities agree that no one, regardless of age, can live efficiently unless he functions well in a total sense and is able to meet successfully the many problems which arise throughout his daily life.

Good health means far more than the absence of disease or infirmity, but rather is a state of complete physical, mental, and social well-being.[1] Possessing such total fitness does, indeed, enable one to "live most and serve best,"[2] for the healthy individual can do his work daily without undue fatigue, face his daily problems, be happy, have an energy reserve for emergency situations, and be concerned about maintaining his own health as well as improving that of

[1] *Handbook of Basic Documents,* 5th ed., Palais Des Nations, Geneva. World Health Organization, 1952, p. 3.

[2] Jesse F. Williams and Floyd G. Wetherill, *Personal and Community Hygiene Applied,* Philadelphia, W. B. Saunders, 1950, p. 13.

others. Such a healthy child or adult radiates and shines; the sickly one droops and is dull. Those with buoyant health work, play, and live with zest. They have a sense of well-being, personal worth, and can adjust to changing life situations.

Good health is far from accidental. It is the result of good heredity, environment, education, and following carefully planned routines. Adequate rest and sleep, a balanced diet, waste elimination, freedom from infection, strain, and worry, coupled with the right amount of exercise, are the ingredients necessary for obtaining and maintaining good health. Parents, however, cannot give their offspring the gift of health, for each child must learn how to use best the responsibilities for his own welfare, and behavior throughout life. A good parent, like a good teacher, becomes progressively unnecessary.

When the child enters the new, exciting world of the school, the administrators, teachers, school doctor, nurse, and other health specialists should become as concerned about his health and well-being as his parents, family doctor, and dentist have been and should continue to be. School and community health agencies must work together in order to obtain the following health priorities:[3]

1. Provide significant experiences for learning to live healthfully in the home, school, and community.
2. Develop better screening techniques for detecting children needing medical attention.
3. Develop local resources for diagnosis and treatment.
4. Orient parents and school health personnel in modern concepts of mental health.
5. Reduce the incidence of dental caries.
6. Detect, diagnose, and treat children with impaired hearing, defective vision, and epilepsy.
7. Recognize special health problems in the community.
8. Provide and maintain adequate facilities to assure safe drinking water in schools.
9. Provide and maintain sufficient, convenient, sanitary toilet facilities in schools.
10. Provide nutritionally adequate and palatable school lunches which meet recommended sanitary standards.

[3] *Better Health for School Age Children,* Federal Security Agency, Washington, D.C., 1951, p. 3.

11. Eliminate environmental hazards and observe safety precautions to prevent accidents.
12. Provide suitable education for children with physical handicaps.

THE SCOPE OF THE HEALTH PROGRAM

The total school health program consists of three interdependent facets: (1) healthful school environment, (2) health and safety instruction, and (3) health services. It should be a program of instruction, guidance, and services which protect and improve the health of each individual. Such a total program must be informative, shape positive health values, and develop meaningful health habits. Its results should produce totally functioning pupils who have developed fitness for living and have an eagerness to serve others.

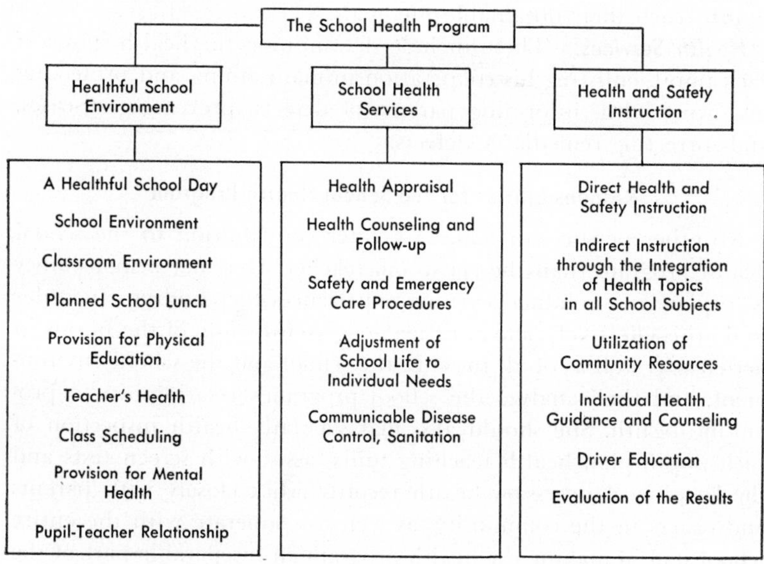

FIGURE 1. The Total School Health Program.

Healthful School Environment. This includes the provision of a wholesome, safe environment, a healthful school day, sound teacher-pupil relationships, and all other environmental factors necessary for the best development for pupils and school personnel.

Health Instruction. This involves the teaching of health facts, values, and concepts in such meaningful ways that individual and community health patterns improve. The product of such instruction should be the desire of each pupil to use the basic health information he has acquired by applying what he knows to what he does in his daily life. Such instruction implies that merely memorizing facts is of little value unless the child applies or uses what he has learned about health. Although one may know the many facts concerning tooth decay and oral hygiene, unless he brushes and cares for his teeth, the information he can repeat to the teacher when questioned is of little value. Education is for use. Its goal is self-directed behavior which will develop and improve both the individual and the community. Health education is a means of helping pupils reach their obtainable life goals.

Health Services. These include determining the health status of each pupil, enlisting his cooperation in maintaining and protecting his own health, informing parents of defects, preventing diseases, and correcting remediable defects.

Responsibilities for the School Health Program

No other person can make a greater contribution to the school health program than the classroom teacher. Her first responsibility is to plan and conduct learning experiences for children. In order to do this effectively, she must make a careful study of the pupils in her class as well as of all those in the school and the school environment, and then analyze the school program's relationship to promoting health. She should also make a daily health inspection of each pupil, plan health teaching units, assist with screen tests and the keeping of necessary health records, work closely with parents and others in the community, as well as cooperate with the entire school staff in making the health program an inseparable part of the total educational program. Although these well-prepared educators should be primarily responsible for instruction in health, the entire program should be the responsibility of the school board, school administrator, health protection staff, and teachers. The specific obligations of each toward this program are listed below.

The School Board

1. Provide in the school budget adequate funds for qualified health personnel, instructional materials, and the proper maintenance of buildings and grounds.
2. See that the parents and other members of the community are well informed about the total school health program.
3. See that all laws pertaining to health are enforced.

The School Administrator

1. Direct and coordinate all phases of the school health program.
2. Secure the services of school-employed medical personnel.
3. Provide and maintain a safe and healthful school environment.
4. Provide for an in-service health training program of all school personnel.
5. Appraise continuously the total school health program in terms of improved health, improved group and individual health behavior, and adequacy of the school plant.
6. Establish good home and community relationships by assisting the medical and nursing staff in interpreting the health needs of children, acquainting the home and community with the school health program, and organizing programs for parent participation and education in that program.
7. Enforce existing laws regarding school health, and work toward obtaining new and better ones.
8. Acquaint school personnel with community facilities and resources obtainable for meeting the health needs of children.
9. Provide for an adequate program of health examinations and remediable follow-up.
10. Provide changes or adaptations in the school program for those with special needs.
11. Ensure an adequate health-record-keeping system.
12. Develop a form or check-list survey which will aid in evaluating the total school health program, the adequacy of the school plant, the efficiency of the teachers, and custodial services.
13. Develop an organized plan for emergencies such as fire, tornadoes, and atomic nuclear fallout.
14. Assign only entrusted and qualified teachers to teach health.
15. Enforce a well-organized program of school safety and emergency care.

The School Physician

1. Conduct health examinations for all school children, keep adequate records, establish remedial programs, and cooperate in getting medical and dental care for children needing them.
2. Conduct an in-service educational program for teachers in the techniques of daily health observation, detecting negative behavior symp-

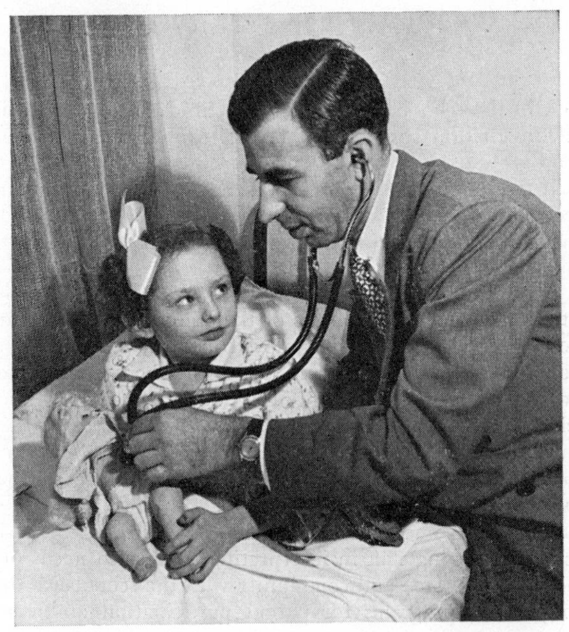

Doctors who are interested in children make experiences such as this one more meaningful. (Courtesy N.E.A.)

toms, tests and measurements of growth and development, and keeping needed records.
3. Develop policies and procedures for the control of communicable diseases and accidents.
4. Assist the school administrator and public health officials in evaluating the school plant, and give skilled leadership in helping to provide a safe and hygienic school environment.
5. Work with parents in helping them maintain, protect, and build good health in their children.
6. Assist the administrator and teachers in evaluating the total school health program.

THE SCHOOL NURSE

1. Assist in conducting health examinations.
2. Administer or train teachers to give needed screen tests for vision, hearing, and in other areas.
3. Work with the physician, school personnel, parents, and others in the community to carry through with adequate follow-up measures recommended as the result of health examinations.

4. Keep adequate cumulative health records.
5. Assist in the special control of communicable disease.
6. Assist in providing a safe, healthful school environment.
7. Contribute to the health education program in as many ways as possible.
8. Help coordinate community and school health efforts and resources.

The Teacher[4]

1. Give health instruction through carefully planned class sessions and at teachable moments throughout each school day.
2. Assist the nurse by giving screen tests, keeping records, and helping to provide a safe, healthful environment.
3. Guide and counsel students in personal health matters.
4. Work as a vital team member with all school-employed personnel in developing fully the three interdependent facets of the total school program.
5. Prepare children for physical and dental examinations and screen tests for vision, hearing, and posture.
6. Observe the health practices of children.
7. Weigh and measure each child at least twice yearly.
8. Isolate those coming down with communicable diseases.
9. Integrate and correlate health education with as many other subjects as possible.
10. Assist in evaluating the total school health program.

The Physical Educator

1. Assist in developing a good total school health program and a school health council.
2. Assist in giving screen tests for vision, hearing, posture, and in physical examinations.
3. Assist in weighing and measuring pupils periodically and in keeping health records.
4. Conduct classes in first aid and in other areas of health instruction.
5. Assist in emergency care, giving first aid and accident prevention programs.
6. Conduct remedial and adapted physical education programs for those with handicaps.

The Custodian

1. Maintain a clean, sanitary, and safe school building.
2. Regulate the heating, lighting, and ventilation of the school plant according to school and public health standards.

[4] See the pamphlet report giving recommendations from five national conferences on professional preparation, *Preparing the Health Teacher,* AAHPER-NEA, Washington, D.C., 1961.

3. Assist all school personnel in matters pertaining to health and especially in the teaching to children, through example, the importance of good health and safety practices in daily life.

THE NUTRITIONIST

1. Conduct and supervise the lunch and cafeteria services.
2. Participate in an in-service training program for teachers in nutrition.

THE DENTIST

1. Make the dental program an educational one.
2. Provide services aimed primarily at teaching children intelligent self-direction, and provide dental treatment.

THE SCHOOL HEALTH COORDINATOR

1. Help teachers make wise selection of educational materials supplementary to the textbook and course of study.
2. Work toward planning for greater emphasis of specific health education areas at specific grade levels in order to avoid duplication.
3. Assist in developing close working relationships between teachers and personnel working in the area of school health service, and closer school-home and school-community relationships.
4. Conduct in-service health education programs for all who are concerned with pupils at the school.

Relationship to Physical Education

Although the goal of physical education, like that of all other subjects in the school curriculum, is to develop students physically, socially, mentally, and morally so that they will become well-rounded, healthy, responsible citizens in our democracy, nevertheless each subject area in the curriculum makes a unique contribution to the attainment of this goal. The major contribution of physical education is in the area of physical development. Commonly accepted objectives of the physical education program are to develop (1) organic vitality and physical fitness, (2) skills, (3) increased knowledge concerning sports, games, and one's self, (4) greater appreciation of one's body, the value of physical activity, and of other people, and (5) more productive use of leisure time through taking part in recreational activities.

On the other hand, the objectives of the school health program are to (1) teach basic facts concerning health, (2) shape positive attitudes toward health, (3) develop beneficial habits for the maintenance, protection and improvement of one's own health, and (4) learn skills for developing and protecting health throughout life.

In every physical education program, numerous opportunities for teaching health education arise. The very nature of this activity requires adequate safeguards for the well-being of those taking part in the program. Frequently the physical educator is the most popular and respected teacher in the entire school and has a close relationship with the students. It is imperative that this adult be worthy of emulation, for children tend to imitate those they admire. The example that this leader sets provides exceptional opportunities to make a major contribution to the health of all participants in the program, but as Oberteuffer points out,

> Whether the physical education program is an asset or liability depends upon its administration. The adult in charge, the principal, superintendent, physical education teacher, coach, medical advisor—these are the ones in the key position who can make physical education, including athletics, a fine experience for growth and development or an experience of human disaster.[5]

Relationship to General Education

Every member of the school staff must understand and contribute to the health program. Likewise, healthful practices should be woven into every part of the child's life. The school should provide a learning atmosphere that is relaxed, cheerful, and attractive, wherein students are both "seen and heard." Any program of education, including health, conducted in such an environment, is unsatisfactory and meager if it revolves around facts alone, or merely reading a textbook aloud in class. Education can and should be an exciting experience.

The school has three major responsibilities in the area of health. These are to (1) develop and improve the health status of each student, (2) provide a safe, hygienic, and stimulating environment wherein learning experiences can take place, and (3) aid in correcting remediable defects by encouraging parents of children with defects to secure medical services, and provide a special, modified educational program for children who need it.

[5] Delbert Oberteuffer, *School Health Education,* 3rd ed., New York, Harper, 1960, p. 492.

Although each school should develop its own objectives for its health program, the following basic beliefs may serve as a guide for the formulation of these objectives:

The total program should strive to:

1. Inspire the child to be well and happy.
2. Convey to the child a public and personal health ideal image, designed to ensure for him the continuation throughout life of wholesome and effective living, physical, mental, and social.
3. Educate the child, according to a definite plan, in the development of those living habits which will promote and protect his present and future health.
4. Impart health knowledge so that he will make intelligent health decisions and choices.
5. Develop in each pupil a scientific attitude toward health matters, and an understanding of the scientific approach to health problems. Help each child to assume responsibility to use scientific knowledge for his own benefit and that of others.
6. Maintain adequate sanitation in the school, the home, and the community.
7. Protect all children from communicable and preventable diseases and avoidable physical defects by providing effective public health control measures, both individual and social, throughout the school and the community.
8. Bring each child up to his own optimal level of health and create in each one a desire to maintain that level throughout life.
9. Extend the school health program into the home by obtaining family and community support for the program.
10. Discover early any physical defects the child may have, secure their correction to the extent that they are remediable, and assist the child to adapt to any handicap.
11. Provide healthful school living for all children and adults.
12. Relate the school health program to the health program in the community by dealing with real, current, and practical problems.
13. Organize effectively not only the program of direct health instruction but the equally important indirect learning experiences of the child in the field of health.[6]

Close cooperation of the home and community is essential before any effective school health program can be developed.[7] Likewise, the

[6] *Health Education and the School Health Program,* Illinois Joint Committee on School Health, Springfield, Ill. Illinois Department of Public Health.

[7] For suggested techniques, see *Your Child's Health, Information for Parents,* Los Angeles City Schools, no. 352, 1957.

health education program must be a primary responsibility of all teachers and staff members. All must work as members of a united team, bent upon helping each child assume greater and more intelligent responsibility for the development and maintenance of his own health in a safe and healthful environment.

THE NEED FOR INCREASED HEALTH EDUCATION IN ELEMENTARY SCHOOLS

Although medical authorities consider American children to be among the healthiest in the world, there is abundant evidence that far too many of them live at a sub-minimum health level and function poorly as human beings. Many are not benefiting from disease-prevention measures, now available at low cost or provided free of charge. It has been estimated that only around 20 percent of all children have received the Salk anti-polio vaccine. An alarming number of children and older students tend to be physically soft because of sedentary living, riding instead of walking to school, and sitting indoors watching television instead of playing rugged games outdoors. Likewise, the American adult tends to be discontented, an avid pill-gulper, a victim of stress, and a frenzied consumer of quick-cure remedies advertised through the media of second-rate television, radio programs, and inferior reading materials. If it is true that the "wealth of any nation is found largely in the health of its citizenry," and that "as a twig is bent, so grows the tree," it is equally true that the education of all children in areas of healthful, wholesome living is of paramount importance. The very foundation and the continuation of our way of life depends largely upon the education of our children.

The following health problems are prevalent in our American elementary schools at the present time:

Physical Defects. These include postural defects, the orthopedically crippled (post-polio, cerebral palsied, post-encephalitic, afflicted with muscular dystrophy or convulsive seizures), the blind, the partially blind, the deaf, the hard of hearing, those with speech deviations (articulation, voice, language, rhythm), those with respiratory diseases, cardiac patients, those that lack good nutrition status, those with rheumatic fever, and those with arrested tuberculosis. Administrators estimate that among the approximate thirty-three million school-age children from 5 to 19 in this country, the following percentages are handicapped:

Blind or partially sighted	2%
Deaf or hard of hearing	1.5%
Crippling defects	1.5%
Delicate and frail	1.0% +
Speech defects	1 to 2%
Epileptic	2%
Mentally retarded	2%
Gifted	2%
Behavior problems	2 to 3%.[8]

It has also been found that for every school system of three thousand students, there will be two deaf children, ten with impaired hearing, two partially-sighted, ten crippled, twenty with heart impairments, and three epileptics.[9] As has been found by Stone and Deyton, out of thirty million school children between the ages of 5 and 17, the following numbers had defects:

Cerebral palsy	106,560
Post-poliomyelitis	62,160
Other orthopedic handicaps	168,720
Epilepsy	180,000
Rheumatic heart disease	300,000
Lowered vitality and delicate health	450,000
Blind and partial sight	60,000
Deafness and impaired hearing	450,000
Speech, including cleft palate	1,500,000
Behavior problems	unclassified number.[10]

Although the above figures are staggering, they are hard to grasp fully. A teacher has only to have had one epileptic or crippled child in a class with normal children to realize the many health and other problems centered around this one individual, problems which also involve the class of which he is a member.

[8] Ethel Martens, *Planning Schools for Tomorrow: Needs of Exceptional Children,* Washington, D.C., Government Printing Office, no. 24, 1944.

[9] Oberteuffer, *op. cit.,* p. 5.

[10] Eleanor Stone and John Deyton, *Corrective Therapy for the Handicapped Child,* Englewood Cliffs, N.J., Prentice-Hall, 1951, p. 29.

Accidents. The chief cause of death among school children is accidents—most of them preventable. Although it would be foolish to restrict the activities of children because they might get hurt, or to remove all hazardous equipment so that they would never learn how to cope with danger or be afraid to take chances (thus developing dangerous behavior patterns which ultimately might lead to disaster), the school does have a great responsibility to teach children to take chances wisely, and to teach them to live and play safely in a hazardous environment. Safety appeals to the aged, danger attracts youth. This does not imply that just growing old (if one survives) will automatically cause a person to be conscious of safety, or that if one believes that children should learn how to take chances he should shove them into the path of fast-approaching cars to give them experience in surviving dangerous situations; it does mean, however, that the school must play a greater role in teaching children both the necessity and "know how" for avoiding unnecessary and foolish risks. Studies show that,

> . . . about 43% of all school age accidental deaths occur either at school or going and coming to school. Of these accidents 20% happen in the school building, 17% on the school grounds, and about 6% going to and from school. In school buildings, the gymnasium is the location of the most frequent accidents, making up about 1/3 of the fatal accidents within the building. Another 2% of the fatal indoor accidents occur in halls and stairs. Shops and laboratories account for about 18% and other classrooms add another 14%. On the school grounds, 41% of fatal accidents occur in unorganized activities, 20% in football, 12% in baseball, 9% in playground apparatus and 18% in other organized activities. The 6% of school age fatal accidents which occur while the pupil is going to and from school are mostly pedestrian-motor vehicle and bicycle-motor vehicle accidents.[11]

Considering that ten thousand school children lose their lives yearly through careless, preventable acts, these percentages are staggering! Carelessness is a major factor in children's deaths caused while riding bicycles, dashing between parked cars, or ignoring traffic signals. In addition, every 24 hours more than 150 American children die from swallowing chemicals, poisons, or small objects—thus, like the cat, they become victims of their own curiosity.

Deviations from Normal Growth. Although every child has his

[11] C. L. Anderson, *School Health Practice,* St. Louis, Mosby, 1960, p. 228.

own growth pattern, teachers can quickly spot the child who is markedly taller or shorter, thinner or fatter than others. Normal growth deviates (and there are many of them in our public schools) often are victims of an uncontrollable appetite, malnutrition, malfunctioning glands, or deep-seated emotional problems. Many of these defects can best be remedied or controlled by both early discovery and treatment, for most of these problems are both physiological and psychological. Contrary to the belief of many parents that their child will "outgrow his trouble," most children usually do not and greatly need expert medical help. The teachers and school personnel should do their utmost to convince parents of the necessity of obtaining medical assistance as quickly as possible.

Cardiovascular Disorders. It has been claimed that every year more than half the teachers of the nation have at least one child with a serious heart disorder in their classrooms. Rheumatic fever and congenital heart defects account for the major proportion of this illness. Many cardiac cases can participate in regular school activities, but some should not. Although this is a decision for the medical specialist to make, it is imperative that the child live as normal a life as possible, that he learn to capitalize upon his capabilities and work around his limitations. Rheumatic fever is far more serious and common among school children than was formerly believed. Since heart disease is the chief cause of death in America, it is evidently true that rheumatic fever does, indeed, "lick the joints and bite the heart of children."

Dental Disorders. Dental disorders constitute the major health problem among public school pupils, for 92 percent of all school children suffer from dental disease. According to the American Dental Association, the first grader usually has three or more cavities, and by the time this child has reached the age of 16 he will have seven decayed, missing, or filled teeth involving 14 tooth surfaces. Thousands of children have serious dental difficulties ranging all the way from carious or missing teeth, abscessed gums, pyorrhea, and gingivitis, to malocclusion with a marked overbite or underbite. A conscientious teacher will do her utmost to help the child receive the dental care he must have, and to teach him ways to protect both his teeth and general health throughout life.

Neurological Disorders. Epilepsy and chorea (St. Vitus's dance), with the former being more common, are serious neurological disorders with which the teacher usually will come into contact sometime during her professional career. It is estimated that a quarter to a half a million Americans are victims of these maladies, and that 80 percent of all those afflicted are below 20 years of age. Epilepsy occurs as frequently as diabetes and tuberculosis, and four times more often than infantile paralysis. Consequently, since this condition is more common than was once supposed, and since epileptic pupils who have mild attacks are often placed in school with normal children, teachers must know what to do should an attack occur in the classroom. Likewise, they should be aware that epileptics are greatly in need of special attention, for the majority of them are fearful, ashamed, shy, and awkward, socially as well as physically. Those who are wisely engaged in satisfying activities are less apt to have seizures than those who are kept idle and fearfully and passively anticipate them. Rapid, successful advances are being made in the treatment for epileptics. These include anticonvulsive medication, diet, education, psychotherapy, improved environmental conditions, and surgery. Here again, the classroom teacher is morally and professionally obligated to see that the parents of the afflicted youngster in her group are somehow made aware of these newly opened avenues of hope for their child, as well as to see that the pupil himself is working and playing in an educational environment which will prove most beneficial both for himself and the class.

Visual and Auditory Handicaps. One out of every ten Americans has some kind of a hearing impairment or is deaf. Although most youngsters who have a hearing loss acquire it gradually, this difficulty can be detected early and treated before the afflicted child develops feelings of inferiority and becomes shy and withdrawn or defiant and rebellious. Almost every school teacher has children in her classes who turn their heads to one side, cup the ear, wear worried, puzzled expressions, are inattentive, fail or do poorly with their school work, have faulty posture with the head and torso held forward, show poor word pronunciation, and have faulty speech habits. The majority of these children have hearing difficulties.

Partially sighted pupils exist in greater numbers than most adults realize, for almost every school has students whose vision is faulty. Since 85 percent of our learning comes through the eyes, the fact that one out of every four school children has a visual defect presents a major problem teachers must both recognize and help solve. Those with partial sight can be enrolled in most public schools if their vision is between 20/70 or 20/200 or if there is no prognosis of vision deterioration, if they have an intelligence quotient of 70 or more, can take care of their own toilet needs, can communicate, have no behavior disorders, can hear, and are ambulatory. Simple tests can quickly detect those children who have more serious vision defects, whereas teacher observation can easily spot those whose poor posture, squinting, inattention, and poor school progress may be due to their inability to see.

Mental Health Deviations. The rapid increase in mental illness is the most serious health problem in this country today. Over 52 percent of those persons ill enough to be hospitalized are mentally and emotionally sick. It is estimated that one out of every ten Americans is emotionally unbalanced enough to need psychiatric care. One does not suddenly go off the deep end and become a raving maniac, or completely withdraw from reality; the mentally ill adult usually showed abnormal behavior as a child. His case history is filled with experiences (terrifying at least to himself) which happened throughout life, but often most particularly during his early years at home and in elementary school. According to psychiatrists, those who show early, markedly significant behavior patterns of withdrawal (moving away from people), or aggressiveness (moving toward people) can and must be singled out and helped during their formative years. Certainly the building of bigger and better mental institutions is not the preventive answer to the increase in the mental-illness problem any more than is the construction of more and more hospitals for wounded veterans the way to eradicate war. The role the classroom teacher can play in the prevention of disease and human tragedy is tremendous. Every elementary school teacher is already engaged in the field of health education—whether it be half-heartedly because of ignorance and an "I don't care" attitude or actively because of knowledge and a desire to see that all children have a "square deal at school." In every classroom throughout the nation many health problems do exist, regardless of whether we ignore them or want to do something about them. If educators who do care only look around at what is not being done, or that which is being so poorly done in the area of health education, they will agree with that wise old man who once said, "We are reaping pigmy results from our pigmy efforts in a time of giant opportunities."

Never before have there been so many children enrolled in our public schools. Never have the opportunities of the real educator been greater!

SUGGESTED READINGS

Anderson, C. L., *School Health Practice,* St. Louis, Mosby, 1960.

Cousins, George F., "32 Important Health Problems," *Journal of Health, Physical Education and Recreation,* vol. 28, no. 7 (October, 1957).

Goodenough, Florence, *Exceptional Children,* New York, Appleton-Century-Crofts, 1956.

Grout, Ruth, *Health Teaching in Schools,* 3rd ed., Philadelphia, Saunders, 1958.

Haag, Jessie, *School Health Program,* New York, Holt, 1958.

Harnett, Arthur, and John Shaw, *Effective School Health Education,* New York, Appleton-Century-Crofts, 1959.

Health Appraisal of School Children, National Education Association and the American Medical Association, Washington, D.C., 1957.

Health Education, North Carolina Department of Public Instruction, Raleigh, North Carolina Department of Public Instruction, 1953.

Oberteuffer, Delbert, *School Health Education,* 3rd ed., New York, Harper, 1960.

O'Daly, Elizabeth, *Dear Parents,* New York, Oceana, 1953.

Priorities in Health Services for Children of School Age, Children's Bureau, Washington, D.C., Government Printing Office.

Schneider, Robert, *Methods and Materials of Health Education,* Philadelphia, Saunders, 1958.

Turner, Clair, *School Health and Health Education,* 3rd ed., Mosby, 1957.

Wheatley, G. M., and Grace Hallock, *Health Observation of School Children,* 2nd ed., New York, McGraw-Hill, 1956.

Willgoose, Carl, *Health Education in the Elementary School,* Philadelphia, Saunders, 1959.

2 TEACHING THROUGH HEALTH APPRAISAL ACTIVITIES

Each child is as different and unique as each of the five fingers on a person's hand. It is imperative that the teacher recognize these differences, for each pupil will react both to this adult and his peer group according to his own growth patterns, his stage of development, his special needs, interests, and abilities. Fortunately, teachers can glean greatly needed health information about each student from a variety of sources. These include (1) daily observation and evaluation of how each child looks and acts, (2) the pupil's health history, (3) screening tests, (4) medical and dental examinations, and (5) psychological tests.

School health appraisal activities abound in numerous opportunities for real health education, such as when the child asks why he should have his teeth examined by a dentist at school, or how much he should weigh in comparison to what he does weigh or the weight of his classmates. All health appraisal activities should be utilized fully by the examining school doctor, nurse, and the teacher at every opportunity throughout the school year. Since we only learn when we want to, the role of the teacher is to capitalize upon as well as to arouse each pupil's curiosity to find out about himself. Children are eager to find out "why are we doing it this way," and about things done to them. Health appraisal activities offer ripe educational opportunities, which when exploited can yield a rich harvest of learning. During such procedures the child should be seen and heard. The basis for health education course materials can be laid preceding and during these activities. Each testing and measuring experience produces many opportunities for "on-the-spot teaching," which can make a lasting impression on the child, and provide a more valuable educational experience for that pupil than a health lesson given to the whole class.

TEACHER'S OBSERVATIONS

The teacher plays a vital role in the development of a child's physical and emotional health. She must learn how to detect deviations from the normal appearance and behavior in her entire class as well as of each child in that class. Unlike parents, the educator can see the individual qualities of each pupil against the background of those of his many peers of approximately the same age and school grade. The teacher learns from the child himself what to expect from him as an individual, as well as a group member, and often her expectations are more objective than those of the parents. Although the teacher, when a normally bright-eyed youngster comes to school looking droopy and dull, or a usually cooperative pupil suddenly becomes inattentive and defiant, cannot and should not attempt to diagnose what is wrong, it is her obligation to see that this change is called to the attention of the school health authorities. Then too, she often can become aware of a change in general health and inform the school medical personnel or parents of the situation. Likewise, she should see to it that parents realize the seriousness of their child's poor posture, crossed eyes, or protruding teeth, which they may have taken for granted or ignored in the hope that the condition would disappear as the child grew older, for sometimes parents are unaware that these deviations are of real importance and can do serious emotional damage to a youngster. Such defects are largely correctable when the child is still a young, growing, pliable being. As is pointed out in the pamphlet, *What Teachers See:*

> The school physician all too often has time only to see that a child has a physical condition which is interfering with the normal functioning of his

body. The nurse is concerned chiefly with the ways and means of getting the condition corrected. The teacher is more likely to see the child held back from what she knows he can be and do by something which is interfering with his expected progress.

School physicians, nurses, and parents are coming to recognize the important place held by the teacher as an observer who may be depended upon to find children in need of medical or dental care. To make the best use of her strategic position as an observer, the teacher herself should be aware of the service she is peculiarly equipped to give, and she should be taken into the confidence of the physician and nurse as a working partner.[1]

The teacher can learn how to observe the daily health status of each person in the class by first being able to pick out deviations in the appearance of one child and then in each of the groups of children encountered daily. She should practice observation for the specific purpose of detecting departures from good health, realizing that she can act for the school nurse as the mother of the child does for the family physician. It is imperative that she know how the child normally looks, whether he usually has a pallid look, or if he ordinarily comes to school with a ruddy complexion and apparently is a happy, smiling youngster or a withdrawn, timid one. Also, the teacher, if she wishes to be a successful health observer, must want to assume the responsibility for the health of her class group, be able to recognize abnormalities, as well as know what constructive things to do when deviations occur.

The daily health inspection may be done informally by the teacher as she greets each pupil as he enters the room. She should carefully note at this time the condition of the hair and face of each child, whether he seems happy or sad, tired or rested, and whether his eyes are clear and bright instead of red and inflamed. Throughout each day she should frequently observe each child's posture, the contents of his lunch box if he brings one, as well as note whether the pupil usually takes time to eat or whether he bolts his food, whether he is usually a quarrelsome social outcast or a person the other children like and readily accept as a group member.

In a self-contained classroom, the teacher has a golden opportunity to observe children as she directs them in periods of physical

[1] *What Teachers See,* Metropolitan Life Insurance Company, Health Education Department, New York, 1958, p. 2. (Free, available upon request.)

education. Educators discovered long ago that if you want to find out what a child is really like, you should *watch* him play, but if you are concerned as to what he will become, you should *direct* his play. Children are their true selves when they are so engrossed in a game that they forget to be the "goody-goody" their mother and teacher expect them to be. Since what a child does is far more important than what he says, all classroom teachers should observe as well as direct children at play.

The teacher should be aware of the following disorders in various parts of the body, as well as of behavior symptoms and emotional problems, as she observes each child daily in her class:

Eyes

Sties or crusted lids
Inflamed eyes
Crossed eyes
Repeated headaches
Squinting, frowning, or scowling
Protruding eyes
Watery eyes
Rubbing of eyes
Excessive blinking
Twitching of the lids
Holding head to one side

Nose and Throat

Persistent mouth breathing
Frequent sore throat
Recurrent colds
Chronic nasal discharge
Frequent nose bleeding
Nasal speech
Frequent tonsillitis

Teeth and Mouth

State of cleanliness
Gross visible caries
Irregular teeth
Stained teeth
Gum boils
Offensive breath
Mouth habits such as thumb sucking

General Condition and Appearance

Underweight—very thin
Overweight—very obese
Does not appear well
Tires easily
Chronic fatigue
Nausea or vomiting
Faintness or dizziness

Growth

Failure to gain regularly over 3-month period
Unexplained loss in weight
Unexplained rapid gain in weight

Glands

Enlarged gland at side of neck
Enlarged thyroid

Ears

Discharge from ears
Earache
Failure to hear questions
Picking at the ears
Turning the head to hear
Talking in a monotone
Inattention
Anxious expression
Excessive noisiness of child

Skin and Scalp

Nits on the hair
Unusual pallor of face
Eruptions or rashes
Habitual scratching of scalp or skin
State of cleanliness
Excessive redness of skin

Heart

Excessive breathlessness
Tires easily
Any history of "growing pains"
Bluish lips
Excessive pallor

Posture and Musculature

Asymmetry of shoulders and hips
Peculiarity of gait
Obvious deformities of any type
Abnormalities of muscular development

Behavior

Overstudious, docile, and withdrawing
Bullying, overaggressive, and domineering
Overexcitable, uncontrollable emotions
Unhappy and depressed
Stuttering or other forms of speech difficulty
Lack of confidence, self-denial, and self-censure
Poor accomplishment in comparison with ability
Lying (imaginative or defensive)
Lack of appreciation of property rights (stealing)
Abnormal sex behavior
Antagonistic, negativistic, quarrelsome[2]

It is not enough, however, for the teacher to spot the child who is coming down with an illness, for although she can do much to prevent the spread of communicable diseases, she should also teach the children how to protect themselves from germs, that they should stay in bed when they have a cold, that they should cover their mouths when they cough, that they should get plenty of good rest and sleep, etc. Every aspect of the health observation program abounds with opportunities for individual health counseling and teaching. Group instruction can develop from any part of such a program. If increasingly more pupils are having colds, it is a good time to stress cold prevention techniques. Likewise, epidemics, accidents, and other types of disasters can be put to positive educational use.

As Haag has pointed out, the teacher must be aware of the range of pupil differences before she can recognize these differences.[3] The

[2] *Health in the Schools—A Manual of the School Health Program,* Massachusetts Department of Education and Department of Public Health, Boston, 1949, p. 91.

[3] Jessie Haag, *School Health Program,* New York, Holt, 1958, p. 15.

more each teacher knows about the needs and interests of each pupil, the better she can guide him to rich learning experiences which can help him find a solution to his own problems, including those in health. This discovery of each pupil's health and safety needs is basic to any sound school health education program. These must be discovered by each teacher herself. She must also find out what the child already knows and does as well as how he feels about himself, life in general, other people, what he wants to be when he grows up, what he fears, and as much other information as possible. The resulting instructional program should be chiefly concerned with everyday health and safety practices as they will affect all the children in the class.

TESTS

Although in large school systems the nurse is usually responsible for giving tests, with the classroom teacher working as her assistant, the teacher in a small or rural school often must assume this responsibility. It is important that those conducting such tests be aware of the possibilities for health education inherent in such situations, as well as knowing what and how to answer the questions childern ask, for it is then that they *want* to learn. It is at this time, too, that fears may be assuaged. Educators call this "having a need for learning" and have discovered that "wanting to know" is basic to "getting to know."

Vision Tests. Children having vision difficulties often display this through the appearance of their eyes (crusted lashes; red, swollen eyelids; sties) or by their behavior (frequent rubbing of eyes, signs of inability to see well or do close work, irritability and lack of attention, holding books too close or too far away, shutting or covering one eye, etc.).

A number of vision tests are available. The Snellen test is recommended for elementary schools, for it is easily given, inexpensive, and enables the teacher to pick out quickly the child who is having vision difficulties and should be referred to an eye specialist. The chart is available in letter or in the E symbol form. The latter is for children who cannot read letters but who can point with a thumb in which direction the "legs" of the letter E are turned (up, down, to the left, or right).

Each child should be tested standing 20 feet from the chart.[4] If he can read the letters in the 20-foot line on the chart, his vision is normal and is recorded as 20/20. If he can only read the letters on the 100-foot line, his vision is 20/100. This means that the pupil is greatly in need of corrective glasses. The teacher must be sure that the child understands what he is to do, has not memorized any part of the chart, and is not afraid to take the test.

Although the Snellen test does not test color blindness, depth perception, or other vision difficulties, it does enable the tester to pick out those who cannot see from a distance of 20 feet, or those who have eye muscle imbalance causing one eye to be used more than the other.

Other recommended screen tests for vision are the telebinocular test (which measures the extent to which the eyes work together), the Massachusetts Vision Test, and the Holmgren Wool Test for color blindness.

Numerous educational opportunities arise each time a child has his eyes tested in school. The teacher can and should prepare each group for this experience. In younger children, interest in the eyes and how we see can be aroused by showing pictures of eyes of different kinds of animals and birds, having each child then look at his own eyes in the mirror, and discussing how our eyes function and can be protected. Older children can become interested in learning about the importance of good lighting and vision by using a light meter and finding the candle power present in various rooms or parts of them in the school building. Regardless of the methods used to teach how our eyes work and should be protected, each pupil should gain from this experience a new appreciation for his own eyes, and use his new knowledge to care for them properly in his daily life.

Hearing Tests. Pupils who have hearing difficulties often turn their heads to one side or cup the ear, seem dull, have a worried

[4] Complete directions for administering the test are available with the chart. It can be obtained from a number of sources including state departments of health, local eye specialists, the local or county health department.

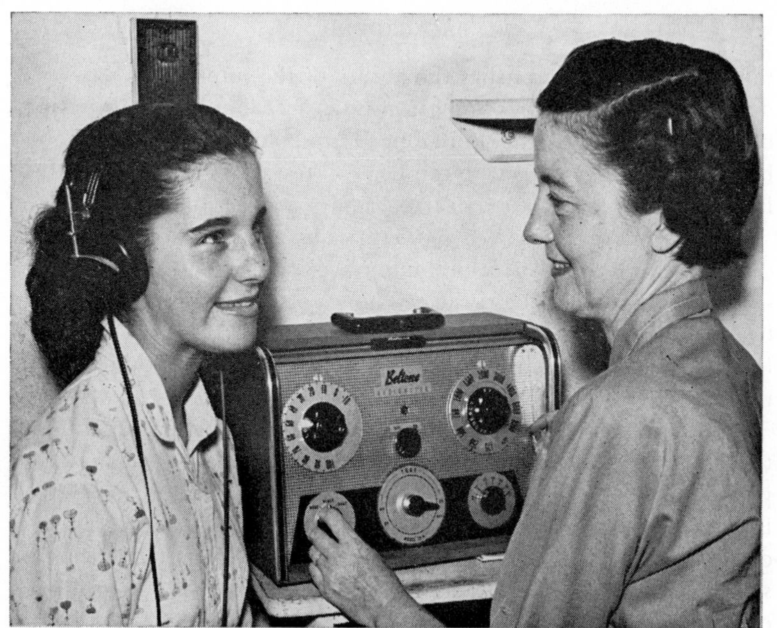

An audiometer test is an interesting educational experience in itself. Its effectiveness can be increased by an understanding educator who capitalizes upon teachable moments which occur during the test. (Courtesy, Los Angeles Public Schools.)

facial expression, or speak in an unusual-sounding voice. Hearing tests include the audiometer (by far the most accurate), the Watch Tick, and the Whisper Test. The most satisfactory testing instrument for hearing is the Discrete Frequency Audiometer, which can be used to test groups as well as individuals. Such instruments can be borrowed or rented from hearing specialists, the local or state health department, or often from a local college or university. Other tests include:

Massachusetts Group Pure-tone Test. This is a group test, using an audiometer, for hearing deficiencies. It can quickly point out those pupils who have normal hearing acuity. Those who fail the test should subsequently be given an individual Pure-tone Sweep Check Test, as a means of checking the results.

Pure-tone Sweep Check Test. This test, given by using a pure-tone audiometer, establishes the ability of the pupil to hear several different tones or pitches at a given intensity. Should he fail to hear certain pitch levels, the Pure-tone Threshold Acuity Test should be administered. Pupils who can hear all test tones at the prescribed intensity have satisfactory hearing acuity and need no referral.

Pure-tone Threshold Acuity Test. This test, given by machine, determines what intensity or loudness is required before it is possible for the child to hear the test tones of varied pitch. Failure to hear certain test tones at established levels of intensity indicates that the pupil does not possess normal hearing and should receive medical attention.

Speech Test. This test measures the most important function of the ear. Under ordinary conditions, however, it is unsatisfactory, for poor acoustics and unavoidable noise may often make it impossible to secure meaningful results. It is especially important to have a quiet room and as little noise outside as possible. The whisper should be about one-third as loud as the voice used in ordinary conversation.

Coin Click Test. In this test, three coins are clicked together behind the head of the examinee several times, and the pupil is asked to count each click. Records should be kept of those who fail to hear all three clicks and these students referred to a specialist. A quiet room is necessary for this test.

Audiometer Tests. In recent years the audiometer has replaced all other methods of testing hearing because it is more accurate, constant, and reliable than any other hearing examination. The tests are made by setting the dial of the audiometer at one intensity and changing the pitch or frequency; at each change the child presses the signal button when he hears the sound.

It is not enough, however, merely to give the child a hearing test, for the class should be prepared for this experience. Lessons or units on the human ear and how it functions should be planned by the class through teacher-pupil planning, and carried out by individual or small committee assignments. This educational experience should enable each pupil to understand better how the ears work, and how hearing can be tested and protected.

Height and Weight Charts. Each pupil should be weighed and measured each month and an accurate record should be kept. A

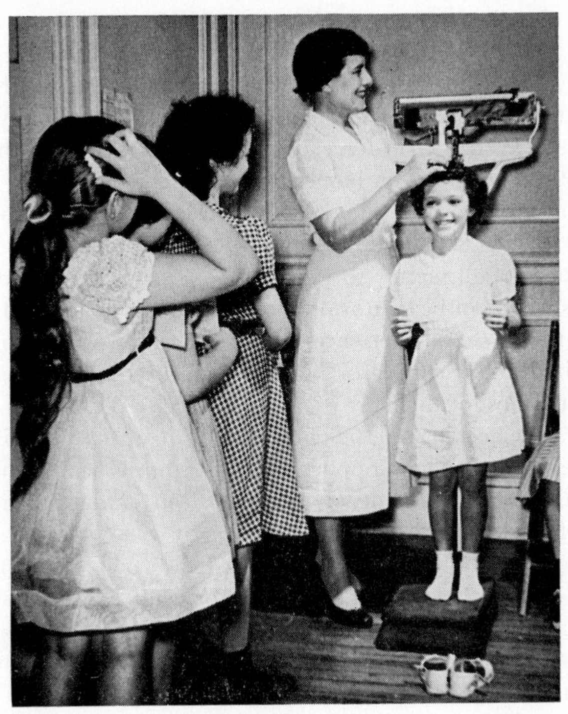

Every child should be weighed and measured periodically. (Courtesy N.E.A.)

scale with an accurate measuring device attached to it may be used for determining height, or a permanent wall marking may be used. Although weight norms are available from insurance companies, the teacher should use these only to compare the height and weight records of *each* pupil to those of many students of the same age and grade in school, for each child has a small, large, or medium skeletal frame, and may have had a recent or lingering illness or deep-seated emotional strain—all of which may influence growth patterns.

The Wetzel Grid is often used in elementary schools to record a child's growth over several years. It is a card on which horizontal lines are drawn to represent body types: (1) stocky, (2) average, and (3) frail, and vertical lines are drawn on which height and weight are recorded. Such a chart is kept for each pupil, and his growth patterns are plotted. It is an excellent way to record and observe normal growth and deviations from the norm. Pupils who skip from one line to another, or who fail to grow over a period of time, should be referred to a physician. Although the school nurse usually records and keeps a Wetzel Grid for each child, in some schools this is the duty of the classroom or home-room teacher. Numerous teaching opportunities occur each time a child is weighed and measured, and the wise teacher takes time to capitalize upon them.

It is not enough merely to weigh and measure a child. Weighing and measuring can be educational experiences for the child and the class. Through such experiences health education can become both personalized and meaningful. Children are extremely interested in growth and most of them are eager to accelerate the process as much as they can. Checking the height and weight of each pupil and of an entire class provides opportunities to build health units into which nutrition, the value of exercise, sleep, and rest, and other aspects of health can be incorporated.

Although most children are interested in growing up, many are unaware of how this process takes place or what happens to them as they do grow. Individual and class interest in this process can be evoked in a number of ways, such as having each pupil bring his baby picture to class, asking such questions as "How much did you weigh when you were born? How much do you weigh now? What caused you to weigh more now?" or by having the class become interested in conducting plant and animal experiments to show the relationship of proper food, sunshine, and other factors to growth. Cattle breeders, farmers, or even rural children can share much valuable information with a city group concerning the type of food given to fatten cows, pigs, or other animals for human consumption. Visits to farms, dairies, ice cream or other types of food plants can make lasting impressions upon children, especially when they hear other adults at these places stress the same good health habits as does their teacher.

HELPING CHILDREN UNDERSTAND THE IMPORTANCE OF GROWTH

School camping experiences are especially valuable as a means of providing youngsters with educational experiences. The program in such camps might well include caring for animals, for such an adventure can give children an opportunity to see for themselves the role that good food and care and other factors play in growth. Those who can be given opportunities to gather and candle eggs, milk a cow, or feed baby turkeys, have learning experiences which remain meaningful, valued, and bright in memory throughout life. Learning to plan menus, shopping for and cooking their own food (whether it be over an open fire outdoors or on a kitchen stove) makes education become alive and far more significant in the lives of boys and girls than the teacher telling or reading aloud about these things to a class; those methods of teaching have value too, but only when properly used at the right time, just often enough, and in small amounts.

Children need to learn that they grow in many ways other than physically. Units on growing up socially, emotionally, and intellectually can help the class learn that growth is more than just an increase in size, nor is it confined only to the body.

Posture Tests. Good posture means comfortable, efficient body alignment when one is both stationary and moving, standing as well as walking. Causes of poor posture are faulty nutrition, poor environmental conditions, fatigue, mental or emotional strain, faulty vision or hearing, or orthopedic defects.

The most common types of posture defects are:

Scoliosis, or curvature of the spine
Lordosis, or hollow back
Kyphosis, or round shoulders
Kypholordosis, or round upper back and hollow backed
Lordosis, both areas with marked curves
Faulty arches, too low or high
Flat feet
Pronated or supinated ankles
Carrying the head too far forward, back, or to the side
Hollow or deformed chest
Winged shoulders
Protruding stomach which throws off body alignment

Although there are many good posture tests, the Posture Test included in the New York State Physical Fitness Test is recommended.[5] In this test the teacher compares the various standing postures of each pupil with those pictured on a card and rates him accordingly. Since few teachers have been educated to pick out postural defects and thus cannot readily detect deviations, the use of picture cards which clearly show any abnormalities is most helpful. The test determines if the child is holding his head correctly, with shoulders and hips level, spine straight, feet pointed straight ahead, arches normal, neck erect, chest elevated, shoulders correctly centered, trunk erect, abdomen flat, and lower back curved normally.

Posture education for many children is dull and uninteresting, for it too often consists of warnings of impending doom if one does not stand up straight. Actually, however, it can become an exciting area of study, especially when related to what one wants to be. At every grade pupils have a fairly good idea of what they want to be when they grow up, even though many fields are "sampled" along the way. Helping the child see the role posture can play in his future success can be an effective way to help him improve his posture.

There are many effective ways to help pupils become conscious of posture.[6] It is the duty of the teacher to provide the right conditions in which healthy growth can take place and wherein the child can make the correct or desired responses. Educators call this "getting the act performed with satisfaction" and stress the importance of having children do things which bring them not only personal satisfaction but also praise by the teacher. Since good posture is an important health factor closely related to mental and physical efficiency and well-being, there should be an emphasis upon this aspect of health in each grade. Good posture results when the mind works together with the body. There are many good postures each person may assume besides the static ramrod once considered to be ideal. It means proper body alignment in standing, sitting, and lying down—all done with a minimum of fatigue, and

[5] Available at small cost from C. F. Williams and Son Printing Company, Albany, N.Y.

[6] Excellent suggestions for teaching posture effectively to children can be found in Ivaclare Howland, *The Teaching of Body Mechanics,* New York, Barnes, 1936, and Ellen Kelly, *Teaching Posture and Body Mechanics,* New York, Barnes, 1949.

with ease, grace, and efficiency. The body should be balanced, the head erect, the hips tucked under rather than thrust out, and the shoulders held straight. The key words to stress when talking about good posture are *balance, rhythm,* and *grace.*

There are as many as seven causes of poor posture—not all of which can be corrected upon command, for the student with bad posture can only develop good posture by developing the muscular strength, energy, and self-confidence which will lead to good carriage and body mechanics. Causes of poor posture are (1) an *improperly balanced diet* which causes the muscles of the body to lack the necessary supportive power; (2) *environmental conditions,* including poor lighting, a sagging bed mattress, or the use of a large pillow; (3) *rapid growth,* which is especially apparent in adolescence; (4) *fatigue,* due to strain and faulty health habits, including lack of sleep and rest, eating irregularly, and lack of exercise (riding and sitting too much); (5) *mental and emotional tensions,* for worry, insecurity, inferiority, and fear all tell on the bodies of their victims; (6) poor vision or hearing, which may cause the head to be carried to one side or the neck to be craned forward; and (7) *structural and orthopedic defects,* which sometimes occur at birth, such as a hunchback or a short leg, or may be due to accidents after birth. Poor posture can best be eradicated when the child is young and in the elementary school, for his body is more pliable and flexible during these years than it will be when he becomes older.

Since good posture is an indication of health, teachers should be aware of how each pupil stands, walks, moves, and sits. Lighting, seating, work and play habits, and the pace of all school activities should be geared toward providing a favorable environment in which each pupil can use his body and grow healthfully. Since young children are restless and tire easily, opportunities should be given them frequently throughout the school day to move about the room and do simple relaxation exercises. Likewise, their recess periods must be closely supervised by the teacher, who should also teach the children many kinds of vigorous activities, including relays and team games. The physical education instruction period should consist of strenuous play activities, and the children should be taught conditioning exercises, rhythmical and self-testing activities, swimming, and simple outdoor camping techniques.[7] It is unreasonable to expect a program of health education in posture or corrective exercises to cure postural defects brought on by fatigue, malnutrition, or emotional difficulties, for these must first be eliminated before the child's posture can ever be improved.

There are many ways to arouse the child's interest in posture education. Slogans, bulletin-board pictures taken from magazines, or better still, actual photographs of the children themselves taken at work and play, can all help do this. Individual learning activities might well include:

1. Making posters.
2. Learning exercises in school which may be done at home and then describing the results; telling the class about teaching these exercises to neighborhood friends or to the family.
3. Practicing good posture before a full-length mirror.
4. Keeping personal improvement charts.
5. Drawing cartoons showing pictures of *poor* posture.

Suggested group activities include:

1. Writing and dramatizing poems and short plays.
2. Judging posture of the children of their own group.
3. Demonstrating sitting posture, showing the correct way and exaggerating the incorrect way.
4. Using blocks to show the relationship of balance to the "straight man," to the "crooked man."
5. Forming a password club and having the class decide on a secret word to be whispered to anyone who is seen slumping.
6. Playing a variety of games to develop strength, balance, and coordination, such as the "Duck Walk Relay," "Prancing Horses," the "Inchworm Race."
7. Doing a wide variety of relaxation mimetic activities such as "Rag Doll," "Floating on Your Back," "Swinging the Elephant's Trunk."
8. Keeping unsigned reports on each child's weekly sleep records. Having groups act out the correct and incorrect ways to get ready for bed.
9. Demonstrating body "unevenness" and "one-sidedness."
10. Making a cardboard skeleton, using heavy paper and string to show the bones of the body; discuss how muscles move bones, and what makes muscles grow.

[7] See Maryhelen Vannier, *Teaching Physical Education in Elementary Schools,* 3rd ed., Philadelphia, Saunders, 1963, for suggested materials and methods of teaching physical activities for this age group.

11. Setting up a posture obstacle course in the classroom which has ropes at varying heights to jump over or crawl under, areas in which one must walk with a book on the head, areas for jumping, etc. Discuss the relationship to body alignment of physical movement.
12. Use a doorway bar for hanging by the hands and by the knees.
13. Teaching rope climbing and chinning.

HEALTH EXAMINATIONS

Although some school authorities believe in giving annual physical examinations, others contend that each child should have a minimum of four periodic examinations. These should be given when the child enters the first grade, during the middle elementary grades, at the beginning of adolescence during junior high school years, and before leaving senior high school. However, throughout a child's experience at school he should be referred to either the school physician or a specialist if a teacher's observation or the results of a test show some health problem. Each school district should determine how often, by whom, when, and where the physical examinations should be given.

The kind of medical examination given will, of course, vary from school to school. In general, however, the examination should test the following:

- Nutritional status
- Eyes and eyelids
- Ears and eardrums
- Skin and hair
- Heart
- Lungs
- Nervous system
- Pulse rate when resting and after exercise
- Muscle tone
- Posture
- Bones and joints
- Abdomen
- Nose, throat, and tonsils
- Thyroid gland
- Lymph nodes
- Teeth and gums[8]

Teachers can and should make a great contribution to this phase of the school health program. Their chief contributions can be in helping each child understand (1) *why* he needs to be examined,

[8] *School Health Services,* Joint Committee on Health Problems in Education of the National Education Association and the American Medical Association, Washington, D.C., National Education Association, 1953, pp. 42–44.

(2) understand *what* the doctor will do (look into your ears, listen to your heartbeat, etc.), and (3) by talking with each pupil after the examination has been given so that he understands what the doctor told him. Although less preparation is needed with older children who have previously been examined, it is still an important function the elementary teacher should perform. Some children magnify previous negative experiences among their peers, and thus a whole cluster of children can become easily upset over being examined. However, the failure of the teacher to capitalize upon the educational opportunities inherent in the physical examination can cause many other similar types of disturbances and emotional upsets to arise. Ideally the parents should accompany their child when the examination is made. Since this is impossible for some parents, the teacher should do so, especially with primary children. Unfortunately, the examining physician too often does not discuss the examination with the child, nor does he spend as much time with each pupil as he should. Consequently, the teacher can be of valuable assistance before and after the examination, and thus make it educational and significant.

As Anderson points out, health appraisal should be a continuing process which ranges from the health examination to the observations by the classroom teacher and to the last health evaluation in the final year of high school. Yet this appraisal is not an end to itself, but rather a means to helping each pupil gain better health.[9]

The purpose of the school health examination should be to ascertain the state of each pupil's health, to discover defects, to provide the pupil with information concerning any existing deviation, to discover if the child can participate fully in the school program and to recommend modifications if he cannot, and most important of all, to provide a valuable positive health education experience potent enough to develop within each youngster an appreciation of the importance of this examination and of similar ones later in life. Unless parents, school authorities, and other adults are informed of the physical examination findings, few changes or real benefits for the children can accrue from this experience.

[9] C. L. Anderson, *School Health Practice,* 2nd ed., St. Louis, Mosby, 1960, p. 121.

Throughout the examination it is the physician who is the educator, whether with positive or negative educational results, for the child being examined. Although ideally as much time as possible should be spent with each child, the large numbers of pupils to be examined at school by one or several physicians prevent this ideal from becoming a reality. The examination itself should take a minimum of ten minutes per pupil, with a comparable amount of time given for counsel and health instruction.

Although health information and findings should be recorded by the school nurse as directed by the examining physicians, in smaller schools this duty is performed by a teacher. All examination records should be available to qualified school personnel. It is important that, since the health of each child can greatly affect his success in school, each teacher closely examine each year the record of every child in her group. This will enable her not only to understand better the behavior of each individual in her class but also assist her in knowing what to expect from each one; such records can also aid her in quickly spotting deviations from the norm in the appearance and behavior of each child.

PREVENTION AND CONTROL OF COMMUNICABLE DISEASES

All schools should have written policies concerning the exclusion and readmission of students who have had communicable diseases, the kinds of immunization required for school admission, and procedures to be followed in the event of an epidemic. Teachers, along with the school administrator, the public health department, local physician, and parents, should work closely together in formulating such policies, and should help enforce these policies once they have been adopted.

The classroom teacher is the key person in the prevention of the spread of communicable diseases in the school. It is her duty to teach children the reasons why they should cover their mouths when sneezing or coughing, wash their hands after going to the bathroom, keep disease-transmitting objects such as pencils, pens, and crayons out of their mouths, not drink from another's cup or use another's personal toilet articles, or avoid getting too overheated, chilled, or tired. Furthermore, they should supervise their pupils as much as possible, to see that these desirable health habits are carried out, for what a child does with what he learns is the key to a successful health education program.

This is real health education and is far more important than following a daily health lesson plan and ignoring health education opportunities which have arisen in the meantime. Children must be reminded again and again to do things before health procedures become habitual. The building of positive daily health habits should be the chief objective of the health education program on the primary level.

The daily health observation program is crucial in the early detection of those coming down with a contagious disease. Should the school nurse be unavailable (sometimes several schools share one nurse), and the teacher know that both parents of the child work and would not be home, she should see to it that the child is isolated at school, and if ill enough, put to bed. Here again the child should be taught why he is being isolated and why he must go to bed. School health policies should contain directives concerning procedures for removing an ill child from school and what to do with him if he cannot be taken home, as well as what to do in other types of emergencies. Such policies should be drawn up by a committee of teachers and the principal. Those who have had courses in health education should take a leading role in the formulation of these and other policies regarding health in the school. It is at such times that they can teach and guide their colleagues. The skilled educator can, should, and does work with people of many ages and educational backgrounds in many kinds of environments both in and away from the school building.

Signs of the early stages of most communicable diseases include:

Flushed or pale face, "glassy eyes," running nose
Excessive sneezing and coughing
Light blue or pale lips and fingernails
Rash, or other unusual skin condition
Swollen glands
Body temperature above 99° F.
Listlessness or unusual overactivity

Both the teacher and her pupils must not only know these signs but also be able to recognize them and know exactly what to do when they appear. Several class lessons can be built around the study of communicable diseases, and emphasis placed in each of these lessons upon preventive measures.

INJURIES AND EMERGENCIES

The school is responsible for the emergency handling of sudden illness and accidental injuries, and there should be written directives concerning measures to be taken. As Schneider and McNeely point out:

> The function of the school is to provide facilities and personnel with proper training to act promptly and intelligently in emergencies for the saving of life, the prevention of further injury, and the alleviation of pain as far as this can be done by nonmedical persons. In all such situations the two most important responsibilities are to summon medical aid and to notify parents or other responsible persons.[10]

Every teacher and upper elementary pupil should be trained in first aid. Even first graders can be taught what to do in an emergency, and how to give simple first-aid treatment for skinned knees or minor cuts and bruises. All children injured at school should receive first-aid attention. Accidents, when they do occur, can often provide the best time to instruct youngsters about the importance of safety. Units of study on playground safety, safety at home, safety measures to follow when coming to and from school, and other aspects of safety education should be included in the health education program on every grade level in the elementary school. Likewise, there should be a review of previously learned materials yearly. New aspects of major safety topics should be introduced at every grade level. Individual attention and frequent talks should be given to each pupil as needed, and especially to the accident-prone youngster. Such personalized education is often the most effective way to teach certain pupils who may be difficult to

[10] Elsa Schneider and Simon McNeely, *Teachers Contribute to Child Health,* no. 8, Washington, D.C., U.S. Department of Health, Education, and Welfare, Office of Education, 1951.

reach in a regular class. Accidents are the chief cause of death among children, and those selecting safety materials for study in school should always be aware of this fact. Accidents can and must be prevented through effective educational programs.

Teachers should remember that they are not doctors and can neither diagnose nor treat injuries. A complete record must be kept of all accidents, filled out in duplicate or triplicate; the teacher should keep one copy of this report and send the other to the school administrators.[11] The report form might well include:

The name of the injured and accident date.
The place of the accident and condition of the environment.
What first aid was given.
The names and addresses of two or more witnesses.

Since it is illegal to give "second-aid" ("treat" an injured person again), teachers should avoid rebandaging an injury, repainting an open cut, or repeating any other type of first-aid given previously.

HEALTH RECORDS

Carefully kept health records provide the teacher with valuable information regarding each pupil.[12] They should also serve as a means of making a careful study of the health needs of each class as well as of each child in the grade. This information should guide the teacher's selection of materials to teach to her class and be the basis upon which the health education program is built. These records should be kept by school physicians, nurses, dentists, secretaries, and teachers. They also better enable the instructor to adjust the school program to the limitations of those needing such an arrangement. The records should be cumulative, from the time the child enters until he leaves school, and should follow him from one school to another. Most states have adopted such records, and they are relatively standardized in schools within each state. Each cumulative record should contain:

[11] See the Appendix for a suggested form.
[12] See the Appendix for a suggested form.

The name, age, and correct address of each pupil.
The name and address of the parents.
The name of the family physician, dentist, and the preferred hospital to which the child should be taken in case of emergency.
How and where the parents or guardian of the child can be reached in case of an emergency.
Where the father works and type of work he does; if the mother works, where, and type of work she does.
A health history, including all communicable diseases, operations, and other pertinent information.
Immunization record.
Allergies or other conditions which affect health.
Height and weight records; body (Wetzel Grid).
Remediable defects and recommended corrections, and a follow-up record.
Recommendations concerning nonremediable conditions (birth injuries, etc.) and suggestions concerning a modified school program, and a record of such adopted program.
Teachers' daily observations of permanent and/or significant deviations which will lead to better understanding of the child.
Dental examination results.
Physical examinations results.
Physical fitness test results.
Results of social tests in which children reveal how they feel about themselves and others.
Record of emotional problems.
Attendance reports.

Individual cumulative health records should be filed in a central office, and be easily accessible to all teachers and other authorized personnel for professional use.

HEALTH GUIDANCE

The health history, physical examination results, and other valuable information contained in each pupil's cumulative health record are the basis upon which an adequate group as well as an individual health guidance program should be built. In cases requiring the school program to be adjusted to meet the needs of any pupil, it is the duty of both the school nurse and teacher to see that such changes are made. There are many possibilities for the development of a splendid program in health guidance built around the teacher's daily health appraisal of each pupil through observation, tests, and physical examinations. Such a guidance program in the elementary school must also reach the parents. Few children know what to do, or have the financial means through which discovered decayed teeth, faulty vision, or malnutrition can be corrected. Somehow teachers must motivate parents to act in the best health interest of their children. In some cases, formal written notes to parents sent by the school nurse or doctor will get results.[13] Personal interviews, at school, or at home if necessary, make for a warmer, more productive atmosphere wherein the teacher can often gain the cooperation of the parents in seeing to it that their child's health deficiencies are corrected so that he will do well in school. A determined teacher will keep trying to reach parents who are almost impossible to motivate into desired action for the well-being of their own child.

Throughout the school day, through her numerous daily close contacts with pupils, the teacher has many opportunities for group or individual health guidance. A chat before or after school with the pupil who returns to class following a long illness, or with the girl who is obviously catching a cold, or a boy who still has not obtained needed glasses, all constitute guidance opportunities designed to help the child want to be in better health. Class discussions during or following a health lesson, or showing a film, or at the many other teachable moments which appear in every school day, open up numerous opportunities. Guidance is more than giving advice or warning, preaching, or praising in an attempt to motivate action, for it requires mature judgment, a deep understanding of human behavior, and a knowledge of ways in which the individual can be directed toward and helped to obtain professional assistance when needed.

As has been often pointed out, each child comes to school wrapped up in a package of his social and economic background, his cultural heritage, and the era into which he is born, and although each child appears to sit alone on his little chair in the classroom, he is far from alone for

[13] See the Appendix for the suggested form letter for writing to the parents.

his family came with him. Their values are present, coloring his values, and therefore his behavior. What he possesses, acquired in a few years, is largely the values current in his household. It is through these meanings that he gives significance to the things that happen in the classroom. The skills and learning which he brings in are home-made. The teacher who receives him, the society which requires his presence, the future which banks on him, must remember this in anything they do for him, or in anything they expect him to do for himself.[14]

Because each child takes his family to school with him, the teacher must get to know, and gain the cooperation of, that closely knit primary group and especially the parents if she is to teach each youngster successfully. Every teacher should know as much about each of her pupils as she can find out, including as much about their home environment as she can discover. Likewise, she and the parents of each child must work closely, striving for the development of each youngster as well as that of all the children in the class.

SUGGESTED READINGS

Absent from School Today, 1958, *What Teachers See,* 1961, *The School Administrator, Physician and Nurse in the School Health Program,* 1960, New York, Metropolitan Life Insurance Company.

Blum, H. L., H. B. Peters, and J. W. Bettman, *Vision Screening for Elementary Schools,* Berkeley, University of California Press, 1959.

Grout, Ruth, *Health Teaching in Schools,* 3rd ed., Philadelphia, Saunders, 1958.

Health Appraisal of School Children, National Education Association and American Medical Association, Washington, D.C., 1957.

Hymes, James, *A Child Development Point of View,* Englewood Cliffs, N.J., Prentice-Hall, 1955.

Johnson, Burt, and Stanley Abercrombie, "A Safe Environment for Learning," *N.E.A. Journal,* October, 1960.

Lowman, Charles, *Postural Fitness,* Philadelphia, Lea and Febiger, 1960.

Neimer, Alma, *The School Health Program,* Philadelphia, Saunders, 1959.

Priorities in Health Series for Children of School Age, Children's Bureau, Washington, D.C., Government Printing Office, 1958.

Rogers, J. F., *What Every Teacher Should Know About the Physical Condition of Her Pupils,* Washington, D.C., U.S. Office of Education, Pamphlet no. 68, 1945.

[14] Marie Ramsey, *Toward Maturity, How Children Think and Grow,* New York, Barnes & Noble, 1947, p. 4.

Schlesinger, E. R., *Health Services for the Child,* New York, McGraw-Hill, 1953.

Turner, C. E., C. M. Sellery, and Sara Smith, *School Health and Health Education,* 4th ed., St. Louis, Mosby, 1961.

Wheatley, G. M., and Grace Hallock, *Health Observation of School Children,* 2nd ed., New York, McGraw-Hill, 1956.

3 TEACHING HEALTH THROUGH THE SCHOOL ENVIRONMENT

There is no justification for forcing children by law to attend schools conducted in dirty, drab, unsanitary, or even dangerously unsafe buildings. Nor is there logic in teaching children the necessity of washing their hands after going to the bathroom, if the school does not provide the soap, warm water, or towels that they might do so. Whether the school building is well kept or neglected, school housekeeping adhered to or ignored, the school lunch program properly or improperly conducted, play space and facilities assigned wisely or foolishly, precautions taken or avoided for protection from fire or other disasters, will, along with other facets of school environmental conditions, accelerate or deter the development of proper health attitudes, appreciation, and understanding. The total school environment and the teachers must serve as models if children are to want to develop good health practices they can carry out while at school as well as at home, and when they become adults. Emerson's phrase, "What you *are* sounds so loudly in my ears that I cannot hear a word you are saying," is well worth remembering. The school administrator, teachers, and all other school personnel must practice what they preach if children are to learn through indirect as well as direct health teaching methods. There is no doubt among educators that the "whole child" who goes to school is greatly affected by the "whole school."

The members of a class of teachers in training were recently required to write a paper relating the most potent learning experiences they recalled when thinking about their elementary school years. The majority of these experiences resulted in fears, foolish concepts, or the use of the fun approach to learning by some ingenious educator. One girl believed for years that she would have a baby if she kissed a boy, for her little friends were convinced and, in turn, "taught" her that this was what caused babies. Another student believed that a pregnant woman was one punished by God for sucking her finger—a practice he was taught at home would cause the stomach to swell. Many of the class wrote that they could "still see" and even "smell" how certain classrooms looked, for either they were unpleasant, poorly ventilated, or made suddenly a place of magic by a color-appreciative teacher who with a few cut-out red, yellow, or green figures could capture and hold the attention of a child and long keep in mind's memory *that* room, *that* teacher, and *that* time in life. Delia Sharp's splendid book, *This I Remember, Teacher,* is full of such lasting learning experiences, as is Leo Deuel's *Teachers' Treasure Chest,* or Alice Humphrey's *Heaven in My Hand.* Most of the memorable childhood experiences related by these authors took place not only in the classroom, but also on the playground, or while coming to or going from school.

Teachers must realize that there is learning wherever there is life, but that learning can be positive or negative depending largely on leadership. Education is by no means confined to a school or classroom nor is it something that can be gained only from reading a book, for children often learn more outside than inside schools, in coming from or going to school rather than from the classroom, and from their playmates and parents rather than from their teachers. Furthermore, the school buildings, grounds, and any other part of the total school environment, like a bulletin board, can be a silent, but powerfully effective, teacher. Teachers do not have a corner on education. Because of their professional preparation, skill in imparting knowledge and shaping attitudes, and sensitivity and belief in children they can, however, become a potent and positive factor in the total development of the children with whom they work.

THE USE AND MAINTENANCE OF SCHOOL BUILDINGS

The "little red school house" of yesterday is rapidly disappearing in America. It is being replaced by school buildings that are attractive, artistic in appearance, and functional. Increasingly, all environmental factors which influence health are being taken into consideration by the architects and school-sponsored committees who plan new buildings or the reconstruction of old ones. Since all plans for new buildings and their sanitation must be approved by the State Board of Education and the State Board of Health, children are now being taught in an improved educational environment.

Whether the building is old or new, it must be more than just a building, for it is a vital part of the environment in which children are educated. It is imperative that the school be a healthy, happy place to which children will look forward throughout their entire education with as much eagerness and joy as they did as first graders. The sharp increase in school vandalism in the past decade is not only a national disgrace, but should be a warning signal to educators as well as parents that children need more than increased discipline. Children must somehow regain the almost reverent feelings the early Americans had not only for education but also for the schoolhouse itself, for this building was preceded only by the erection of the church in any newly established community or settlement. In our time of distorted values, wherein the rights, privileges, and property of others never become the concern of the "me-first" individual striving to get ahead at any cost, children must be given more opportunity to do things for themselves instead of being waited on and pampered by adult servants (teachers and parents included), who rob the child of learning experiences every time they tie his shoes or zip up his snowsuit. There is wisdom in Bernard Shaw's statement, "If you teach me, I shall never learn."

One reason the Tyler Public School Camp, and other school camps throughout the nation, rarely have walls defaced or ruined by children, is that the youngsters at these camps are given increased responsibility for the care and maintenance of their own living environment. The program at many of school-sponsored camps is built around (1) learning to live with others out of doors, (2) healthful personal and community living, (3) basic campcraft skills, (4) work experiences, and (5) conservation projects. According to school camp directors, the favorite camp activities are taking care of animals, cabin clean-up duties, making dams, meal planning and outdoor cooking, lard and soapmaking, milking, and weather forecasting.[1]

Although millions of children do not attend any kind of camp, educators might well seriously consider just why the outdoor educational experience of camping is so appealing to children. One reason could well be that in camps children are given *real* responsibility for their own well-being and that of others. Every teacher, whether she works as a camp counselor or classroom educator, must provide opportunities for children to form desirable health habits in their daily lives and instill in them a feeling of responsibility for controlling and improving their own working, playing, learning, and living environment.

THE TEACHER'S EXAMPLE

Although an abundance of well-selected teaching aids coupled with an attractive, sanitary, and well-kept building are vastly important in teaching health and instilling positive health habits, without a good teacher these are of little value. A real teacher is one who not only sets a healthful example worthy of pupil emulation, but also provides a stimulating classroom learning atmosphere. All children need teachers who are emotionally well balanced and calm persons who enjoy being with and working with children, who respect them as unique individuals, and who set firm but secure behavior boundaries. Such adults are loved and respected by children, who want to be like them.

Teaching requires good health, stamina, patience, a sense of humor, plus many other qualities which will enable an older person to work patiently and successfully with youngsters. It is important

[1] George Donaldson, *School Camping,* New York, Association Press, 1952, pp. 114–115.

that educators have recreational outlets during their leisure hours every day, as well as finding legitimate outlets for their normal feelings of hostility and rejection, which build up daily through association with others, through sports, games, or other types of recreation. Those who balance work and play in their daily lives will be less apt to project feelings of aggression felt toward a superior upon their smaller charges who cannot fight back. Interests in many outside activities and periodic health checkups help teachers to maintain an even keel in the classroom, as well as help them become outstanding leaders for children. Such teachers are both fun and profitable to be with and are the ones most eagerly sought by children.

THE CLASSROOM AND OTHER FACILITIES

Children who go to school in a relaxed but controlled learning environment feel both secure and happy. In such an atmosphere of security they are given freedom of movement, responsibility in planning what they are to learn (guided by the teacher), and greater responsibility in helping make and keep the classroom their own—a place of friends, fun, adventure, and beauty. The modern schoolroom is full of fascinating equipment, movable furniture sized correctly for each pupil, and a happy, relaxed, and cheerful atmosphere permeates it. Here the curriculum is both carefully planned and flexible, and each child is made aware that what he learns today or this year will dovetail into tomorrow or the next grade, and into what he wants to be and do when "grown up." Each child finds that planning what he will do in order to learn is an adventure in itself. Helping children plan for, select, and carry out what they will learn is masterful teaching and requires far more skill than telling children what to do and how to do it.

Students should be encouraged to move their seats around in the room in order to obtain the best light. Likewise, since so many health learning opportunities are inherent in the care of plants and animals, pupils should become responsible for the daily care of fish, birds, hamsters, rabbits, a garden, flowers, etc. Facilities should also be provided for the group so that each can hang up his own hat and coat and put his rubbers or boots in an assigned space. Each child should be encouraged to become increasingly independent from adults by receiving praise from his teacher for taking such good care of himself and his possessions.

The emotional climate of the classroom is extremely important. Learning can be greatly encouraged or inhibited by teacher enthusiasm and encouragement or pupil frustration and fear. Jealousy, lying, cheating, tattling, and obvious signs of inferiority feelings are warning signs that pupil-teacher relationships are strained. All children should feel secure and adequate and believe that going to school is a great adventure. The slow learner must feel as secure as the rest of his classmates. Although the teacher should discuss with the children behavior standards that are to be maintained in order that the classroom and school be a place in which the best kind of learning, work, and play can take place, the pupils should also help devise conduct rules which will provide a desirable educational and living environment. All adopted rules must be promptly, firmly, and consistently enforced and pupils made well aware that all such standards have been established primarily for their benefit. The teacher should treat all children alike. Studies show that children like teachers best who are firm, fair to all, and are consistent in what they do. The most successful educators are those who can share magical things with children and make them excited about what they are learning, and who expect success for each learner in each group. Children, as well as adults, respond to such an adventure and to such a challenge! It is imperative that each pupil feels that he is making progress, for nothing destroys learning desire and self-confidence more than repeated failure without hope of success or motivating words of encouragement to keep on trying. It is unwise to take away the recess periods from those who misbehave or fail to complete their work, for these are often signs of pent-up tensions and rebellion which can best be relieved through increased physical activity.

Although the physical maintenance of the room is the responsibility of the school custodian, the teacher and the children should make every effort to see to it that their room is as clean and attractive as possible. Included below are suggestions of things pupils can do to make this phase of the total school health program functional and meaningful:

LIGHTING

1. Adjust the window blinds according to changing light conditions.
2. Move seats around so that the light can be used most advantageously.
3. Keep window ledges free from boxes or anything else which might interfere with proper lighting.

VENTILATION

1. Assign to one student the honor of reading the room thermometer, or to regulate the thermostat properly under supervision. Rotate this privilege among different members of the class.
2. Adjust windows, if the building is not air-conditioned, to changing weather conditions. Use air deflectors when necessary so that no child sits in a draft.
3. Open doors into halls and ventilate the room frequently.
4. Adjust seating according to temperature readings, if necessary.
5. Help children become conscious of the weather and room temperature. Teach those in the upper elementary school how to forecast the weather. Have a monthly or weekly weather forecaster.[2]

DRINKING FACILITIES

1. Provide adequate facilities (1 drinking fountain for every 75 pupils).
2. Teach children to use the fountains properly.
3. Devise a few strongly enforced rules regarding pushing and shoving around the fountains or while someone is drinking.
4. Insist that no one drop gum or other objects into the basins.
5. Keep fountains clean and sanitary at all times.
6. Require each student to have his own marked cup when necessary, or provide individual paper cups.

HANDWASHING FACILITIES

1. Provide adequate facilities (1 wash basin for every 50 pupils).
2. Demonstrate the correct way to wash one's hands; supervise each child as he washes the first days at school, and frequently thereafter.
3. Provide adequate warm water, soap, and paper towels.
4. Enforce the rule that those who soil the basin must wipe it clean again. Enforce all other rules devised by the class. Have certain children be monitors, but make such an office a privilege.

[2] Robert Fisher, *How about the Weather,* New York, Harper, 1951; *Weather,* Boy Scout Handbook no. 3816; *Girl Scout Weather Handbook,* no. 19-503, New York, 1959.

5. Provide mirrors near the basin and encourage children to keep themselves neat and clean at all times.

TOILET FACILITIES

1. Provide adequate toilet facilities (1 commode for every 30 girls, 1 for every 60 boys, 1 urinal for every 30 boys).
2. Teach children the necessity of flushing the toilet every time it is used; build in them a feeling of civic pride for having a well-cared-for rest room.
3. Take all children on a complete tour of the school building and grounds the first day of school so that they know which is the boy's rest room and which one is for the girls. Explain carefully the reason each has a room for themselves, in contrast to the family bathroom.
4. Train and encourage children to report uncleanliness in use of facilities or writing of "dirty words" on the walls to the teacher, janitor, or principal.
5. Supervise frequently the use of toilet facilities by class groups. Be sure each child knows how to use each facility properly.

THE SCHOOL LUNCHROOM

Although the consolidation of small schools into larger districts has resulted in lunchroom service in many rural areas, there are still isolated one-room school houses to which children come on horseback or on foot instead of by school bus or in the family car, and many areas where pupils bring their own lunch in a paper bag or lunch box, instead of buying it at low cost from the school cafeteria. Regardless of where the children eat or who prepares the food, the lunch period should be a time of rich learning experiences, for this period in the child's school day abounds in many daily, life-related educational opportunities. Although basic nutritional principles can be taught in the classroom, the lunchroom is the laboratory wherein those principles can be put into practice, and teachers can see for themselves how effectively the children have learned and are applying what was taught them about nutrition. Likewise, the school lunch offers a wide variety of opportunities to integrate materials from all areas of the curriculum, but especially in social studies, arithmetic, health, and physical education. The school lunch program should be concerned with far more than merely feeding.

Its success depends primarily upon the knowledge, desire, and interest of the classroom teacher, who should either eat with her class or supervise them as they eat, and her cooperation with all the other personnel who are connected with this phase of the school program.

Learning experiences which are inherent in the school lunch program include:

1. Developing proper handwashing practices which are actually carried out and supervised before each meal.
2. Creating an interest in choosing food wisely.
3. Selecting a nutritious lunch in the classroom as guided by the teacher from the menu written on the board before the actual lunch period begins.
4. The proper way to store lunches brought from home.
5. Enlisting the cooperation of parents in helping their children select or bring to school a nutritious lunch by sending them in advance the weekly lunch menu and encouraging them to guide their children into selecting the right foods.
6. Encouraging children to eat new kinds of food and making efforts to develop good food selection an intelligent habit; gauging serving size to fit child-sized appetites.
7. Helping children learn the value of eating slowly, the necessity of chewing food thoroughly, and being relaxed and happy when eating.
8. Encouraging the practice of good eating habits such as using silverware and napkins correctly; not talking with food in the mouth; contributing to the conversation and listening to what others say; keeping one's voice low and avoiding unnecessary noise; waiting until all are served before starting to eat; saying "thank you," "please," or "excuse me" at the proper time.

THE SCHOOL PLAYGROUND

There should be more to playground activities than the pleasure of a game, for they should enrich the leisure time of all children as well as develop physical fitness. By teaching obedience to rules, taking turns, accepting defeat as well as victory, children learn to get along with others, as well as help gain a working set of life values. No child can live in a world by himself, even though some few may escape through daydreams to such a desired place. Consequently, the school playground can be a valuable area in which the child learns the give and take of life, a lesson he must learn if he is ever to grow up.

For all recess and supervised free-play periods, pupils should be assigned a specific play space. Most play activities can be dangerous if unsupervised. Although children are not as interested in safety as they are in being daring, adults must help them realize that they can have the most fun over a longer time period if they remain free from accidents or injury. Safety education means learning to take chances wisely. When an accident happens can be the best moment to impress upon others why one should be careful, for then children can see what actually happens when a person has not done the right thing.

The teacher and pupils must jointly assume responsibility for safety on the playground as well as in the gymnasium. The specific duties of each might include the following:

The Teacher

1. Check and keep all equipment in good repair at all times.
2. Find all hazards with pupils and mark them in bright yellow paint.
3. Direct all pupils in safety measures to be taken.
4. Teach all children how to use all apparatus and equipment correctly.
5. Discuss with the class why they should not do anything on the playground which might interfere with the safety of anyone else.
6. Use activities which minimize accident possibilities.
7. Insist that all children wear suitable apparel for all activities.
8. Do not permit pupils to try new, more dangerous activities until they become skilled enough to do so.
9. Insist that all game rules be obeyed at all times.
10. Never leave an assigned group.

The Children

1. Stay in assigned play areas.
2. Assist the teacher in discovering all hazards and painting them with bright yellow paint.
3. Take turns using swings and other equipment and report to the teacher those who do not.
4. Report to the teacher any equipment which is broken or is faulty.
5. Come to the teacher when hurt in any way so that needed first-aid treatment can be given.
6. Serve as a member of a school playground safety patrol club.

7. Tour the grounds accompanied by the teacher discussing and discovering safe and unsafe play places.
8. Dramatize going to the right person in case of an injury.
9. Dramatize safe and unsafe ways to play.

Since the vast majority of all accidents which occur at school happen on the playground during unsupervised play periods, it is imperative that children become especially safety-conscious during recess and before and after school play periods. The school administrator and teachers assigned to teach physical activities or supervise free play periods are legally responsible should an accident occur, if it can be proved they were negligent in their duty, which can easily be done if they were not with the group of children they were assigned to supervise during the play and recess periods. Likewise, the school administrator and teachers must work closely together and plan recess activities wisely, provide safe play equipment, and assign space in the playground for each class. Areas should be assigned so that the greatest number may play safely at one time. At least five acres should be provided for elementary schools, or a minimum of 100 square feet per pupil. The grounds should be fenced in, and the youngest grades assigned space closest to the building and widely separated from the older children. Regardless of whether the surface is cement, blacktop, grass turf, or sawdust combined with asphalt, it should be an area wherein play will be safe and healthful. Backstop fences for softball and enclosed swing and apparatus areas are recommended. Space should be provided for sandbox play. All outdoor equipment should be chosen from the viewpoint of safety. Jungle gyms and horizontal bars should hang 36 inches from the ground for primary children, but may be up to 54 inches for older groups. Canvas-seat swings hung 10 to 12 inches from the ground, slides, monkey rings, parallel bars, merry-go-rounds, manila or hemp climbing ropes, horizontal ladders, low and high traveling rings, and a heavy rope giant stride are exciting facilities on which children love to play. One reason they are so attracted to these types of apparatus is that their use presents a challenge, contains elements of danger, and are challenging fun to master.

SCHOOL SANITATION

One of the best ways to impress upon pupils that their school is a sanitary place and that they have an important part in keeping it that way, is to take them on a complete tour of the building. They should visit the furnace and air-conditioning rooms in order to learn how the temperature is regulated, see how the school disposes of its sewage, garbage, and rubbish, observe how school lunches are prepared, food stored, dishes washed, and the procedures used for proper food handling. A visit to the city water department and water filtering plant will help impress upon young minds the value of pure water, as well as inform them of the methods used to make and keep it safe.

Thus we see that children can and should be taught valued health practices through the school environment itself by (1) giving them direct purposeful responsibilities in the care and maintenance of their own assigned areas at school, and (2) having them actually visit and see for themselves, rather than reading or hearing about, the environment at school in which they learn, work, and play.

SUGGESTED READINGS

Conditions of work for Quality Teaching, Department of Classroom Teachers of the National Education Association, Washington, D.C., 1959.

Creating a Good Environment for Learning, Association for Supervision and Curriculum Development, 1954 Yearbook, Washington, D.C., 1950.

Haag, Jesse H., *School Health Program,* New York, Holt, 1958.

Healthful School Living, National Education Association and American Medical Association, Washington, D.C., 1957.

Irwin, L. W., J. H. Humphrey, and W. R. Johnson, *Methods and Materials in Health Education,* St. Louis, Mosby, 1956.

Martin, Ethel, *Robert's Nutrition Work with Children,* Chicago, University of Chicago Press, 1955.

Oberteuffer, Delbert, *School Health Education,* 3rd ed., New York, Harper, 1960.

Planning America's School Buildings, National Education Association, Washington, D.C., 1960.

Planning Facilities for Health, Physical Education and Recreation, National Facilities Conference, rev. ed., Chicago, The Athletic Institute, 1956.

Safety in Physical Education and Recreation, National Safety Council, Chicago, 1941.

Safety Education (a Magazine for Teachers and Administrators), National Safety Council, Chicago.

Standards for Schoolhouse Construction, West Virginia State Department of Education, Wheeling, 1951.

Strang, Ruth, *Introduction to Child Study,* 4th ed., New York, Macmillan, 1959.

Vannier, Maryhelen, and Mildred Foster, *Teaching Physical Education in Elementary Schools,* 3rd ed., Philadelphia, Saunders, 1963.

4 THE CHARACTERISTICS, HEALTH NEEDS, AND INTERESTS OF CHILDREN

Although all children are basically alike, each is as unique and different as each leaf, grain of sand, or snowflake. In order to be a successful teacher the instructor must know as much as possible about every individual pupil, his rate of development, where he is in his development, his family background and living environment, as well as his own special needs, interests, desires, and problems. Likewise, the teacher must know (1) the characteristics of all children according to their class in school and what to expect of them as a group, (2) what subject matter to teach each grade, and (3) what methods and materials are most appropriate to use in order to teach each pupil and the entire class most effectively.

Children today are part of our vast, rapidly changing, and anxiety-ridden world. The 7,000 delegates attending the 1960 White House Conference on Children and Youth were given carefully gathered statistical facts for study and discussion concerning the most important changes affecting children and family life in the United States today. These data must be taken into account in planning the kind of life and opportunities adults want to provide for youth when drawing up the blueprints for a better, safer, and more abundant life for children in the home, school, and community. These significant facts concerning life in the United States today are of vital importance to teachers as well as parents.[1] Our population patterns are changing drastically, and our nation has grown by the addition of twenty-eight million people since 1950. By 1980 there will be far more children and old people than the number of citizens now in the most productive age groups. School enrollment will zoom upward on all educational levels. The individual child as well as the older student will be lost in the crowd. Although at the present time 36 percent of our total population is composed of those below the age of 18, this percentage will increase rapidly in each new decade, for even today families are getting larger and 58 percent of our children are members of a family composed of three or more children. Our child population is being concentrated into fewer areas, however; seven states (New York, California, Texas, Illinois, Michigan, Ohio, and Pennsylvania) now have 44 percent of the total number of children under the age of 18. Our cities are not growing as fast as our suburbs. Home ownership is at an all-time high. We have more mothers working outside the home than ever before in our history, yet the greatest increase in working mothers (83 percent) has been among those with children under six years of age. Among older youth, although more are now in the labor force than were ten years ago, far more teenagers also are now in school. Nonschool enrollment occurs far more in rural than urban areas. Family income has increased and is rising, with family spending patterns showing higher living levels. People are working fewer hours and now have more leisure than any Americans have ever known, and yet this is only the beginning of tomorrow's new age of leisure, which will only be golden when those of all ages have been educated to use it in positive and creative ways, in contrast to the violent, passive, and mediocre leisure-time patterns found among far too many Americans of all ages today. Likewise, more people are church members and go to Sunday and Sabbath Schools. More people are living longer, for the life expectancy for the female today is 70 years,

[1] Materials condensed from *Children in a Changing World* (*A Book of Charts*), prepared by the Interdepartmental Committee on Children and Youth for the 1960 White House Conference on Children and Youth, Washington, D.C., 1960.

for the male, 68 years. By the end of this century, it is estimated that it will be 100 years for the American woman, and 98 years for the American man. Thus, we have more people who are living longer and have more leisure and better health, and there are far more students in our schools on all educational levels. In turn, we have a brand-new group of problems at school, in the home, industry, medicine, and in every area of life.

It is hard to imagine that sixty years ago Americans did not have telephones, automobiles, or electricity, or that air travel, the radio, and television were unknown. Today's children are now living in a world of speed and luxury that their grandparents could not even imagine. Science will bring even greater changes in the next few decades. Youth living in this time of explosive change and changing values is unaware and largely unconcerned with what is happening around them. It has been said that most of the major problems which so drastically affect children today grow out of the fact that there are so many of them. The increased number of pupils attending schools can easily result in larger class size and consequently a diminishing personal relationship between the teacher and the learner. Children today, living in a permissive atmosphere in the school as well as in the home, are often insecure, undisciplined, "bratty," and rude. Their sense of security is further weakened by the ever-growing size of the school, church, and community. Few children have time alone, and most are lost when they have free time, for they do not know how to create their own fun. Children of nonwhite or other minority groups have never been burdened with problems of insecurity and hatred as they are now. Many youngsters face special physical, mental, and emotional problems, and others have economic and educational ones related to the area in which they live. In addition, there are far more broken homes, and yet the number of births is increasing.[2] Today in America 40 percent of all mothers of illegitimate children are below 20 years of age, and 2 percent are under the age of 15 years (significant and useful facts for those who endorse and conduct family-life education in our schools). Juvenile delinquency, a social cancer, is spreading at an alarming rate in rural as well as urban areas. Manpower shortages

[2] *Ibid.*

in public health and welfare departments are serious. City slums, an unsolved problem, continue to be a hotbed for the increase in disease, infant death, tuberculosis, venereal diseases, robbery, and homicide. The poorest housing from the standpoint of healthful and sanitary facilities is found in rural areas and small towns.

On the educational scene, although all but three states have compulsory school attendance laws, under many of these laws children may be excused to work in agriculture. Of the 4,491 children employed in farm work in 1957–58 who were under 16 years of age, three out of five were found to be in grades far below normal for their age. Many migratory workers are children. In 1957, among 77,000 of such laborers, 18 percent were below the age of 18. Children who drop out of school are most likely to become common laborers or service workers. Unemployment is highest among young workers with the least amount of schooling. Those with a college education have the widest and best choice of jobs, and the demand for highly trained workers is increasing rapidly.

In all public and private schools, classroom and teacher shortages persist. Some few children receive a better education than the majority; this depends largely upon the economic status of the parents and the area the child was fortunate enough to live in. Although child mortality is decreasing, among nonwhites it is still high, and for Indian children the situation today is similar to that of the general population 25 years ago. Accidents and cancer are the most common causes of death among children. In spite of our wealth and abundance of food, many children have poor diets. Dietary habits of adolescent girls tend to be poorer than those of boys in this age group. In spite of our many advances in education and science, the number of children with mental and serious emotional problems is increasing.

UNDERSTANDING CHILDREN IN GRADES 1 AND 2

Physically, children in the primary grades are extremely active, and joyously run, skip, jump, and hop but are not yet able to use effectively the small muscles of their bodies in such activities as catching a ball, sewing, or writing. Their bones are soft, their eyes far-sighted, and their permanent teeth gradually replacing the baby, or deciduous, ones. Since this is a period of rapid growth, in which the normal child gains from 3 to 6 pounds in weight and 1 to 3 inches in height, these children need plenty of sleep and rest (10 to 12 hours daily), rugged outdoor play, and much nourishing food.

Socially, primary children question continually as a means of gaining attention from adults and will do almost anything to be noticed by them, and are selfishly egocentric, with little concern for others or desire to share with them. Some few are beginning to show sex differences in interests and play activities. They are extremely sensitive to ridicule, failure, or loss of adult approval, and thrive on praise. Often they experiment in testing how far they can go in order to rile adults and do so through "shocking" language, unkempt appearance, or boisterous horseplay. They often show many fears, including those of the sight of blood (which is significant for accidents are numerous in this age group), death, fainting, darkness, being left alone or deserted, dentists, doctors, or even nurses. Minor changes in their daily routine upset them. Some are curious about sex and seek information from their playmates in secretive ways, or by means of blunt and direct questions to their parents or other adults such as "Where do babies come from?" and "How does the baby get out of (or into) the mother's stomach?" Many are shy, sensitive, stubborn, and selfish.

Intellectually, this is a period of great curiosity, and in their eagerness to smell, touch, taste, and explore these children are like hummingbirds—flitting quickly from this to that and drinking in as many brief moments of living as they can. They like to experiment and use their own ingenuity rather than follow a set of definite directions. Most of them respond wholeheartedly to a challenge and are talkative in their desire to exchange information (secret or otherwise) with their teachers, neighborhood adult friends, and peers. Certain favorite words and expressions, such as "actually," or "my mother always," etc., are used almost continuously to start each sentence.

Sex Differences. Girls during this period of middle childhood tend to grow and change slowly. Each has her own pace and pattern, whether it be a skinny or a chubby one. Gradually the former begin

All children need opportunities to be alone sometimes, and to wander as well as wonder. (Courtesy, AAHPER.)

to fill out in shape, while the latter begin to taper down and lose their baby roundness. Most children get their permanent front teeth at the age of seven. Although small-muscle coordination is poor, it is improving and girls at this age are increasingly more able to write and print more legibly. Respiratory diseases, which have reached their peak at six years, tend to diminish in frequency, but still remain a health hazard. This period is the age for mumps, measles, and chickenpox. Since girls in this age group fatigue easily, they should have at least four hours of outdoor play and eleven hours of sleep in well-ventilated rooms.

Mentally, girls in this age group are full of imagination, and they delight in make-believe play. Although many no longer believe in Santa Claus or the Easter Bunny, practically all of them have favorite television characters, alive or animated, which seem real to them. They ask many questions in this stage of their development. They are extremely creative and delight in expressing themselves in original dances, drawings, and in many other ways. Their response to rhythm is great. When speaking to others, they are unable to put themselves in the role of the listener, for they still are controlled largely by their own egocentric drives. Since their sense of humor is undeveloped, they fail to see much that is funny in what they hear and read. Although their memory tends to be good, their attention and interest span is short. They delight in enacting adult heroine roles, including being mothers, teachers, actresses, and greatly enjoy dressing up in high heels, enormous hats, flowing dresses, much jewelry, and, of course, lipstick and heavy face powder. Girls go quickly from one interest to another, but tend to cling to "favorite" games with a fierce conservatism that is amazing to adults. These children love pets and try to "mother" them. They enjoy going on trips and are especially fond of hearing about other children in other lands.

During the formative years of middle childhood, a girl's feelings largely center around herself and gaining approval from adults. Teachers working with girls in Grades 1 to 3 should be cognizant of the areas in which these children need the most help. She can contribute greatly toward the development of each girl in each of these grades by assisting her to:

1. Feel wanted, needed, and loved in her own peer group and by the adults in the school, and help her feel that she is worthy of this acceptance and love.
2. Become increasingly more independent by giving her tasks of real importance to do which call for her to make decisions.
3. Accept and prefer the feminine role.
4. Develop physical skills through increased and well-directed play activities.
5. Find things she can do exceptionally well for a young girl of her age and help her enjoy doing self-chosen activities.
6. Increase her appreciation for rules, her ability to take directions from others, and to conduct herself according to accepted behavior standards.

Boys in Grades 1 to 3 are in a rapidly changing and kaleidoscopic period of dirt, noise, questions, skinned knees and treasure-filled pockets. Although their growth is relatively slow, they are increasing in ability to resist many diseases, except those which are respiratory in nature, for it is during the beginning of this period that such diseases reach a maximum peak. By the age of 6, most boys have reached over half of their final height. This is the period of missing teeth for boys as well as girls. These boys fatigue easily and need eleven hours of sleep. Although they are slower in learning to read and write than girls, they are faster at numbers. Increasingly, their questions become more intelligent, and their desire "to find out" about a wide variety of things makes teaching this age group of young males an exciting and challenging experience. Those in the first grade have about a 20-minute attention span, which gradually increases as the pupils advance in school. Although during this period writing ability lags behind speech and reading skills, nevertheless, boys of this age are beginning to enjoy reading for pleasure, and delight in selecting their own books to read from the school and town library.

Physically, boys in Grades 1 to 3 dote upon games which involve much chasing and fleeing, horseplay, and large-muscle activity. Although they are gaining a concept of rules and their necessity in games, they are often quicker to label a classmate as a "big cheater" than to realize that they frequently disobey game rules themselves. Imitative play patterns change from wanting to be a daddy, doctor, or policeman to those of being a cop or robber, Indian or cowboy, spaceman or skin diver. Like girls of this age, boys are also keenly interested in learning about faraway places and people in distant lands. Their pockets are miniature museums, and many of their fights with classmates revolve around endeavors to swap or barter "this treasure for that one." Radio, television, and comic series which stress western and adventure stories are favorites. Although their attitudes toward parents and adults are changing, they still seek their approval. Increasingly they engage in exploratory behavior by frequent use of "cuss words" or daring actions. Sibling rivalry becomes more apparent, especially when they feel a threat to their own security, which they will often strive to maintain by regressing back to infantile behavior. Although they crave adult and peer approval, they also seek gradually increasing independence. They constantly must be reminded to be neat and clean, for most boys during this time are inattentive and just plain messy. Truthfulness is not as common as lying or deceitfulness, but this should be recognized as a type of "finding out how far they can go" behavior. By the age of eight, most boys have learned their school role, have tried out their teachers and know fairly accurately how far they can go with them. In their search for friends, they seek out those who will satisfy their own needs, and friendship becomes all-important to them. Fighting is characteristic behavior, and by the age of eight, fist fights often replace name-calling and threats.

As the boy grows older, there are many important "life lessons" he must learn in order to get along with people around him. Freedom of pressure from overanxious adults will aid children in this age bracket in bridging successfully the gap between middle and late childhood. Since the difference between childhood and adulthood is that between being and becoming, those teaching developing and rapidly changing boys should have the utmost patience, understanding, and serenity. Teachers of this age group need to know when "not to see," when "not to hear," and when "to step in" to give greatly needed help and encouragement.

A teacher can most successfully work with boys in Grades 1 to 3 by helping them:

1. Gain a sense of worth in the eyes of their parents, for they are the chief source of each child's feelings and attitudes toward himself.
2. Gain love, recognition, and acceptance from their peers and adults without feeling they have to fight for these.
3. Recognize their role in the family as a group member and not as the hub around which the family wheel rotates.
4. Gain security through firm, consistent routine and discipline.
5. Widen their circle of friends; assist in the development of social and physical skills.
6. Learn why and how boys are different from girls; help each accept the male sex role.
7. Answer all sex questions briefly and honestly, always avoiding giving the child the feeling that sex is dirty or secretive.
8. Develop large-muscle control, especially in running, throwing, and catching.
9. Feel successful in their attempts to learn or succeed.
10. Take part in meaningful small tasks at home, school, and play.
11. Channel needs for adventure into increased opportunities for learning more about their own environment and more about the exciting new world of nature and living things.

12. Increase their ability to follow directions given by others, as well as to become more self-directing.
13. Develop an increased sense of values.

Health Interests and Needs. Both boys and girls at this stage are not at all interested in health or safety except when they themselves are ill or have an accident, but they do have a mild interest in learning how to play without getting hurt, or how to come to or go from school safely, especially if they like school. However, they can be made actively interested in safety when stimulated by an expert teacher who knows the events of a child's world, such as a new baby sister, puppy, or pony. The children get keenly interested in taking good care of these newcomers and in turn, taking good care of themselves. They are only faintly interested in keeping themselves neat and clean, but can be easily motivated to do so if they are made aware that this is one sure way to gain approval and recognition from the teacher. Their concern for public health is practically nil, as is their general indifference concerning loss of their baby teeth, an abundance of freckles on the face, or the necessity of wearing thick glasses in order to see or braces in order to walk. In their eagerness to express themselves as they wonderingly explore their world, regardless of how they look when they laugh or how they seem to others, their enthusiasm carries them into many glorious adventures. They need adult supervision and protection while they play (for they are awkward and almost totally unaware that there are others near and often become venturesome daredevils in order to attract attention), while they eat (for they bolt their food in their eagerness to get outside and play), and while they work at school (for their attention span is extremely short). Provision should be made for them to engage in activities involving the large muscles—in vigorous games, and using large sheets of paper and large pencils and brushes in writing and creative art. Brief, repeated safety instructions should be given to instill desirable habits in each child as he plays, rides his bicycle, walks, or is driven to and from school. Each one should also be provided with the proper seating facilities and have his seat moved according to his hearing and seeing needs as discovered through testing. Health habits and a knowledge of "why" should become a part of all children's actions and understanding in such things as using one's own towel and other toilet articles, use of handkerchief or tissues, keeping objects out of the mouth, nose, and ears, what to do in case of an emergency or accident, teeth and mouth care and hygiene, as well as how to wash and bathe properly. Good eating habits should be developed, but the teacher should be more concerned that the child eats a balanced lunch than with how he eats. Likewise, she must always be aware of each pupil's need for encouragement, and help him gain self-confidence, self-control, and acceptance from his peers and from his parents and family.

Teaching Implications. The teacher should make every effort to capitalize upon the children's natural curiosity and their eagerness to learn in her efforts to help them develop good health habits ranging from washing their hands before eating and after going to the toilet to getting enough sleep. Furthermore, she must realize that her primary task is getting the children to *want* to do these things. Since so many first graders are venturing away from home for the first time, she should place stress upon good safety practices coming to and going from school, as well as repeatedly cautioning them not to accept rides from strangers, and not to pet strange dogs, cats, or other animals. From the standpoint of mental health, she should make every effort to see that each pupil is accepted by the group and overcomes his many fears of being away from home for the first time and being on his own. By getting the children to talk and express themselves in other ways, she can gain a better understanding of the feelings, tensions, and anxieties each one has. Child psychologists claim that the more the teacher talks the less she will learn about children. Friendliness is one of the best approaches to use with these primary pupils, for as Hymes points out, "When you are friendly you turn the air-conditioners on. The climate is right. You tone down the distractions. Your children like you so the working conditions are good. Now you are ready to teach."[3] Much can also be done in helping each child feel that the teacher, as well as the entire class, is concerned about his well-being and happiness. This can best be accomplished by treating each child kindly, by not

[3] James Hymes, *A Child Development Point of View,* Englewood Cliffs, N.J., Prentice-Hall, 1955, p. 47.

showing favoritism, and by being firm and consistent in one's behavior and attitudes toward the class. It is also important that each child succeed in some area, whether this be in learning to read or cleaning out the cage of the class pet. Group discussion and "show and tell" periods are effective, valuable techniques in the teaching of health on all levels of the elementary school, but especially in the primary grades. Bauer suggests that, since research discloses that attitudes *can* be changed greatly as a result of talking things over in a group, teachers can best guide class discussions by:

1. Giving children a chance to think before they talk.
2. Referring questions back to children now and then by saying, "Helen, what do you think of this?" or "Jim, how do you feel about that?"
3. Bringing into the discussion a child who rarely volunteers.
4. Listening closely to each child's remarks and commenting upon them.
5. Occasionally telling of her own experiences or her own opinion.
6. Summarizing the main points of the discussion.[4]

Because second graders often tend to become too dependent upon adults, emphasis in health education for the seven-year-old should be in helping him become more self-directed concerning his own health and safety. Again, the emphasis should be placed upon stressing why he should do this or that for his own well-being and protection. Since many in this age group have their first experience with operations (usually tonsillectomies) and more painful experiences than they had as six-year-olds with a dentist, the teacher should devote time periodically to discussions of what a hospital is like, why the dentist is our friend, what we can do to recover quickly from an operation, and how to prevent tooth decay. A good time to do this is when an absent pupil who has been to the hospital returns to the class or when the teacher knows that certain pupils have dental appointments. Likewise, second graders should be given increased opportunities for more vigorous types of outdoor play, and for experimenting with self-testing activities such as cartwheels or handsprings, and opportunities to do creative dance. In safety education, attention should be given to safety en route to school, on

[4] W. W. Bauer, Dorothy Baruch, Elizabeth Montgomery, Eleanore Pounds, and William Gray, *Just Like Me* (teacher's edition of the Picture Primer of the Basic Health and Safety Program), Chicago, Scott, Foresman, 1957, p. 22.

bicycles, riding the school bus, or in the family car. Fire and air-raid drills should be held periodically so that each child knows exactly what to do in case of such an emergency. In the area of mental and social health, many opportunities should be provided for the children to express their feelings toward themselves, school, families, and life in general. Stress should be placed upon helping the children become kind and considerate to others, as well as upon good sportsmanship. Likewise, the pupils should be taught how to profit and learn from their mistakes, and that failure as well as success are parts of life. The teacher should avoid comparing children within the class, but should, instead, help each pupil feel that he has a secure and needed place in "our class." Field trips taken to visit a bakery, farm, or other places all help make health education exciting. Simple experiments, movies, filmstrips, and other visual aids give children opportunities to learn new things and to connect them with previously held ideas and attitudes concerning health. Role playing, as well as other dramatic activities, will enable the children to gain insight upon healthy ways to handle their feelings and pent-up emotions. Since sex education cannot be taught solely with facts suitable for the seven-year-old to learn and understand, a good classroom emotional environment is of paramount importance in helping boys and girls learn to accept their own sex roles in life, consideration of other people and all other aspects of good human relationships, which in reality is sex education suitable for all primary children.

Third graders are ready for more advanced work in health education and for receiving an increased amount of specific information. At this stage in their development, muscular coordination is improving, for the eight-year-old is in what experts call "the rhythmical stage." Teachers can capitalize upon this increased skill and desire for self-expression by having pupils increase the number and quality of visual aids they make to illustrate what they are learning in health. Since the permanent teeth are continuing to come in, dental care should be reemphasized, along with the value of a balanced diet as a means of preventing decay and stimulating growth. Those who are thin, tall, and growing rapidly are most apt to develop poor posture. Consequently, stress should be placed upon developing and maintaining good posture, as well as learning the reasons for doing so. As leaders, children at this age are going through a "bossy period." The teacher can do much to help them desire to become popular democratic leaders through committee assignments in health instruction, as well as by incorporating units of study on how to become a leader or group member in larger areas of mental and personal hygiene. Children in this age group tend to be more competitive than they were previously, and will delight in all types of contests which can be utilized in helping to learn health facts, such as modified forms of spelling bees. Health clubs can well be introduced in this grade level; these activities will not only help the children express their needs to belong and "boss," but can be an avenue for helping them learn many things about getting along with others, or almost any aspect of physical, mental, and social health. Cub Scout, Brownie, and Bluebird groups all provide opportunities for youngsters to put in practice things they have learned in school and at home about health, but can, if the teacher will work closely with the leaders of these groups, add to and make more meaningful many new experiences in health which can best be learned outside the classroom, such as campfire safety or first-aid treatment for heel blisters or sunburn. Boys and girls at this period increasingly seek friends of their own sex. This provides many opportunities for an alert teacher in the area of sex education, such as "Why Boy Friends Should Also Like Girls," or "How Our Parents Work Together." Since reading comics becomes a favorite pastime of children this age, parents as well as teachers should recommend and guide youngsters to well-written adventure stories, animal tales, and Indians, which have educational as well as entertainment value. The wise adult will help them grow in ability to understand, react, and make use of what they read. Weekly scheduled discussion hours built around the theme "What I Did This Week in My Leisure Time," in which each child tells his classmates what he did for fun that week can help the instructor gain insight into what each pupil has done, his actual feelings, or other valuable information. In turn, the class can benefit and learn from such experiences. The wise educator realizes that the children can and do learn much from each other about many things, including health.

CHARACTERISTICS OF CHILDREN IN GRADES 4 TO 6

Physically, children in these grades continue to grow rapidly in weight and height, tire easily, and are in a period of development when there is danger of overexertion, with consequent damage to the heart. They have a higher degree of endurance, vitality, and resistance to disease than younger children. Some show a growth spurt and become awkward much earlier than others. Boys increase more rapidly in strength and endurance, making it wise to separate the sexes in most physical education classes starting in the fourth grade. Body-build differences and family characteristics become more apparent. Boys tend to be noisier, more active, and daring in sports, whereas girls prefer rhythmical activities and sports and games rather than unsupervised, physically exhausting, and often roughhouse gang play.

Socially these children often manifest emotional instability due to their rapid growth. They begin to show less emotional attachment to parents, teachers, or other adults and develop almost inseparable bonds with their own same-sex gang to whom they vow (sometimes in blood) to remain forever devoted and loyal. Although boys often show more timidity and reluctance than girls in social situations, they are more apt to take daring chances or do things they know are harmful or wrong in order to gain group acceptance and status. Individuals of both sexes, in their attempts to belong to desired groups, often do strange and outlandish things which are shocking and puzzling to adults. Most show an increased desire to make more of the decisions which affect them and seek independence in caring for their own personal needs, appearance, and making their own clothing selections. There is a marked interest in organized and competitive games and a strong desire emerging in a few to learn and perfect physical skills, but the majority still just want to play on a team, without striving to be its "star" or captain. This is a period when there is danger of developing morbid fears and guilt complexes concerning one's own changing body, masturbation, and "sexy" thoughts. Both boys and girls show an increased interest in community and world affairs. They are apt to be restless, eager for activity, and although they attempt many things, still are not too concerned about finishing them. Likewise, they become discouraged easily and often are surly and uncooperative when frustrated by failure. In the latter stage of this period, they frequently become overly critical of others, especially adults (including teachers). Some become extremely aggressive, and are often cruel to smaller children and animals. Because this is a period of crushes and hero worship, an adored adult can do much to mold these plastic personalities into good citizens, or can be the deciding factor in their career selection for later life. However, the adult must be careful to handle these "crushes" carefully, realizing that they are temporary and a phase of growing up. This is also a time for extreme loyalty to a team or club group. These children can still be influenced and controlled by earned adult praise but not if gaining it will in any way be detrimental to their group acceptance by major or even subpeer groups. Many become emotionally upset because they are treated "like a baby" and told to "act your age," when at the same time adults often expect more of them in accepting responsibility or making grown-up decisions than they are able to do.

Intellectually, these children are imitative, imaginative, and creative. They seek to know the reason behind things instead of blindly accepting facts or concepts adults claim to be true. They want to know how things are put together and can be taken apart as well as what makes them work, and delight in experimenting and discovering these things for themselves. Their attention span has increased, as well as their ability to think more logically. Toward the end of this period most have developed a strong sense of right and wrong, are loyal, and have an awakening sense of fairness and a concern for the rights of others. Most are idealistic and optimistic about themselves, and life in general.

Sex Differences. Girls during this period of late childhood are exploring and testing their relationships with others and experimenting with their own abilities to cope successfully with assuming a more grown-up and responsible role in life. They want their own way, and they want to be popular with their peers. Each likes to play at being an adult, but in a different and more meaningful way than she did as a child; she now tries wearing face makeup not just for fun but as a means of making herself more desirable to her circle of friends. Her dresses and shoes resemble those of adult women. For her friends she chooses a group in which she can feel adequate, but will seek again the security of her family when tensions or conflicts threaten her security. The ninth year is a clear dividing line between childhood and girlhood for most girls. A new growth spurt begins at the age of ten when they become and remain taller than boys for the next three years, but at 13 the boys regain a height lead. During this period, girls are giggly, untidy, noisy, and often rude. By the age of 11 the hips begin to widen, breasts begin to develop, and pubic hair appears. Some few begin to menstruate before they are eleven, and the majority do so by the age of fourteen.

Although girls in Grades 4 through 6 still have a relatively short interest span, they are starting to understand causal relationships and abstractions, as well as developing a budding interest in the personal problems of other people. Television programs, usually romantic in nature, keep them glued to the set for hours, and listening to rock-and-roll records, and long telephone conversations become favorite pastimes. This is also a period of great curiosity, alertness, and eagerness for many new kinds of experiences. Although she can understand what is right and wrong, by the time she is in the sixth grade, she delights in discussing what is good or bad, fair or unfair. Although there is little interest in boys during this period, girls have many romantic attachments, but they are with remote, older movie, television, or recording stars. Physical skills which require many hours of determined practice are popular with this age group, especially swimming, dancing, or learning how to play a musical instrument. The family remains their mecca of security, and parents become more important to them, even though girls during this stage in their development take their first real steps toward independence. Adults wisely do not decrease family rules, but instead increase some possibilities of free choice and provide helpful behavior suggestions. Adults outside of the home begin to carry more importance, and girls aged nine to eleven begin to place more value on the judgments of their adult teachers or club leaders. These girls also begin to reflect more clearly the prejudices of their parents, and are becoming increasingly concerned about the welfare of others. They also welcome opportunities for community service. Although their desire to serve others is real, it is often a part of a more subtle and strongly felt need for recognition and attention. Each has some insight into her strengths and weaknesses, yet disappointments can often deal crushing and long-lasting blows. In the desire to do well and have everything go right, they often spend needless energy, tears, and worry about the great injustices they find in life, or about the guilty, secretive thoughts or acts they have and are afraid to share with their parents.

As each girl grows, she has special problems she must solve and adjustments she must make if she is to progress successfully to her next developmental stage in life. Adults who provide guidance and encouragement can assist each one in making a smoother, happier transition from childhood to girlhood, for these youngsters need a warm, friendly response from adults as well as their friends if they are to develop a healthy aspect of self-acceptance. Teachers especially can be of tremendous help by assisting each pupil to:

1. Feel accepted, needed, and valuable.
2. Find happiness in making others happy.
3. Become an effective family member who is becoming increasingly skilled and secure in her relationships with others outside her own home.
4. Enlarge her social horizon, develop new interests, and deepen life values.
5. Accept her feminine role and develop a growing appreciation in feminine interests and skills.
6. Develop a growing understanding and appreciation of her own changing body.
7. Increase skill competency; encourage interest in many creative things which will add to her enjoyment and that of others around her.
8. Experience a wide range of recreational activities and to take an active role in positive group fun.
9. Increase and deepen a growing appreciation for justice and fair play.

As Clarence Moser has said, "a boy is nature's answer to the false belief there is no such thing as perpetual motion." In later childhood, the boy in Grades 4 to 6 seems to have a superabundance of energy and is ever on the move. He has been described as one "who can swim like a fish, run like a deer, balk like a mule, bellow like a bull, act like a pig, or carry on like a jackass according to climatic conditions."

A growing child is an adult in the making who has a long way to go before he finally arrives at maturity. It is a long, slow, and often painful journey for many. Each one is not only different, but reacts, thinks, looks, acts, and feels differently. Physically, the growth of boys during this period is slow, but by the age of eleven, each is about four-fifths of his adult height. Because of his increased activity, his appetite is amazing. Most need between 10 and 11 hours of sleep nightly. Although hand-eye and foot-eye coordination is increasing, there is limited skill in most sports during this period and not as much natural interest in competition as those who promote Little League softball, Biddy basketball, or sandlot football claim to be present. In fact, too much competition in sports can be extremely harmful to boys in this age group. Shocking words, crude jokes, and increased sex curiosity are characteristic of fourth, fifth, and sixth grade males. Mental development is often far more rapid than physical growth, for this is a great period for expanding curiosity, experimentation, and adventure. Animal stories, tales of heroes, mysteries, and comic books are eagerly read. Although their interest span and ability to concentrate are increasing, interest in their own activities often makes them seem ruder and cruder than they actually are. They can completely block out the words of those speaking to them and are frequently lost in an adventurous Walter Mitty dream world of their own. Those who seemed slower in previous grades often show marked improvement in the fourth grade, while those who previously seemed the brightest before often now need special guidance and help. Play interests center around the more manly team sports, which they play with more aggressive spirit than physical skill. They are still avid collectors of almost anything which embraces science, prehistoric animals, and discoveries. Friendship of each with his buddies or "gang" is characterized by roughhouse play, pushing, and sometimes vicious practical jokes. This is the age for a boy to like to the utmost what he is doing, and he will try to do plenty! Some of his explorations into the forbidden and unknown get him into serious trouble with his parents and sometimes with juvenile authorities. His eagerness to please his gang instead of his parents often causes inner guilt feelings and many family conflicts. Although he frequently complains that adults do not "understand" him, it is really his own lack of self-understanding that is at the root of much of his difficulty. Although he is not as anxious to have his mother at home when he comes in from school, he feels hurt when he is not sure where his parents are or when to expect them back. His adult hero is usually one who is good in sports and is available for a talk, or to lend a listening, sympathetic, and understanding ear. His dislike for girls and taking part in social activities with them is real and intense; he is extremely critical of the opposite and "weaker" sex. Inwardly, he longs to be independent, yet is usually proud of his parents and feels close to his home environment. He is well aware that his body is changing, and because of his embarrassment refuses to undress in the presence of his mother. His fear of being labeled sissy, coward, or not as good as others around him is a nightmare. At times he seems increasingly conscious of wrongdoing, yet often cheats in game situations in order to gain group status and recognition.

Teachers of boys in the upper elementary grades can be of great help to them during this stage in their development. Above all, they should help each boy to:

1. Feel wanted and accepted by his family, other adults, and peers.
2. Find real satisfaction in making other people happy.
3. Feel he can respond to and please his group without coming into conflict with his parents.
4. Get started in a group; increase his circle of friends.
5. Accept his sex role in life.
6. Decrease his fear of failure or doing things wrong.
7. Feel assured that he is useful and of value to others.
8. Share and voluntarily assume group responsibilities.
9. Find positive outlets for his increased need for adventure and desire to "find out" more about life.
10. Increase and deepen his sense of values, and respect for fair play.
11. Provide an environment of love and understanding for others.
12. Develop a realistic ability to evaluate what others have done well or failed to do correctly.
13. Profit and learn from his mistakes.
14. Develop self-confidence.
15. Talk with adults he trusts when things are bothering him.
16. Establish a consistent routine for work and play so that he can operate as freely as possible without unnecessary rules or regulations.

Health Interests and Needs. Children of this age group need longer periods of outdoor play, coupled with skilled instruction, for these are the skill-hungry years wherein basic movement patterns and many lifelong habits and interests can be developed most successfully. In their exuberance to succeed in play or other activities, however, the majority need additional time for rest and relaxation and should be helped in gaining an understanding of why they need this rest, as well as taught the way to do so. Many desperately need help and guidance in making adjustments in order to gain group acceptance, and the extra time and energy the teacher spends in individual guidance for self-improvement are well worth the effort. The pimply faced girl, the fat boy who cannot catch or kick a soccer ball, or the near-sighted class scapegoat all need personal encouragement and assistance. The vast majority of pupils in this age group are keenly interested in learning about how to be popular, what qualities are needed for making and keeping friends, and how to be more physically attractive. Most want to receive specific, accurate sex information. Girls especially are eager to know the true facts about menstruation, for some of them will have already started to menstruate—a fact well-discussed, whispered, and worried about among themselves and their girl friends. This is also a period of marked need for adequate nutritional education and increased guidance in selecting food wisely, and a time when pupils need help and increased motivation to take good care of their eyes, ears, skin, and teeth. During these important and formative years, it is imperative that children have a home and a school that are as attractive, stimulating, and magnetic as the ever-expanding, longed-for, danger-filled great world of adventure unfolding before them.

Youngsters in the upper elementary level differ in height, weight, and body build, in things they have seen, heard, done, or read about, as well as in their social and emotional maturity. Starting in the fourth grade, specific health interests and needs center around teeth-straightening and braces, the care of the new first and second bicuspids, and their own changing bodies. This is the school year when reading abilities become apparent, and therefore the time when both teachers and adults, who are aware that the total personality and educational future of any child with reading difficulties may be in jeopardy, should see to it that such a child is helped immediately. Since pupils at this age are trying to develop standards of right or wrong, they are interested in learning what happens to the "bad" as well as the "good" guy. Dr. Gesell claims that "Nine is finally becoming what his parents have been striving for." Consequently, if the child's parents are interested in health, this pupil will also show a marked concern in learning more about health and for developing good health habits at this age. The ten- and eleven-year-olds are in that phase which Dr. Fritz Redl has characterized as "when the nicest children begin to behave in an awful way." Their interest in what is happening to their own bodies is of paramount importance to them. Likewise, because of the many physical changes which are taking place at this time, great energy spurts and periods of keen interest in what they are doing and learning in school are often followed by laziness and lassitude. Each child has his own unique maturing and growth pattern. Consequently, some are still "little girls or little boys" while others of the same age have grown up faster and have more advanced interests and needs. This great variation makes this age group hard to plan for as well as reach as a class. Likewise, since their emotions fluctuate very rapidly the need for wise counsel and steady guidance is paramount. Although they want to be attractive and well liked, boys (and sometimes girls) do not brush their teeth unless checked, or even bathe as frequently as they should. Having the same age, being in the same grade, or living on the same block are the principal criteria for group membership at first, but because of differences in the rate of growing up, groups change membership frequently, and there is usually much quarreling, "dropping out," and "leaving out." Groups of boys tend to be more stable in membership than those of girls. Both sexes work and play well together with those of their own sex. Both boy and girl "gangs" or "clubs" often take on service projects with a real zest. Many youngsters are interested in learning more about a vocation they are interested in entering when grown up. Boys as well as girls often voluntarily take on work experiences not only for monetary reasons but because they want to find out what it is like to "have a paying job." Hobbies are all-important to those in the fifth and sixth grades, and often these pay rich dividends in helping the children learn faster and more about the things in which they show interest, whether this be in some phase of health or in any other school subject. Stories of other lands and people and love of country cause them to want to become good citizens and to do a good deed daily. Children of this age need and seek frank answers to their questions about sex; they need to belong to a gang they can be loyal to; and they should have increased responsibilities in the home, school, and the community. They are now ready for more advanced school work and challenging educational experiences. Wise supervision and patient understanding from friendly adults can help them become outstanding youngsters, which is what most of them really want to be. Membership in clubs or school activities which help them work toward "worthy goals" should be encouraged. Since skill mastery is one of the great desires of youth, they should receive expert instruction so that they can win both group status and recognition for their physical, social, and mental accomplishments.

Teaching Implications. The health education program for pupils in Grades 4 to 6 should:

1. Place increased emphasis upon reasons why healthful living habits should be developed.
2. Provide numerous opportunities and activities through which pupils can develop a good sense of values and gain a sense of personal worth, responsibility for their own actions, and increased insight into the rights of others.
3. Devise committees wherein boys and girls can work and play together, make plans and carry them out, and learn through trial and error.
4. Build wholesome attitudes toward self, the opposite sex, and life.
5. Provide counseling for those with individual problems, either through individual or group guidance.
6. Offer a wide variety of health education activities, including learning how to give simple first aid, and what to do in order to be well, happy, and safe.
7. Provide opportunities for self-evaluation as well as for group evaluation, stressing "What did you learn from this experience?" and "How could you have done this better?" (rather than "What did you do that was wrong?").

Teachers of this age group can create through their example and direction a friendly classroom environment wherein pupils can learn readily, gain new friends, and succeed in their attempts to grow up. Since boys and girls in this crucial stage in their development can be

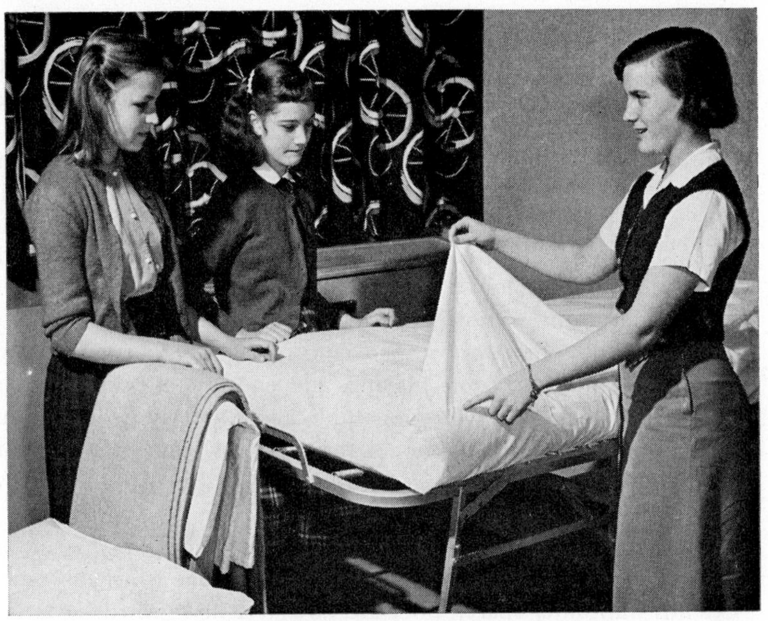

Home nursing can be an important part of a health education program for sixth grade girls. (Courtesy, N.E.A.)

helped or hindered in their trial-and-error attempts to learn, it is of utmost importance that their teacher accept each pupil as he actually is, not as she wishes he would be. She must remember that all behavior has a cause, and she must be cognizant that when her students do "bad" or negative things it is because of an apparent or concealed reason and not because they deliberately "want to be bad." Care must be taken not to label a pupil as "lazy," "stupid," or anything else, for such tags remain with children longer than adults realize. Since the parents know more about their children than does anyone else, they and the teacher should become working partners interested in the welfare and full development of each youth. It has often been said that the more a teacher knows a child as a human being, the better she can help him grow and learn. The teacher's enthusiasm for health and her own well-being will do far more to encourage youngsters to want to become healthy than anything else. These children need to be guided and taught by skilled teachers who will challenge them to reach new learning heights, will help them to broaden and deepen life values, and can laugh with them and like the things they enjoy. Those who provide a stimulating, personalized classroom learning atmosphere will find that their pupils will not willingly skip school because they will miss doing and learning things that are exciting to take part in and do. Because some children have difficult home lives, the teacher should provide many harmless ways to work out feelings of hostility and frustration. Conversation periods, making things which require hitting and pounding, providing chances for getting dirty, encouraging creative art work, role playing, and encouraging the pupils to write down what they feel or think about, all provide growing youngsters with good emotional safety valves. Cooperative group activities should be emphasized rather than individual competitive ones.

Interests of children in the intermediate grades are expanding from their own ego-centered world to a wider one which now even extends into outer space. They are now at a new growth level and are ready for more challenging and exacting types of learning experiences. Since they are more curious than ever before, they especially like to experiment and find out things for themselves. It has been said, in truth, that

> The ingenious teacher, eager to vitalize teaching beyond texts and outlines, need only center planning around her group of 9 to 12 year olds to find important needs to be met, real life situations to be faced, and challenging problems to be solved. With teacher and pupils together setting goals, deciding upon ways to achieve them, executing their plans, and evaluating their success, a more dynamic health education program for the middle grades will take shape. It can be one that will provide significant learning experiences.[5]

While building desirable health practices should be stressed in the primary level, health instruction in the intermediate grades should emphasize helping the children learn the "why," the "how," and the "what" of health education. In some schools, health science now becomes an important part of the basic science program. Like-

[5] *Health Education,* 5th ed., Washington, D.C., National Education Association and American Medical Association, 1961, p. 165.

wise, health instruction should become more scientific, and the pupils be provided with increased opportunities to study and learn physiological facts from simplified anatomical charts. Leading questions such as "What do you think you look like inside?" will not only help motivate interest but give the teacher insight upon just what the pupils do or do not know about their own bodies. It is important in this age of scientific marvels, wherein men are pushing out into new frontiers into the space above as well as below the earth and sea, that the pupils gain a sense of deep appreciation of the greatest wonder of all creation—their own bodies.

The health education program should be based upon the health needs and interests of the pupils. These may be found by preliminary fact-finding research, which might well entail a careful study of:

The kinds of accidents her pupils usually have at home, school, or play
Their health practices and knowledge as exemplified by their behavior in the classroom, lunchroom, on the playground, or elsewhere
The causes of most school absences
Their past health education experiences; how potent and meaningful these have been in shaping behavior, health attitudes, and values
Mistaken ideas they have about health and safety
Community and national health problems that should be of concern to them
Ways to better the family's health through educating the pupil
Specific health problems of each pupil as observed, discussed with the nurse, or found from a health record

It is relatively simple to discover the health interests of these children. These can be disclosed by listening to and reading their questions, adjustment inventories, problem check lists, diaries, autobiographies, and other techniques. In a study to determine the health interests among the elementary pupils enrolled in the Denver public schools in 1954, the most frequently checked interest among boys in the intermediate grades was "to learn how to build muscles," and among the girls it was "to wear clean clothes."[6] Other major interest areas were health and safety, cleanliness and good grooming (girls), first aid, social adjustment and popularity (girls), muscle building

[6] *Health Interests of Children: A Report of a Research Study*, rev. ed., Denver, Colorado Board of Education, 1954.

and sports (boys). It is interesting to note also that these children wanted to learn about these areas by "doing" activities rather than by listening or memorizing. This study could be used as a pattern by any instructor who wants to discover the real health interests of her own pupils, and go on from there to provide a vitally important health education program for them.

The major health problem areas which should be studied in these grades are:

1. Nutrition and growth.
2. Safety and first aid.
3. Healthful living at school, at home, and in the community.
4. Infection and disease protection and control.
5. Sex education and social adjustment.
6. The structure, function, and care of the body.
7. Mental and emotional health.
8. Care of the eyes, teeth, ears.
9. Good grooming; the importance of cleanliness.
10. Sleep, play, and rest.
11. Posture and body control.
12. Self-medication, health products, and consumer education.
13. Community health.

In some schools, these areas may be integrated into larger units of study in social studies or science and may be called "Twentieth Century Man" or "Our Environment and How to Better It." However, regardless of how the health instructional materials are organized or the content of each lesson, it is the teacher alone who can make these learning experiences become important, meaningful, and personalized. The use of increased teacher-pupil planning, motivational techniques which can range all the way from leading questions such as "Do we have adequate protection from food poisoning in the food we buy in our town and in our school?" to seeing a film on how to become attractive, popular, and well groomed, and to activities in which each pupil can be actively engaged and is challenged to master new and important materials—all these can motivate increased pupil interest in health, deepen their health values, and improve their attitudes and behavior for healthier, happier, and more productive living. Wider use of community resources with and by these children will add richness to this phase of their education and growth.

BASIC NEEDS OF ALL CHILDREN

Needs basic to all children are (1) physiological (food, elimination, rest, exercise, and fresh air); (2) social (to belong, feel secure, gain recognition, and be loved); and (3) ego, or self, needs (a sense of pride and well-being, a need to love and build in conflict with a need to hate and destroy, to dominate as well as to cooperate, and to serve oneself first). All these needs combine to cause behavior. When a child's drives are adequately met, he is balanced, happy, and outgoing. When they clash, become thwarted, or submerged, atypical behavior often results, unless the child can be taught to rechannel negativeness into socially approved patterns. The "well" child needs help to remain well; the "sick" one needs assistance in order to become well.

No teacher can work successfully with a child who has deep-seated behavior problems, and no child needs help more than those who are burdened with problems, for no subject matter in school can receive their full attention, or have meaning until their own pressing problems are taken care of first.

Some of the most fruitful health teaching in the elementary school can be done through individual or group health guidance, wherein each pupil is aided to help himself face and solve his own problems. Frequently, a teacher can best reach problem-burdened pupils outside the classroom, and by indirect methods such as lending a sixth grade girl the splendid little booklet, *On Becoming a Woman,* when this youngster displayed an interest in it and asked if she could borrow it to read at home.[7]

Group guidance helps boys and girls achieve their own self-direction through increased cooperation with the group. It can be developmental, diagnostic, and therapeutic. Group influence, when guided by a skillful teacher, can do much to help a child with personality and behavior problems overcome these difficulties. The class bully can often be helped to understand his actions and improve upon them by a class discussion evolving around the question, "How can we become a good leader without bossing people around?"

[7] Mary Williams and Irene Kane, *On Becoming a Woman,* New York, Dell, 1959 (25¢).

or "What makes some children act mean or bully others?" The teacher can best reach the individual through the group when she has a genuine personal interest in the pupil having difficulty, and a friendly, sincere attitude toward him. The use of a sociogram can help the teacher locate leaders, cliques, and isolates, as well as serve as a useful guide in organizing the class into committees. Helping children become democratic group members requires patient guidance in living, working, and planning. This, too, is an important task for the teacher concerned about the development of each pupil to his utmost as a healthy, productive citizen.

Individual guidance has an important place in the health instructional program in elementary schools. Some pupils can best be reached through a more personalized approach. Atypical children need extra help; whether the handicap be orthopedic or mental-social, the exceptional child has all the adjustment problems of a normal child plus others of his own. These may be due to his own sensitivity and fears, familial overprotection, or the inability to keep up with more active and alert classmates. For these children, sometimes the best assistance can be given in building personality and character strength as well as in actual adjustment to school. The gifted child in this group should receive special attention and increased educational challenges which will help him make the contributions he can to society in the future and to his own present class group.

Projective techniques for studying individual children include (1) oral and written work, (2) sociodrama, (3) play, and (4) creative expression in arts and dance. All these methods help children act out needs and unconscious drives; they all give teachers insight and understanding into the behavior of children. Since it is a biological principle that all living organisms seek harmony and equilibrium through their behavior, the teacher who knows that this is the root of much overt negative behavior of many so-called "problem cases," can do much through example, by providing an environment wherein growth can best take place and by knowing as much as possible about each individual pupil. She can do much to assist each child, whether he be a cooperative pupil or a little devil, succeed in school and in life.

All teachers should capitalize upon the youngster's eager curiosity to find out all they can about themselves and the world in which they live. They should not only guide them in discovering the magic and wonder of life, but also create and capitalize upon classroom situations and experiences so that the children may find answers to their many questions and are stimulated, through a rich educational program, to a whole new widened and wonderful world!

SUGGESTED READINGS

Almy, Millie, *Ways of Studying Children,* New York, Teachers College, 1959.

Baldwin, Alfred, *Behavior and Development in Childhood,* New York, Dryden, 1955.

Breckenridge, Marian, and E. Vincent Lee, *Child Development,* 3rd ed., Philadelphia, Saunders, 1955.

Burrows, Alvina, *Teaching Children in the Middle Grades,* New York, Heath, 1952.

Children in Focus, Their Health and Their Activity, American Association for Health, Physical Education and Recreation, Washington, D.C., 1954.

Cunningham, Ruth, *Understanding Group Behavior,* New York, Teachers College, 1951.

D'Evelyn, R., *Meeting Children's Emotional Needs,* Englewood Cliffs, N.J., Prentice-Hall, 1957.

Florio, A. E., and G. T. Stafford, *Safety Education,* 2nd ed., New York, McGraw-Hill, 1961.

Health Interests of Children, rev. ed., Denver, Denver Board of Education, 1954.

Humphreys, Alice, *Heaven in My Hand; Angels in Pinafores,* Richmond, John Knox Press, 1951, 1955.

Jenkins, Gladys, Helen Shocter, and William Bauer, *These Are Your Children,* New York, Scott, Foresman, 1951.

Kyte, George, *The Elementary Teacher at Work,* New York, Dryden, 1957.

Lee, Harper, *To Kill a Mockingbird,* Philadelphia, J. B. Lippincott, 1960.

Lee, Laurie, *The Edge of Day,* New York, Morrow, 1960.

Linkletter, Art, *Kids Say the Darndest Things,* Englewood Cliffs, N.J., Prentice-Hall, 1959.

Martin, William, and Celia Stendler, *Child Behavior and Development,* New York, Harcourt, Brace, 1959.

Prescott, D. A., *The Child in the Educative Process,* New York, McGraw-Hill, 1957.

Reeves, Katherine, *Children—Their Wants and Needs,* New York, Educational Publishing Corp., 1960.

Redl, Fritz, *Understanding Children's Behavior,* New York, Teachers College, 1950.

Schneider, Elsa, and Simon McNeely, *Teachers Contribute to Child Health,* U.S. Office of Education, Bulletin 1951, Government Printing Office, 1951.

Smith, Helen, and Mary Wolverton, *Health Education in the Elementary School,* New York, Ronald, 1959.

White, V., *Studying the Individual Pupil,* New York, Harper, 1957.

Willey, Roy De Verl, *Guidance in Elementary Education,* rev. ed., New York, Harper, 1960.

TWO

TECHNIQUES FOR TEACHING

"IF YOU HAVE EVER SEEN THE LIGHT OF UNDERSTANDING SHINE IN ANOTHER'S EYES WHERE NO LIGHT SHONE BEFORE, IF YOU HAVE EVER GUIDED THE UNSTEADY AND UNPRACTICED HAND AND WATCHED IT SUDDENLY GROW FIRM AND PURPOSEFUL, IF YOU HAVE EVER WATCHED A YOUNG MIND BEGIN TO SOAR TO NEW HEIGHTS AND HAVE SENSED THAT YOU ARE PARTICIPATING IN THIS UNFOLDING OF THE INTELLECT, THEN YOU HAVE FELT WITHIN YOU THE SENSE OF BEING A HUMBLE INSTRUMENT IN THE FURTHERANCE OF MANKIND . . ."

SAMUEL GOULD, "DEFINITION OF A TEACHER," FROM WHY TEACH?

5 HOW CHILDREN LEARN

Children are in love with life! Watch, as an adult, any child having his very first "finding out about" experiences—he inspects and smells a strange flower, holds a brand new baby sister, first touches so very timidly and then finally ever so softly pets a cow, kitten, puppy, or any other animal, or tries to turn a somersault or roller skate. Such total absorption, delight, and sheer determination! Look closely, as a teacher, at the two wonderful books of photographs of children at play, work, and camp—*The World Is Young* and *Summer Magic,* and note how totally absorbed the children are in what they are doing and learning about.

The desire to learn is present in all normal human beings, but in youth it is a strong, forceful flood. To learn means to discover—to find ways to make satisfying adjustments to new situations. Learning also means changed behavior in relationship to obtaining desirable goals. Children need not be driven to learn the things they want to learn, although they sometimes must be prevented from learning or experiencing negative or harmful things too suddenly, or too early in life. Our old folk saying that "you can drive a horse to water but you cannot make him drink" is truer than was once realized. The learner, not the teacher, controls the learning situation. Pupils discover early in their school experiences how to tune the teacher out, and how to give the impression of full attentiveness and at the same time be far away in the golden land of their daydreams.

The desire to learn spurs the child on and often gets him into all kinds of trouble, for he usually acts first and thinks later in his attempts to satisfy his curiosity and find out. Any child who fails to learn may be stymied by physical or emotional blocks, which must be removed before any real progress can be made. Sometimes these clogs are due to an inability to see or hear, fear of failure, or the dread of loss of parental love. The six-year-old boy who refused to take part with his class in any type of supervised play activities on the playground, finally, after many tears, confessed to his teacher that he was afraid to play for fear he would get dirty, knowing that if he did so "Mamma wouldn't love me anymore; she hates dirty boys!" Regardless of what deterring factors are present, they must be discovered and eradicated before the child will give his whole self to learning.

Learning involves the entire child; there is no separation into physical, mental, and emotional selves. One cannot draw a picture, catch a ball, read a book, or master any learning task by only using one's head or "learning it through one's body." The mind of man is a central clearing house, a transfer station, a switchboard which can only function when messages come to it, are received, sorted, clarified, or filed, and sent back out again. As William Kilpatrick has said, "what we live, we learn. Where we live, with whom we live, toward what ends we live—these determine what we learn." The whole community educates, but the learner teaches himself. No one can really "teach" anyone else to do anything. The person learning teaches himself by some magical process which includes his own fumbling attempts. Most of our learning comes from first making mistakes and then discovering how to avoid them. Without failure there can be no success. The role of the teacher is to guide the pupil around learning pitfalls that are sure to stymie him and lead to failure, as well as to "egg him on" to keep trying until he succeeds (riding the bicycle after falling so many times, or finally pronouncing and spelling a new word correctly), and to lead him to new learning thrills and adventures he never dreamed existed. Learning can be speeded up when the learner sees the relationship between what he is trying to learn, and his own chosen goals. Although children change their minds many times before actually selecting a life goal or a chosen profession, most know definitely what they want to be or do at every grade in school. The child who wants to be a traffic policeman must see the necessity for developing good health habits, learning arithmetic, or doing anything else in relationship to that desire to be a policeman. Past experiences, goals, and drives are the foundation upon which new and often more lasting experiences are built. Each child, in order to succeed as a student, must clearly see where he is in relationship to where he wants to go, as well as have carefully selected and well-planned educational experiences which will enable him to arrive at his goal.

TYPES OF LEARNING

Most of what children learn comes through the senses of hearing, seeing, tasting, and touching, and the more these can be used and stimulated, the richer the learning experiences will be. For example, the child being taught the meaning of the word "papaya" will more quickly gain an understanding of it if he sees it written (sight), hears it spelled and pronounced correctly (hearing), and actually eats (taste) the fruit. A child learns when he:

1. Understands words and their meanings.
2. Can communicate with others.
3. Develops and uses new skills.
4. Forms new habits.
5. Develops new attitudes.
6. Builds new interests.
7. Gains new understandings.
8. Makes generalizations and uses learned facts.
9. Develops social skills.
10. Becomes more concerned about his environment and other people around him.
11. Develops favorable attitudes toward himself and others.
12. Shows concern for the rights of others; has good conduct.

Although theorists vary as to the number of different kinds of learning there are, most agree that the various types are not wholly dissimilar and that some of the same factors operate in all of them. All stress that one learns by doing, or from his own experience. A learner must learn something, or to put it another way, one learns when he can respond correctly, such as when he jumps a rope without missing, or recognizes "cat" when he sees c-a-t written out. The most frequently found types of learning are (1) *conditioned re-*

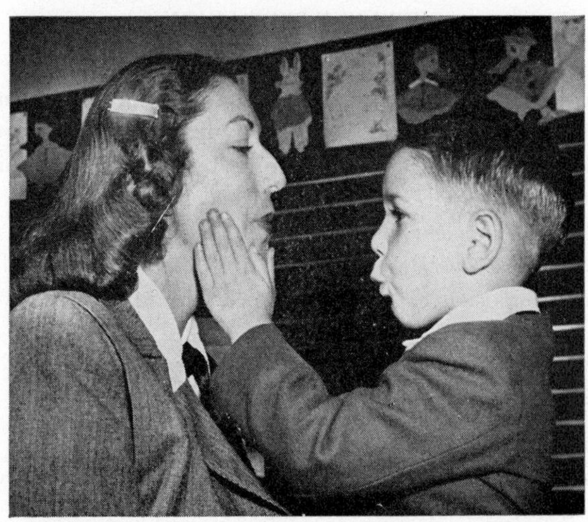

Most of our learning comes through the senses. Here a pupil is learning how the voice vibrates sound through the sense of touch. (Courtesy, N.E.A.)

sponses (the result of forming a patterned reflex), (2) *autogenous responses* (the result of self-initiated actions), (3) *sociogenous responses* (the result of social stimulation), (4) *incidental learning* (the result of exposure to a set of stimuli or to a single stimulus), and (5) *insightful learning* (the result of suddenly seeing relationships and meaning in what is being learned).

Many educators feel that the central task of the teacher is to help each pupil develop self-discipline. Although this cannot be imparted directly from one person to another, it can often be instilled best by setting high standards and by example. A self-directed learner, who is strongly motivated to attain goals he has clearly in mind, can and usually does obtain them. It is the job of the teacher to provide the stimulus which sets off this magical process of self-education. However, it is the school's task to provide time for learning, studying, developing ideas and concepts, reading, thinking, and discussing ideas. Education, then, is a long, slow process that lasts a lifetime. It should be shared by the school, the home, and the community. If in these places there is a real respect for learning, education becomes easier and more enjoyably and productively fruitful, for as Plato has said, "What a nation honors it will cultivate." Much of the child's attitude toward school and his own ability as a learner is a reflection of those closest to him—his family, friends, and members of the school and community.

There are four significant elements in the learning process: the *drive* (the stimulus that triggers action), the *cue* (the stimulus that guides action), the *response* (the action itself), and the *reward* (the result of action). If the child is to learn, he must (1) *want something* (the drive), (2) *notice something* (pick up a cue and relate it to his past knowledge of similar words or experiences), (3) *do something* (the response), and (4) *get something* for his efforts (the reward. A skillful teacher uses positive motivation and is adept at providing children with cues which they can readily pick up and use in their own learning attempts. Such an educator also provides the drill necessary for retention of what has been previously learned, and establishes a warm and friendly classroom environment so that positive attitudes can be shaped and healthy emotional responses can be established. Lucky, indeed, is the pupil who knows as well as feels that his teacher likes him and is there to help him learn to help himself grow. Parents who daily ask their children, "What did you learn in school today?" and who are sincerely interested and concerned about what they hear in reply, can do much to help teachers aid children gain a great respect both for education and the pupil's progress as he strives to become educated.

Conditioning

The simplest type of learning is conditioning, or establishing a patterned reflex response to a repeated stimulus. Pavlov, in his famous experiments with dogs, proved that the animal could be conditioned to salivate when a bell was rung and food was expected. We all show that we have been conditioned when we automatically pick up the phone when it rings, stop at the red light, turn over and sleepily push the alarm off on the clock at our bedside when it awakens us, or do numerous other automatic acts to the same repeated stimuli because within us a habit has been formed. The pupil who can give back the right response when asked to spell the word "boy," or how much is 2 + 2, or what is the capital of Texas, has been trained to do so. However, education which stresses understanding far transcends such training, for it makes paramount the full development of each person. Educators are not trying to train robots or talking parrots, who can repeat a dictated and meaningless vocabulary. The role of the educator is to develop each rational human being to his highest potential for our free but controlled democratic society.

Connectionism

This theory, which results largely from the work of Thorndike and his associates at Columbia University, stresses that human beings, as well as animals, will voluntarily select things which bring them the most pleasure, satisfaction, and best fill their needs. Although this is similar to the theory of conditioning, connectionists contend that learning must be on a higher plane, for the purpose of education is *not* to create human vending machines who will give back to the teacher an answer upon demand, but to develop educated citizens who can solve their own as well as help solve group problems intelligently in many ever-changing situations.

Simply, this concept known also as the *S-R*-bond theory of learning, means that when a stimulus (*S*) brings about a response (*R*) which is accompanied by satisfied feelings, the connection between that stimulus and that response is reinforced (bond). The intensity of these positive feelings can produce either an advancing, positive response (choosing it again, joy, satisfaction), or a retreating, negative one (not choosing it again, anger, disappointment, frustration).

According to this theory, the greater the need and inner pressure for learning, the keener and more productive are the attempts to satisfy this need and relieve this pressure. All human beings, children and adults alike, have certain common needs. These drives make up the underlying cause of all human behavior:

1. Physiological needs (food, water, air, temperature regulation, rest, exercise).
2. Love needs (sex, mutuality, belongingness, affection).
3. Need for esteem (recognition, mastery, approval, status, adequacy, self-respect).
4. Self-actualization (desire to succeed at tasks for which one is best suited).

5. Need to know and understand.
6. Need for ambiance (balance between love and hate, desire to destroy and build).
7. Need for adventure (to seek ever-greener pastures).

A skillful teacher can and does capitalize upon these drives common to all. She, like a tour director, can help the learner discover many wonders created by God and man, as well as awaken in him a desire to contribute to humanity, and to find the good life.

Field Theory

This concept, developed first by Koffka and Koehler, and later advanced by Hartmann and Wertheimer, stresses that one learns best by grasping whole concepts. It holds that one learns by trial and error plus "insight"—suddenly "seeing" how to do something. Anyone who has ever tried to learn to ride a bicycle usually was battered and bruised before he suddenly found he could do it. The novice swimmer learning the crawl stroke has a great moment of triumph when he finds he can synchronize his arm, leg, and head movements and can move rhythmically through the water using all of these coordinated actions. Insight is "getting the hang" of anything we are learning; it can only be the result of previous trial-and-error attempts. The task of the teacher is to encourage the learner to keep trying until this thrill of accomplishment comes. Here again, she must take care not to nip learning struggles in the bud by being too much of a perfectionist, overly critical, or impatient.

This concept of learning, known also as "Gestalt psychology," places the emphasis in any learning experience upon the learner, and stresses that he knows more about his own values, desires, capacities, and preferences than the teacher. The instructor should help the learner to (1) set his own goals, (2) determine his plans, and (3) judge the results. This does not mean that the teacher is unnecessary but does imply that her main task is that of guiding and directing. Students gain much more from such skillful leadership than from being told what to do, for there will be less friction and more rapport, fewer failures and more success, less boredom and far more excitement in learning.

If the main purpose of education is to help each person increase the number of socially approved things he can do well which are beneficial to him and society, teaching is more than either an art or a science, for it becomes a combination of them both. A skilled teacher will (1) provide the best kind of learning atmosphere—warm and friendly, yet controlled; (2) motivate pupils to desire worthy goals by making them as attractive as possible; and (3) make even disagreeable tasks seem agreeable and interesting to a bored, uninterested learner by changing negative attitudes to positive ones; and (4) help the learner develop finer and deeper appreciation of himself, others, and what he is doing.

Gestalt psychology also stresses that the best learning will result when the learning environment is used to its fullest extent; and also that the learner can and will learn only when he has a need to do so, and that he will learn best when he can do so under the friendly, consistent guidance of a firm teacher who regards him as a unique human being. It also contends that learning will come about faster and be more lasting when large blocks of material are mastered. Educators call this the whole-part-whole method of teaching and learning. They agree that it is superior to piecemeal learning attempts, for it will bring desired results more quickly by stressing relationships.

THE ROLE OF MOTIVATION

Learning is an individual and progressive experience that is closely associated with goal-seeking. Every human being learns in his own way and at his own rate of speed. Pupil and teacher goals are too often widely separated and different. The best educators are those who help each child select for himself higher, broader, obtainable, and more meaningful goals through the use of the right kind of motivation. Since motivation is the basis of all learning, teachers must be aware of and skilled in using a wide variety of ways to interest children in wanting to learn. Motives which can spur or check a desire to learn include:

Wants and needs	Attitudes
Individual behavior traits	Interests

Habits and skills	Rewards
Knowledge of progress	Punishment
Purposes	Group recognition
Emotions	

The teacher has the major role in motivation. However, she must be careful that children do not become overly motivated, especially in the areas of health and safety, for there are dangers in causing children to become too health-conscious or fearful. Likewise, there are great dangers in overemphasizing competition. The best form of competition is self-competition, in which each child tries to improve upon his previous record. Punishment, whether it be by isolation, physical measures, or ridicule, must be used with great caution. Teachers should realize that praise is far more effective than blame in motivating pupils to learn. However, undeserved praise or praise given too frequently has little, if any, educational value.

Children can be effectively motivated to learn more about health and safety through classroom teaching when they:

1. See meanings and relationships in what they learn. Overviews of study units or other materials can quickly accomplish this, as will skimming through a book before reading any part of it.
2. Are assigned tasks which are not beyond their abilities.
3. Know and understand what is expected of them in the way of assignments, behavior, or in other areas.
4. Can see clearly that what they do each day in class will bring them closer to their goals.
5. Participate in activities which are meaningful and important to them.
6. Are guided into developing good study habits.
7. Gain recognition for accomplishments.
8. Like and respect their teacher, and know that she, in turn, likes and respects everyone in the class.
9. Can relate what they are learning with what they are doing in the whole school program, at home, and in their community.

A child's natural urges of curiosity, to communicate, to engage in dramatic and physical play, and to create often present an "open sesame" for learning. The purposes, ambitions, drives, and values of each child should be channeled to help him develop along his natural abilities. Teachers must help children value well-earned

Motivation is the key to all learning. (Courtesy, N.E.A.)

achievement. Marks and verbal rewards, as well as reproofs, can play a powerful role in the development of a child's performance. It is imperative, however, that the teacher discover what motivates each pupil best, as well as what most whets his curiosity and sustains his efforts until he accomplishes his own desired goal.

The following principles will assist in motivating pupils to positive action:

1. Become familiar with each child's drives and plan learning experiences that will arouse his interest.
2. Motivation is more potent when the learner sees the relationship between what he is learning and his own goals.
3. Motivation is more effective when the children are involved in setting goals.
4. Pupils should be encouraged to set both short- and long-range goals for themselves as well as to help formulate group goals.
5. Negative motivation (fear of punishment) usually retards learning, whereas positive motivation (anticipation of reward) elicits more favorable responses.

6. A child learns to do best what is the most satisfying to him. The teacher should help boys and girls gain satisfaction from right responses and right conduct.
7. Children are ready to learn when they are healthy, well adjusted, mature enough, and interested.

Almost every learning situation abounds with character-shaping and value-developing opportunities. Since character can often be best "caught" rather than taught, the behavior patterns and attitudes the teacher displays at all times are of paramount importance, and especially so in the area of health, for children are great imitators, but they copy only those they most admire. Leadership through example is the best way to help children develop positive attitudes and learn to behave in socially accepted ways as developing young people in a democracy.

It is of vital importance that each child have a favorable and realistic attitude toward himself, his teacher, family, friends, and life in general. Children learn attitudes in many places, and from unpleasant as well as pleasant things which happen to them. The school can do much to develop in children desirable attitudes toward their own sex, classmates, as well as the valued concepts of fair play, friendliness, and cooperation. The teacher can also help children develop desirable attitudes toward school, work, educators, and toward the value of a good education in their own lives. Those who develop proper attitudes toward health have a strong foundation upon which lifelong positive health habits are built.

LEARNING PRINCIPLES

Basic beliefs and action guides are known as principles. They result from experience, the opinion of experts, research, and education. The best learning will result if the following principles are used as springboards for action:

1. *Children learn experimentally with their whole bodies.* Trial and error plus insight produces changed behavior, or learning. In this process, mistakes are necessary and success comes from failure. The whole child is involved in learning, not just his mind alone. Just as all of Johnny goes to school, the whole school educates Johnny.
2. *Learning is doing.* Discovery results from searching. We learn mostly

from doing, not from being told, or from watching others perform. In order to learn one must try out things for oneself and through one's own experience gain skill, understanding, concepts, and appreciation.

3. *The learner controls the learning situation.* If the learner is in situations in which he feels secure and confident, he progresses faster. He will be handicapped when dominated or told by adults what, when, and how he is to learn. Knowledge of his progress in relationship to that of others can both be an asset or a liability, depending upon the amount of self-confidence the learner has.

4. *Each pupil learns in his own way.* Every learner goes about learning tasks differently, and each develops his own learning progress pattern which leads to victory or defeat over what he is attempting to do. For the majority, this pattern shows a sharp rise at first, tapers off to a plateau, then rises again as the pupil becomes increasingly aware he is reaching his desired goal. Learning is a personal experience, and every person has his own unique method of learning.

5. *Overlearning results in longer retention.* Practice of the correct pattern until what is to be learned is mastered or becomes automatic will keep it longer in the body's memory storehouse. The more a learned skill or concept is used and reviewed, the more valuable it will become. Just as unused silver tarnishes quickly, so do once-learned things. Practice must be done correctly if it is to produce mastery. Practice makes permanent, whether for doing things the right or wrong way.

6. *Emotions retard or accelerate learning.* Learning occurs more rapidly if both the pupil and the teacher are enthusiastic about and see purpose in what is being learned. Fear and insecurity are clogs and dam up desire until it stagnates; confidence and encouragement plunges learning on.

7. *Short practice periods are more productive than long ones.* The length of each practice period should be determined by the interest level and potency of desire to accomplish the learning task that the pupil has. Practice will be fruitful only if it brings satisfaction to the learner and is recognized as a basic task necessary for improvement. A "cooling off period" is needed before a renewed and recharged learning pursuit can become potent enough to lead to final victory, for a learning pause can bring real refreshment, as well as desired results more quickly. Learning attempts must be balanced with play, for the latter is a "battery" recharger.

8. *Transfer will occur when situations are recognized to be alike.* The transformation of anything learned in one situation to another will take place only when the learner sees similarities in the two situations and continues to do in the second one what he did in the first. Mastery of health facts will have no relationship to health practices unless the learner sees the togetherness of what he has learned to what he does. The child who can name the parts of a tooth, recite in squeezed-sponge fashion the rules of proper mouth hygiene, but does not brush his teeth has failed to transfer

meaningless information into practice. Teachers must be ever aware of opportunities to help pupils recognize existing relationships which exist among all things being learned. Knowledge is for use, and the real goal of education is improved action.

9. *Learning can be an exciting, challenging adventure.* One has only to watch the happy face of any youngster who first discovered that he can swim, recite the multiplication tables, or sing all the way through any song without a single mistake to see the truthfulness of this principle. The child who wants to learn what he has chosen to master can have a glorious time doing so. The real teacher is one who can inspire him to want to make many new and thrilling learning discoveries, and can guide him to where these treasures are.

10. The learner reacts to a cluster of stimuli. The teacher must eliminate those which are distracting.

11. Since the learner is motivated by his urge to explore, act, create, and grow, the setting must provide freedom to explore, create, solve problems, and to find new and better ways of working, playing, and learning.

12. The learner is both an individual and a social being. Consequently, he must be allowed to work on learning projects which are of vital importance to him as a unique person as well as participate in and contribute to a class group.

13. The learner should be taught to see relationships and aided to understand the whole process before he begins to drill on any specific parts.

14. A child can only learn when he is ready to learn. Such readiness varies in every grade and in every activity taught at each grade level.

15. Recognition works as a powerful motivator to children. Every pupil should receive approval for tasks well done or attempted, to build his self confidence. Only when praise is seldom given, does a child prefer criticism to being ignored.

16. *Evaluation is an essential part of learning.* Improvement and evaluation are inseparable, for one can only improve when he sees his mistakes and cares enough about what he is attempting to avoid them. It is a difficult task for the teacher to know when to stop muddling learning attempts or how to go about it, for doing so at the wrong time and in the wrong way may destroy the pupil's zest and zeal to reach his desired learning goal to such an extent that he will give up trying, or quit. There is truth in Pope's wise statement that "only fools rush in where angels fear to tread."

SUGGESTED READINGS

Allport, Gordon, *The Course of Becoming,* New Haven, Yale University Press, 1955.

Brogan, Peggy, and Lorene Fox, *Helping Children Learn: A Concept of Elementary School Method,* Yonkers, N.Y., World Book, 1955.

Cunningham, Ruth, *Understanding Group Behavior of Boys and Girls,* New York, Teachers College, 1951.

Deese, James, *The Psychology of Learning,* New York, McGraw-Hill, 1958.

Fessenden, S. A., R. I. Johnson, and P. M. Larson, *The Teacher Speaks,* Englewood Cliffs, N.J., Prentice-Hall, 1954.

George, Jean, "There's Always a Time to Grow," *Reader's Digest,* April, 1960.

Guthrie, E. R., *The Psychology of Learning,* New York, Harper, 1952.

Johnson, G. O., and K. A. Blake, *Learning Performance of Retarded and Normal Children,* Syracuse, Syracuse University Press, 1960.

Lawson, R., *Learning and Behavior,* New York, Macmillan, 1960.

Laycock, S. R., *Teaching and Learning,* Toronto, Coppelark, 1954.

Leadership for Improving Instruction, 1960; *Learning More about Learning,* 1958; *Learning and the Teacher,* 1959; *Freeing Capacity to Learn,* 1959; *Continuity in Learning,* 1957; *Creating a Good Environment for Learning,* 1954; *Toward Better Teaching,* 1949; Association for Supervision and Curriculum Development, Washington, D.C., National Education Association.

Logan, Lillian, and Virgil Logan, *Teaching the Elementary School Child,* New York, Houghton Mifflin, 1961.

Lowenfeld, Viktor, *Creative and Mental Growth,* New York, Macmillan, 1958.

Miller, Wayne, *The World Is Young,* New York, Ridge Press, 1958.

Morgan, Barbara, *Summer's Children,* Scarsdale, N.Y., Morgan and Morgan, 1951.

Mowrer, O. H., *Learning Theory and Behavior, Learning Theory and the Symbolic Processes,* New York, Wiley, 1960.

Moustakas, Clark, *The Teacher and the Child: Personal Interactions in the Classroom,* New York, McGraw-Hill, 1956.

Prescott, Daniel, *The Factors That Influence Learning,* Pittsburgh, University of Pittsburgh Press, 1958.

Remmers, H. H., Harry Rivlin, D. G. Ryans, and Ernar Ryden, *Growth, Teaching, and Learning,* New York, Harper, 1957.

Schmuller, Allen M., *The Mechanics of Learning,* Denton, Tex., Texas Women's University Press, 1959.

Shane, Harold, "Children's Interests: How Do They Affect the Elementary Curriculum?" *NEA Journal,* vol. 46 (April, 1957), 237–239.

Spence, K. W., *Behavior Theory and Learning,* Englewood Cliffs, N.J., Prentice-Hall, 1960.

Zirkes, Laura, *Spurs to Creative Teaching,* New York, Putnam, 1960.

6 CURRICULUM PLANNING

The school curriculum encompasses all the many kinds of experiences which children have under the guidance of the school. The curriculum can be different for each child and affect each one differently. Essentially it is living and learning in a democratic problem-solving educational environment. In its broadest sense, the curriculum refers to the whole life and program of the school. Seen in the narrowest aspect, it refers to school subjects taught or to a course of study. Modern educators contend that the curriculum can be found only in the actual reality-centered experiences of children and not in a textbook or on a piece of paper. To them a course of study has about the same relationship to the curriculum that a road map has to taking a trip.[1] The modern school is primarily concerned with the development and direction of the interests and abilities of each pupil toward his active and full participation in the life of his school, community, nation, and world. The curriculum in such a school is no longer subject-centered, nor is it child-centered, but it is life-orientated. The problems studied at such a school revolve around developing new and better ways to improve living for the present, as well as for the future.

Curriculum planning in an elementary school should be a continuous, cooperative experience shared by the teachers, state and national educational authorities, parents, and the children them-

[1] William Ragan, *Modern Elementary Curriculum,* New York, Dryden, 1954, p. 4.

selves. The final results should be a definite course of action to be used for the primary purpose of achieving the objectives of the school; it should be subject to continuous study and modification. The following principles may well serve as useful guides for those engaged in constructing a curriculum.

The curriculum should:

1. Coordinate the efforts of all teachers and avoid duplication or repetition.
2. Provide a well-balanced school day wherein children will find opportunity to work cooperatively in groups as well as alone. Work activities should be balanced by carefully selected play activities which have educational value.
3. Be based on graded content and standards which challenge and encourage each child to master the skills and knowledge necessary for effective living in a democracy.
4. Be organized to orient the child to the life and world in which he lives.
5. Provide broad, meaningful experiences which cut across all subject lines.
6. Provide for the development of the fundamental skills and subjects, plus social living and health.
7. Provide for pupil participation in curriculum planning.

Education is largely a process wherein learners are guided to choose wisely, directed toward higher appreciations and values, and are aided in discovering how to act wisely according to social and ethical customs and mores. The total school health program should be centered around the goal of helping each child develop his ability to make wisely the many decisions and choices which relate to his own health. The real aim of any health education program should be to help others develop positive behavior patterns which will enable them to live well, scientifically, efficiently, economically, and happily. As Oberteuffer says, "Action is the thing. To live healthfully, to practice what one knows, to do the scientific thing, and to be creative—these are the principal objectives for which teaching exists."[2] The real purpose of any health education program should be to help each person learn (1) how to promote and protect his own health and general well-being, and (2) have the desire and

[2] Delbert Oberteuffer, *School Health Education,* New York, Harper, 1960, p. 7.

knowledge to become a healthier and happier individual and group member. The test of any teacher's or parent's effectiveness as an educator is what the child does when away from his sight, warning cries, and protection.

The interrelated and reciprocal objectives of any health education program should be to help others develop (1) positive health habits, (2) acquire correct knowledge concerning the development and maintenance of good health, and (3) favorable attitudes concerning good health. The emphasis placed upon obtaining each of these goals varies with each grade level, as do the teaching methods used to secure them. Primary pupils respond well to any health program which helps them develop good health habits and independence, such as learning how to brush their teeth correctly, or comb their hair neatly. Proper health attitudes gradually will develop (but not automatically, for they must be carefully shaped). Simple sentences repeated frequently for emphasis will help children grasp the reasons behind taking a bath (to feel clean, and to wash off the germs), getting enough sleep (to help you grow and feel good), or drinking milk with every meal (milk helps children grow faster). Major stress in the lower grades should be placed upon developing good health habits, with secondary emphasis on positive attitudes toward health, oneself, and others, and with still less emphasis upon health facts. During early formative years, children are most receptive to conditioning and will find security in receiving praise for repeating simple, habit-forming daily tasks, such as always washing their hands before going into the school lunchroom. Carrying out these routinized habits should be accompanied by adult recognition and approval, for this will not only bring satisfaction to the child, but will also help him to realize more quickly the relationship of his own actions to his own welfare and what admired adults want him to do.

On the upper elementary level, emphasis in the health instruction program should be placed primarily on the development of proper attitudes, secondarily upon reinforcing previously learned practices and developing new ones, and thirdly upon gaining new knowledge. During this period children have numerous problems which revolve around the changes taking place in their own bodies and have an increased need for positive attitudes toward their own rapidly changing selves. As each pupil progresses in school, he should develop more firmly-grounded health habits coupled with an appreciation of the value of good health. As he matures he needs to know increasingly more about the meaning of life and his role in the world. Consequently, the teacher of this group should utilize the desire of these older pupils to know and understand the scientific facts of health, as well as help them grasp the significance of this knowledge in relationship to their daily lives. As each pupil grows up it is important that he knows why it is necessary for him to safeguard his own health, as well as to have the desire and skills necessary for doing so. As great educators throughout the ages have declared, the real purpose of education is not acquiring knowledge—it is action!

GRADE PLACEMENT

Since the scope of learning in health education is as all-inclusive as life itself, it is the duty of the school to include in the health education curriculum the study of children's problems, interests, and needs relating to growing up. It is the task of educators to select which interests, needs, and problems are most pertinent and suitable for each grade to study. Above all, duplication of course content should be avoided, for children have the right to an exciting adventure in health education directed by a skilled, enthusiastic, and capable teacher who can take them to new "places" or make many new kinds of discoveries in areas previously only partially explored.

Although most states and large school systems have recommended courses of study in health education for each grade on both the primary and secondary levels, there is no standardization of these courses, nor should there be, for such materials should be used primarily as guides. Each teacher should be aided by health education experts and a curriculum guide devised for her school to discover what major health areas she should cover and what are the sources of the supplementary materials and aids, suggested teaching methods, and activities she should use. In order to avoid duplication, any recommended course of study for all the elementary grades should be carefully studied by teachers from each grade and changes made in the original plans when necessary. Many schools use the block plan for health instruction, in which certain major health areas receive stress during alternate years. Thus, nutrition may be emphasized in Grades 1, 2, 3, 4, and 5, and community health and sanitation in Grades 1, 2, 3, and 6. Table 1 shows the distribution of course content for the health instruction program used in Oregon:

TABLE 1. Four-Cycle Plan of Health Instruction in Oregon Schools, Grades 1–12

		Cycle 1 Grades			Cycle 2 Grades			Cycle 3 Grades			Cycle 4 Grades		
AREAS	HEALTH UNITS	1	2	3	4	5	6	7	8	9	10	11	12
I	Structure and Functions of Human Body	x			x			x			x		
II	Personal Hygiene[a]	x			x			x			x		
III	Physiology of Exercise		x			x			x			x	
IV	Nutrition		x			x			x			x	
V	First Aid and Safety Education		x			x			x			x	
VI	Choice-use of Health Services Health Products			x			x			x			x
VII	Communicable Diseases[b]			x			x			x			x
VIII	Community Health and Sanitation			x			x			x			x
IX	Mental Health[c]												x

Source: *Handbook of Health Instruction in Oregon Elementary Schools*, Salem, Ore., State Board of Education, 1952, p. 14. (Reprinted by permission.)

[a] This unit also includes instruction in the area, "Effects of Alcoholic Drinks, Stimulants, and Narcotics."

[b] This unit also includes instruction in the noncommunicable diseases.

[c] On the three lower cycles, appropriate instruction in mental health is included in the units on "Personal Hygiene." The unit on "Mental Health," recommended for grade 12, also includes instruction on "Family Life Education."

Some state courses of study and those devised by local committees in large school districts recommend that the health instruction program be built around broad areas such as Nutrition, Safety, Family Life Education, Sleep and Rest, Care of the Special Organs of the Body, Mental Health, Exercise, Personal Hygiene, and Growth and Development. They also suggest that each of these major areas be included in the program on all grade levels, but that the materials under each area become increasingly more difficult and broader in scope.[3] Outstanding courses of study are available for use as patterns for curriculum development from the state of Oregon, California, Ohio, Indiana, and North Carolina, and from the cities of Los Angeles, Nashville, and Seattle.

TIME ALLOTMENT

Although this varies with each state, all schools must set aside a certain amount of time in the school year for instruction in health. Some schools, in order to comply with the law, do devote the time to health but fill it with a makeshift and poorly taught program. Still others combine it with physical education and conduct classes in health on rainy or alternate days during the week. Since no one can be sure when the weather will be bad, teachers are often caught unprepared and have no health lessons prepared, with the result that the students read aloud to one another from a health textbook. In a certain school system in one of our southern states, when the weather is bad the children who eagerly look forward to their physical education class are appeased by a doting teacher who lets the disappointed class read comic books, even though the class understands that they will "have health" instead of physical education on such days. In such a city, health education is a farce and rightly held in contempt by the pupils, as well as by their parents. On the other hand, many schools have a definite time allotted daily or weekly to a well-planned health education program.

Authorities are agreed that daily meetings for a shorter time are superior to sharing health instruction time with physical education, with health classes being held either once or twice weekly. In every grade of the elementary school a definite time should be set aside

[3] See Part Three of this book for a suggested graded program in the major areas of a recommended health education curriculum for elementary schools.

each day for health instruction and children provided with meaningful opportunities to learn about health, discuss it, and take part in health education activities which will increase their understanding, as well as shape desirable behavior and attitudes toward this subject. Starting in the seventh grade and continuing on through the twelfth, all students should have an opportunity to have at least one full semester of health education. Such a program necessitates careful planning and skillful teaching in order to avoid repetition of course content and dullness.

Found below is a suggested time allotment plan for school health instruction in Grades 1 through 12.

TABLE 2. Time Allotment for Direct Health Teaching

Grade	Best	Next Best	Least Desirable
1, 2, 3	1 period a day	1 period twice a week	1 period once a week
4, 5, 6	20 minutes 3 times a week	20 minutes once a week	20 minutes once a week
7, 8	1 class period a day for the year	1 class period 3 times a week for a semester	1 class period once a week for a year
9	1 class period a day for a semester	1 class period 3 times a week for a semester	1 class period once a week for a year
10, 11	1 class period a day for a semester	1 class period 3 times a week for a semester	1 class period once a week for a year
12	1 class period a day for a semester	1 class period 3 times a week for a semester	1 class period once a week for a year

Source: Oberteueffer, *op. cit.*, p. 129.

CURRICULAR PATTERNS

There are four types of curricular patterns found in today's schools. These are (1) the subject curriculum, (2) the broad-fields curriculum, (3) the core curriculum, and (4) the experience curriculum. Each employs subject matter and makes use of experience, and in each content is stressed, pupils take part in some kind of activity, the needs and interests of the learners are taken into consideration, and teacher-pupil planning should be utilized.[4]

The Subject Curriculum. This is the most widely used of the four types. It is the oldest, and somehow withstands the attacks made upon it by modern educational leaders. In this pattern, each subject exists as a relatively independent and isolated teaching area. The chief purpose of this type of curriculum is for the pupil to gain factual information and to understand it. Lecturing to more adult students and explaining or "talking" to young children is the chief method of instruction, although more and more instructors are using problem-solving units and laboratory experiments. Since most adults are familiar with this type of curriculum, it receives strong support among insecure and frightened parents who want to return to the "good old disciplined days" they knew as youngsters because it represents a familiar and safe period (much glamorized by memory) in their lives. Critics of this type of curriculum claim that much of the subject matter taught in any given field is too often meaningless, compartmentalized, and fragmentary, presenting out-of-date and inaccurate information, and that the teaching of the subject to the child may become more important than the teaching of the child himself. Advocates of this type of curriculum declare that good teachers will overcome these faults, and they have only scorn for those in their own group who assign "the next ten pages for Wednesday." Perhaps the greatest criticism which can be made of this type of curriculum is that it chops learning up into isolated segments, each of which can become overly important or totally disregarded by a "talking" teacher who does all the planning and carrying of what is to be learned, and in so doing robs children of an educational adventure.

The Broad-fields Curriculum. This pattern is not new, for it dates back 80 years. In most of the public schools using this plan today, such a curriculum usually contains Social Studies, General Science, Language Arts, Health and Physical Education, General Mathematics, and the General Arts.

[4] *The American School Curriculum,* American Association of School Administrators, Thirty-first Yearbook, Washington, D.C., 1953, p. 58.

The chief purpose of this type of curriculum is to systematize, reinforce, and bring together related subject areas so that teachers can spend more time on any one of the larger areas, and pupils can be aided in seeing relationships in what they are learning so that it becomes more meaningful to them.

Three practices are commonly used by educators in this type of curriculum to help pupils see relationships within what they are learning. These are (1) correlation, (2) fusion, and (3) integration.

Correlation is often used as a means of bringing out reciprocal relationships among subjects. Health and science are often correlated, as are American history and American literature. Although there are advantages to this practice, it also has many limitations. When the teacher correlates science with health education, often too much emphasis is placed upon the science, and students end up learning about the bones in the feet without knowing about proper foot care. Often, too, some of the major health areas are given brief attention or no attention at all by the instructor. Science teachers tend to be too scientific when teaching about health, just as classroom teachers tend to know too little about science or its relationship to health and so, consequently, are unable to help children learn about or understand this relationship. In order that correlation of health education with another subject be fully used by two or more teachers it is necessary that (1) they be well enough versed in both areas to do justice to each as the materials are presented; (2) each be willing to work hard to make such a program successful; (3) an in-service training program be given in both areas so that each instructor becomes fully aware of the materials to be presented, their relationship, and importance; and (4) conferences or workshops be held periodically so that all involved in the program become cognizant of new materials and of problems which have arisen.

Health can and should be correlated with all the basic academic areas as well as with all other subjects in the curriculum. Readers in health are widely used in all elementary grades. These can be not only a means of developing reading ability and comprehension, but also inform children about the body and how to keep it well. In the language arts, pupils should be encouraged to make oral or written reports about health topics which interest them, or about field trips the group has taken, in order to learn more about any aspect of individual or community health. New words, such as "nutrition" or "relaxation," can be introduced and children taught their spelling, use, and meaning. There are also numerous opportunities to correlate health with art, for making of puppets, posters, health record charts, or coloring fill-ins delight as well as teach children.[5] Music can also be used, although care must be taken that children do not create nonsense jingles set to popular tunes which have no value except to entertain them. Keeping accurate height and weight charts, making bar graphs or charts to illustrate special class reports can all help children master the mysteries of mathematics, as well as give them opportunities to practice their newly acquired arithmetic skills. The field of geography abounds in opportunities for children to gain an understanding of other peoples in other lands and their health habits, such as learning about the children of India and their nutritional problems, or how and where the boys and girls of Africa live. Likewise, history contains much of interest to children, especially those on the upper elementary level, who are in the hero-worshiping stage and delight in reading about the life of famous health heroes like Florence Nightingale or Louis Pasteur. Nature study can easily be correlated with health education for children intrigued by caring for animals, learning how birds build their nests, or watching plants grow. In fact, any and all school subjects can easily be correlated with health by a creative, imaginative teacher who is determined to share with youth unusual and meaningful experiences.

Fusion combines and condenses several previously separated, but naturally related, subjects into one course. A common practice under this plan is to merge government, economics, and sociology into a course entitled "American Problems," or to offer a biology course composed of a combination of zoology and botany. In health education separate courses in first aid and home nursing are often

[5] The Continental Press, Elgin, Ill., has excellent preprinted master carbon units for coloring and use on any liquid duplication for health instructional purposes in each elementary grade. Children using these materials should be asked to explain what each picture means to them.

These pupils are correlating things learned in arithmetic with health education. (Courtesy, AAHPER.)

fused into a course entitled "Emergency Care and Safety Education." It is also possible to fuse or telescope units within a subject by combining closely related areas or topics. One advantage of such a plan is that unnecessary materials can be discarded. Its chief disadvantage, however, is that since "something will have to give" to fit materials to be covered into a reduced time schedule, that "something" may be vitally important to certain students who were victims of the teacher's final decision to "skip lightly" over this, but to "tread heavily" over that. Too often, under such a plan, health education is eliminated or briefly mentioned by an unknowing teacher who too often assumes that the children are not interested in health, especially since they all seem to be happy, healthy, normal children. Actually, every child has a great need for accurate health information.

Integration is a plan whereby subject matter boundaries are nonexistent or ignored. It is a unique rearrangement of materials devised to help the learner recognize and profit from closely linked subject areas. It is both a state (completeness) and a process (a means of bringing about a harmonious working unit made up of separate parts). Integration, then, is a mosaic created out of many tiny pieces which have been carefully fitted together into a clearly recognized pattern.[6]

Integration in health education is used to organize learning and concentrate efforts on large problems or areas. For the elementary school these may be:

1. School living
2. Health and safety
3. Leisure and play
4. Consumer problems
5. Personal development
6. Family living
7. The control of disease

Fragmentation, or the old-fashioned method of teaching health by day-to-day assignment, such as posture one day and the care of the eyes the next, is rapidly becoming an educational antique that is being replaced by the newer, more functional concept of integration. As a result, children are both seeing more meaning in what they are learning, and mastering more worthwhile materials.

The Core Curriculum. The chief characteristic of this type of curriculum is its emphasis upon the present-day needs of America and the world. It is centered upon life today. Advocates of such contend that schools should deal with socially significant content—namely, problems which revolve around living in a democratic society. They stress teacher-pupil planning and purpose, rather than "turning the school over to the kids" or "keeping them busy." This type of curriculum is sometimes called "areas of living," "integrative

[6] The Denison Publishing Company, Minneapolis, now has five new books available outlining daily integrated lesson plans in reading, writing, arithmetic, social studies, health, physical education, library time, etc., for Grades 1–5. They are entitled The First Grade Log, The Second Grade Log, etc. These splendid materials will prove valuable to all teachers as patterns for integrating subject matter.

Education can never be confined to a classroom. Here school safety patrols enter an airplane to see what safety devices and precautions are provided air travelers. (Courtesy, Nashville Public Schools.)

core," or "centers of interest." It contends that the school must assume greater social responsibility if democracy is to survive, let alone extend itself in the world.

In the elementary school core programs are organized around units, problems, or areas of living, such as (1) protecting life and health, (2) living at home and school, (3) conserving and improving material conditions, (4) cooperating in social and civic action, (5) earning a living, (6) securing an education, (7) seeking religious beliefs, (8) enjoying and expressing beauty, and (9) engaging in leisure-time activities. In this type of curriculum, stress is placed upon that which is realistic to both the pupils and teachers, upon teacher-pupil planning, and the sharing of many learning experiences. As applied to health education, the core curriculum means a theme or a unit made up of many facets or problems. Frequently, such a core program reaches beyond a single period and extends into the major portion of the school day or into several school weeks. The library is one of the main resources used at school or in the community by students to discover the answers to problems arising in each major unit. Constant evaluation is necessary in order that the learners and the teacher see how much progress they have made toward reaching their goals. The use of resource people, such as the nurse or dietitian in the school, or the mayor or firemen in the local community, is a means of providing children with opportunities to become acquainted with a wide variety of people from different ages and occupations in order to help them see that one can learn much from life and persons in it, instead of just from reading books or by listening to teachers. The instructor is of paramount importance if the core curriculum is to be used successfully. She must be a democratic leader who can skillfully guide and channel the enthusiasm of the children, as well as create in them an eagerness to learn about unknown and interesting things, direct them to many learning resources, help them devise workable plans, see meaning and purpose in what they are doing, aid them to relate what they are learning to their daily lives, and finally, assist them in learning how to evaluate their efforts objectively.

The Experience Curriculum. This curriculum is built primarily around the needs and interests of the pupils. Since each group is different, each curriculum must be unique. Consequently, major emphasis should be placed on pupil interest. Planning by pupils, under the guidance of the teacher, is considered essential and receives great emphasis, as do teaching methods which center around problem solving, group activity, and laboratory experiences. Weaknesses of this type of curriculum are that often teachers cannot discover the real and lasting needs of children, and that a careful study of the present and future problems of children is too often neglected. Then, too, the interest span of children is fleeting, so that although they may be engaged in many different kinds of activities, they often do not get very far, educationally speaking. The mere expenditure of energy cannot result in progress unless the work done is meaningful and has educational value.

CURRICULUM PLANNING

Many people should determine what children learn at school. As Willgoose states, "The curriculum is part and parcel of the society, the local community, the pupils, and teachers,"[7] Basic factors which must be taken into consideration by all curriculum committees are the health needs, interests, individual capacities, and the stage of development of each class group, for *what* is to be taught as well as *when* it will be taught must be determined if each class is to profit from taking part in a carefully planned program. Firstly, all such planning groups should be aware of those with whom the materials will be shared. Secondly, they must take into consideration state laws and the recommendations from the State Department of Education, as well as the objectives and the purpose of their own particular school. Thirdly, they must be cognizant of national needs, recent curriculum trends, and the scope and sequences of major materials which should be included in the school program. Total participation in such planning can be made possible by representatives from those to be taught and those directly and indirectly concerned with education within the school, community, and state. Short- and long-range planning should be done in both the broad subject areas and the special subject fields.

Regardless of which type of curriculum pattern is developed as the result of careful planning, the focal point of such a plan must be the pupils. From these curriculum plans, the teacher and children should determine their own objectives and course of action in the pursuit of knowledge in all learning areas. In schools using the core curriculum, group planning among teachers should result in suggested ways in which the health program can be incorporated in the core content. Where a departmental type of organizational pattern exists, activities selected by teachers engaged in group planning of the curriculum should focus upon the needs and interests of the children, and the allocation of health educative experiences to home rooms or departments. The teachable moments

[7] Carl Willgoose, *Health Education in the Elementary School,* Philadelphia, Saunders, 1959, p. 125.

which occur during each day should be discussed, and plans drawn up for how best to utilize them. Health education can be taught most effectively by some teachers using the direct method, while others create marginal and indirect learning experiences. Both techniques are recommended; it is not a question of which method is superior, for this depends largely upon the group being taught and each individual in it.

There are many ways to discover the needs of pupils, the knowledge of which is a necessary prerequisite of good curriculum planning. These include the following:

Steps in Studying Needs

Collect facts related to	*through*
the pupils' health status and behavior	teacher group planning
the pupil environment, including the home, school, and community	teacher-pupil group planning and activities
	student council and committee activities
	community group activities
	individual activities[8]

Awareness of pupil interests and needs is basic in planning health education programs. No list of needs should become static, for it should, like the children, grow and change with the passing of time and with each new pupil and each new group of children. Following the discovery of needs, pupils should be guided to think, plan, choose, judge, take initiative, develop knowledge, appreciation, and skills, and evaluate and draw conclusions through assuming an active role in the learning areas which they help develop. They must come to realize that taking part in desired activities is vitally important to them for their present and future well-being.

Every teacher must be actively and wholeheartedly involved in the school health program. In a real sense, each must feel a responsibility for it and contribute to its success. Each must become a health educator, regardless of whether she is the music or art teacher or any other kind of specialist teaching at the school, for no

[8] *The Problem Solving Approach in Health Teaching,* Michigan Joint Committee on Health Education, Lansing, Mich., 1943, p. 9.

part of the health instruction program should ever become the responsibility of one person, or only of the professional health educator. Every teacher must be involved to the extent that she will do her utmost to help young people find the way to live abundantly, productively, healthfully and happily.

Curriculum development is a continuous, ever-changing, and growing process. Some school systems supply teaching guides and aids that not only assist the teacher in planning the health education program, but suggest ways to interpret the program to the parents and general community. Such guides often contain:

A statement of the relationship of health education to general education.
A statement of the purpose, philosophy, policies, and scope of the school health program.
Suggested standards, policies, and procedures in the school health service program.
A survey of current health programs and major health problems in the community.
An outline of the scope and content of the school health education program.
A study of the health needs and interests of children.
Suggested resource units.
List of available resources for health education.
Suggested units in health problems in related areas of learning.
Suggested student references in health education.

If the health education program is to become meaningful and dynamic to all concerned with the education of children, each must have a vital part in shaping and reshaping a devised program. In order to achieve this goal, all teachers must believe that health education is as important as anything else taught in schools, whether it be reading, science, or mathematics. There are those who claim that the development of good health is the foundation upon which a sound educational program for the individual and the nation must be built.

PRINCIPLES OF CURRICULUM PLANNING IN HEALTH EDUCATION

Guiding principles for the development of a schoolwide health education program might include the following:

1. The health education program should be an integral part of the total school curriculum.
2. All school personnel should share in the planning for the school health program as well as for health instruction.
3. Representatives from the community as well as the school should play a major role in planning the health program.
4. Pupils should share in planning the program through committees and as individuals.
5. Planning should be continuous, and gains made through experience should be utilized.
6. Leadership for planning should be provided by the school administrator, classroom teachers, and professionally trained health educators within the school and community.
7. Planning should result in a workable, reality-centered course of action which is to be put into practice as quickly as possible.
8. The curriculum for all grades in the elementary school should cut across subject matter lines and core areas in the overall school curriculum.
9. All subject areas included in the health instruction program for the elementary school should be carefully arranged in a graded health education program.
10. Each classroom teacher should assume the major responsibility for carrying out the results of coordinated planning for a health education program and tailor it to fill the needs, interests, and abilities of her pupils in each class.
11. Representatives from parent groups, teachers, the board of education, pupils, and school administration should study, improve upon, and approve the planned health education curriculum.

UNIT TEACHING IN HEALTH

A teaching unit is a plan that is drawn up jointly by the teacher and the pupils. It should be built around life-centered learning experiences and should cut across subject lines. Likewise, it should be based upon the personal and social needs of children, and provide them with opportunities for growth as individuals and group members. Although there are many ways to organize a teaching unit, basically each should contain a title, an overview or introductory statement, objectives to be reached, content guides and possible approaches, teacher and pupil activities, suggestions for evaluation, as well as references for the pupils and instructor.

In the primary grades, children should be given many opportunities to learn how to live healthfully and safely at home and at school. Health for this group should be taught informally and indirectly. Emphasis should be placed upon the development of good health habits and the learning of simple health concepts. For this group, teaching units should largely consist of meaningful and challenging activities. On the upper elementary level, each unit must be planned in greater detail and in relation to broad experience areas. All State Departments of Education states have devised handbooks or guides for health instruction. Naturally there is a wide variation in these materials, as is shown in the three sample units included below, which have been selected from widely separated geographical areas and illustrate various ways in which health units can be presented:

GRADE 1: GETTING READY FOR SCHOOL[9]

Suggested Approaches

1. Conduct an informal discussion on what pupils do in order to get ready for school, who helps them, and things they can do for themselves.
2. Read story to class relative to getting ready for school.

Problems and Pupil Interest

1. How much time do you need in order to get ready for school?
2. What kind of clothes should one wear to school?
3. How do you fasten your clothes properly?
4. How and why should you brush your teeth?
5. How do you comb and brush your hair properly?
6. What do you need to do in order to keep clean and look nice or "well groomed"?
7. Why is it important that you eat breakfast before coming to school? How much time is needed for breakfast?

Suggested Group Activities

1. Investigate the amount of time it takes to get ready for school, to eat breakfast, and to get to school from home.

[9] *A Guide for the Teaching of Healthful and Happy Living to Children in the Elementary Grades,* Department of Education, Columbus, Ohio, 1958, pp. 10, 11. (Reprinted by permission.)

2. Discuss and illustrate with cut out pictures proper clothing for different kinds of weather.
3. Dress dolls in seasonal costumes according to weather.
4. Discuss what to do to keep clean and look nice.
5. Discuss the importance of the following:
   Using individual towels and drinking cups.
   Washing, combing, and brushing hair frequently.
   Taking baths frequently.
   Hanging up clothes removed at night.
6. Demonstrate a good manicure.
7. Demonstrate proper way of combing and brushing hair.
8. Secure one's own toilet articles for use at home and at school.
9. Demonstrate how to brush teeth properly.
10. Make drawings or cut out pictures showing children getting ready for school.
11. Read stories relative to personal appearance and cleanliness.
12. Plan suitable dramatizations on "Getting Ready for School."
13. Bring pictures of children to class and discuss which ones are ready for school.
14. When playing with dolls get dolls ready for school.
15. Have pupils tell about experiences of sisters and brothers in grooming animals for fairs or pets for pet shows.
16. Make individual charts on essential items for getting ready for school and have pupils check daily for a period of two or three weeks.

Application for Teachers

1. Encourage pupils to bring to school their own toilet articles, such as comb and handkerchief.
2. Provide time for washing hands after play periods and before the noon lunch.
3. Place a mirror at convenient height for the pupils in the room. It will be conducive to good grooming.
4. Provide facilities for shining shoes and for cleaning shoes before entering the building.
5. Provide hangers for coats, with clothespins attached for overshoes and mittens.
6. Prepare mimeographed letters to parents suggesting things essential for preparing children for school.
7. Discuss problems of this unit with parents in individual conferences and at Parent-Teacher Association meetings.

Teaching Aids

PUPIL REFERENCES

See the list of basic textbooks in the Appendix.

TEACHER REFERENCES

Johns, Edward, Wilfred C. Sutton, and Lloyd Webster, *Health for Effective Living,* New York, McGraw-Hill, 1954. Nemir, Alma, *The School Health Program,* Philadelphia, Saunders, 1959.

VISUAL AIDS

Filmstrips *Getting Ready for School,* New York, Popular Science Publishing Co.

MISCELLANEOUS

Articles for demonstrating manicure and the brushing and combing of the hair.
Pictures of children getting ready for school.
Individual charts for recording and checking items related to getting ready for school.

GRADE 3: FIGHTING THE GERM[10]

Objectives of This Unit

One of the major health problems of the elementary school level is the prevention and control of communicable diseases. While the fundamental responsibility for prevention and control should be centered in the child's home, the school must assume a certain amount of responsibility in preventing and controlling the spread of disease. Health instruction concerned with communicable diseases plays an important role in this program.

The purpose of this unit is to build an elementary understanding of germs and how they are spread, with special emphasis given to the common cold. This unit should help the children realize their responsibility for helping prevent the spread of disease. The students should be familiarized with conditions that encourage the spreading of germs and what can be done to limit or control these conditions.

More specifically, the objectives of this unit may be stated as follows:

1. The children should learn that many germs enter the body through the mouth.
2. The children should learn that such articles as pencils, money, books, or other foreign objects may carry germs to the mouth.
3. The children should learn to cover coughs and sneezes with a handkerchief to avoid spreading germs.
4. The children should learn that sickness can usually be avoided by staying away from sick people.

[10] *Idaho Study Guide for Health Education, Grades 1–6,* State Department of Education, Boise, Idaho, 1956, pp. 25–27. (Reprinted by permission.)

5. The children should learn to stay at home when ill.
6. The children should learn to report first signs of illness to parent or teacher.

Teaching Suggestions

A. By the teacher:
   1. Talk about cleanliness and its relationship to preventing the spread of disease germs.
   2. Discuss doctors, nurses, and dentists as being our friends who work to keep us from getting a disease by immunizing us against certain diseases.
   3. Discuss the dangers of picking up disease germs from animals when they are friendly pets.
   4. Discuss with the children some of the ways of preventing the spread of colds and some ways to care for colds.

B. By the pupil:
   1. Demonstrate the use of the handkerchief to cover coughs and sneezes and relate why it is important in the prevention of diseases.
   2. Demonstrate the proper use of the drinking fountain.
   3. Do an experiment to show that warm water and soap is the best means of removing dirt. Wash something with cold water, then with warm water, then with cold water and soap, and last with warm water and soap.

C. By all pupils:
   1. Work out a dramatization showing how germs will not associate with clean boys and girls but follow around those who have dirty hands or put dirty things in their mouths.
   2. Demonstrate in a skit the ways cold germs may be taken into the body—trading bites of food, putting objects in mouth, handling objects handled by persons with a cold and then putting fingers in mouth, etc.

Basic Content

A. What germs are
   1. Size of germs
   2. Where germs are found
   3. What are bacteria
      a. Helpful
      b. Harmful

B. How germs are spread
   1. Coughing
   2. Personal contact with dirty objects
   3. Improper use of public facilities
      a. Drinking water
      b. Washrooms

4. Food and water

C. How can we control the spreading of germs
   1. Vaccination-immunization
   2. Quarantine
   3. Avoid ill people
   4. Don't spread germs you may have

Evaluation

A. By the teacher:
   1. Do the children know that many germs enter the body through the mouth?
   2. Do the children realize that pencils, money, books, fingers, and other foreign objects carry germs to the mouth?
   3. Do the children know the distinction between germs and bacteria?
   4. Do the children know that germs are spread through food and water?
   5. Do the children know what causes a cold?

B. By the pupil:
   1. Do I appreciate the doctors and nurses who can help me stay well?
   2. Do I appreciate the sanitary conditions of school, home, and community?
   3. Do I accept a personal responsibility for helping to prevent every possible disease?
   4. Do I realize the importance of pure food and water supplies?
   5. Do I know how cleanliness helps prevent the spread of diseases?

C. By all pupils:
   1. Do we report the first signs of illness to our parents or teachers?
   2. Do we avoid people who are ill?
   3. Do we stay at home when we are ill?
   4. Do we cover our mouth when coughing and sneezing?
   5. Do we keep foreign objects out of our mouth?
   6. Do we respect quarantine regulations?
   7. Do we avoid using others' personal objects such as towels and wash cloths?
   8. Do we drink properly from the water fountain?

GRADE 5: SAFETY AND FIRST AID[11]

Desired Outcomes

Children know

1. How to help the corridor and playground patrols prevent accidents.
2. How to prevent fires.
3. How to extinguish fires of all types.

11 *Handbook of Health Instruction in Oregon Elementary Schools,* State Board of Education, Salem, Ore., 1952, pp. 56–58. (Reprinted by permission.)

4. How to enjoy vacations without being hurt.
5. How to keep from being hurt at home.
6. How to keep wounds from becoming infected.
7. How to acquire a tan without being sunburned.
8. How to identify and use safe places to play.
9. How to use a saw, hammer, pliers, and similar common tools without being hurt or hurting others.

Activities

1. Make a survey of the school building. Check amount of traffic at intersections, along corridors, and on stairs. Make floor plan of building showing each floor. Study floor plan to determine whether pupil traffic should be divided, rerouted, or in some cases eliminated in part. Draw up plan to handle pupil traffic most effectively.
2. Field trip to fire station. Find out what constitutes the different types of fires (wood, chemical, electrical). Learn best means for extinguishing each type. Use commercial and pupil-made fire extinguishers to extinguish the different types of fires.
3. Make a survey of school building noting location and type of each fire extinguisher. Make floor plan showing location of each fire extinguisher in red. Study floor plan to determine whether or not the right type of extinguisher is in the right place. If not, contact principal with suggested plan for relocating fire extinguishers. Note date of last inspection of extinguisher.
4. Make a list of accidents and their causes common to different types of recreation engaged in by the pupils. Indicate on a chart which ones pupils have experienced, which ones people in the community have experienced, and plan ways to prevent such accidents.
5. Make a survey of pupils' homes to determine whether or not potentially dangerous situations are present. Plan how to correct undesirable situations. Report later on extent of correction achieved.
6. Have teacher, nurse, or doctor set up microscopes showing sterile and contaminated slides. Find out way in which wounds become contaminated and the resulting dangers. Practice handling sterile gauze and covering minor wounds.

The Use of State Courses of Study

State courses of study and health teaching guides should be used only as starting points for curriculum individualization. Just as a dress designed and made for a chubby ten-year-old girl living in Des Moines, would be totally inadequate and unsuited for a frail little lass in the first grade in Dallas, no state course of study or health teaching guide will "fit" all children even in the same grade in the same school in that state. An ideal health instruction program is one specially adapted to each class in each school in every locality throughout the land. Such a plan should be a flexible and elastic one which is just right for each child in each school grade. No two instructors, children, or teaching situations are identical. Consequently, no one plan is best for all concerned. Courses of study do have value, but only when used as a suggested pattern or course of action. Skilled teachers will create new and better plans from these suggestions and ideas found in all such materials obtained from the state education department or a local school system.

Every teacher is a builder. Each constructs her own educational house. The superior builder, realizing that such a dwelling is to be erected for the education of children, will quickly enlist the co-operation and capabilities (both apparent and half-hidden) of the youngsters to help build a wonderful place of their very own. Such a master builder will use an already-devised blueprint only to check on minute details which will prove helpful to the group's own creative efforts, and to avoid sure-to-fail attempts along the way. The house, when it is completed, will be a place of pride, joy, and wonder wherein many magical experiences can take place for all who live and learn there. The average builder will stick closely to a preplanned blueprint made by and for somebody else, and she will build just another house, which cannot and will not last long, or become a learning landmark worthy of anyone's remembrance. The poor builder, alas, will not even know that somewhere a blueprint does exist, or that it could be used as a starting point, so her house is never built, and the busy children who were longing to accomplish something merely mill around instead, and leave the incomplete foundation in search of adventure and meaningful accomplishment elsewhere.

Educators, unfortunately, seldom capitalize upon their gains. They could do so, however, by using what has already been achieved as a starting point. Existing, obtainable courses of study, teaching guides, and other such materials are such starting points.

THE RESOURCE UNIT

The resource unit is an organized, preplanned collection of materials and suggested teaching methods developed by one teacher for her own use, or by a committee composed of several instructors and health specialists. These units are also often devised by school health education specialists on the state level and are made available to educators upon request. Such a unit should contain a list of books and other printed references, teaching aids, and people or other community resources which could become most helpful to a project and could share valuable educational experiences with the children. Such units may be built for each health unit included in the subject-centered curriculum, or they may be planned to fit health into a broad-field, experience, or core curriculum. Professionally trained health authorities, including the health supervisor or coordinator, can be of invaluable help to any group of teachers engaged in developing such units of work. All completed unit projects should be kept in a central file so that many teachers may profit from this work done by their coworkers or predecessors. Each instructor should be aware, however, that she must bring life into such a plan that exists only on paper by modifying it to fit her own particular group before using it. Likewise, the teacher or the working committee groups should revise and keep such units up to date, so that children might benefit from current materials. The pupils should assist in the development and revision of such units. A resource unit might be patterned after the following one:

A RESOURCE UNIT IN COMMUNICABLE DISEASES FOR GRADE FIVE

Visual Aids

The Story of Dr. Jenner, Teaching Film Custodians, Inc. (10 minutes).
I Never Catch a Cold, Coronet Films (10 minutes).
Your Health: Disease and Its Control, Coronet Films (11 minutes).

Pamphlets

The Control of Communicable Disease in Man, American Public Health Association, 1958.

References for the Pupils

Jones, Edwina, and Jane Morgan, *Keeping Healthy,* Laidlaw.
Schacter, Helen, and William Bauer, *You and Others,* Scott, Foresman.
Ways to Keep Well and Happy, National Tuberculosis Association.
Winter Enemies, John Hancock Mutual Life Insurance Company.

References for the Teacher

Health Education, American Medical Association and National Education Association, Washington, D.C., 1961.

The Science Book of Wonder Drugs, Pocket Books, 1959.

The Control of Communicable Diseases in Man, American Public Health Association, 1958.

Personal and Community Health, Turner, C. E., St. Louis, Mosby, 1960.

SUGGESTED READINGS

Anderson, C. L., *School Health Practice,* 3rd ed., St. Louis, Mosby, 1961.

Beauchamp, George, *Planning the Elementary School Curriculum,* Boston, Allyn and Bacon, 1956.

Beck, Robert, *et al., Curriculum in the Modern School,* Englewood Cliffs, N.J., Prentice-Hall, 1960.

Foster, Julia, *Health Activities,* Philadelphia, Lippincott, 1950.

Godshall, Frances, *Nutrition in the Elementary School,* New York, Harper, 1958.

Grout, Ruth, *Health Teaching in Schools,* 3rd ed., Philadelphia, Saunders, 1958.

Hanna, Lavone, Gladys Potter, and Neva Hagaman, *Unit Teaching in the Elementary School,* New York, Rinehart, 1955.

Lees, Joseph, and Kenneth Jones, *The Teacher in Curriculum Making,* New York, Harper, 1961.

Los Angeles City Schools-Health in Elementary Schools (An Instructional Guide), Division of Instructional Series, Publication no. EC-201, 1959.

Loze, Frances, "Teaching Health in Life Science and Physiology Classes," *Health Education Journal,* September, 1958.

Health Education, National Education Association and American Medical Association, Washington, D.C., Report of the Joint Committee on Health Problems in Education, 1960.

Health Education, National Education Association and American Medical Association, 5th ed., Washington, D.C., 1961.

Safety Education in Rural Schools: Safety Education Methods, National Safety Council, Chicago, 1960.

Otto, Henry, *Principles of Elementary Education,* New York, Rinehart, 1955.

Phillips, Beeman, Ralph Duke, and Vere DeVault, *Psychology at Work in the Elementary School Classrooom,* New York, Harper, 1960.

Ragan, William, *Modern Elementary Curriculum,* New York, Dryden, 1954.

Remmers, H. H., David Riulin, and Einar Ryden, *Growth, Teaching and Learning,* New York, Harper, 1957.

Rucker, W. Ray, *Curriculum Development in the Elementary School,* New York, Harper, 1960.

Rugen, Mabel, "Working Together for Better Health," *Journal of Educational Sociology,* vol. 22 (1948), 91.

Schneider, R. E., *Methods and Materials in Health Education,* Philadelphia, Saunders, 1958.

Smith, Henry, *Psychology in Teaching,* Englewood Cliffs, N.J., Prentice-Hall, 1959.

Strendler, Celia, *Teaching in the Elementary School,* New York, Harcourt, Brace, 1958.

Warner, Ruby, *The Child and His Elementary School,* Englewood Cliffs, N.J., Prentice-Hall, 1957.

White, Verna, *Studying the Individual Pupil,* New York, Harper, 1958.

Willey, Roy DeVerl, *Guidance in Elementary Education,* rev. ed., New York, Harper, 1960.

7 TEACHING METHODS

To teach means to guide, lead, inspire, share, discipline, and discover with others. Success in this all-important professional field is due largely to skill in human engineering and to educational development. Those best prepared for their positions know something about *what* to teach but a great deal more about *how* to do it. The latter comes from experience, experimenting and adapting principles and methods to fit one's own situation. To teach also means to impart information through skilled techniques so that others will learn, for to educate means to bring forth latent possibilities and to "lead forth."

Good teaching results will accrue more abundantly when each instructor, through the use of teacher-pupil planning: (1) sets desired goals and individual objectives to be reached, (2) selects and sees values in materials to be learned in order to obtain these desired ends, (3) shares planned, purposeful learning experiences, and (4) evaluates the final results in light of the original goals. Through the use of a wide variety of methods, the skilled teacher will see pupils improve in skills, make positive attitude changes, develop deepened and broadened understanding, and use the things they have learned by applying them in their daily lives.

TEACHING METHODS

There is no single best teaching method. A good teacher is one who can obtain results, using the best method from the many she

Children learn many health habits at school for use in their daily lives. (Courtesy, Nashville Public Schools.)

can skillfully use in order to succeed in reaching an objective. The use of variety by any teacher will bring more than spice and life into her work, for it will increase pupil interest and add to the excitement of learning new things. Each instructor who wants to become a master in her chosen professional field must experiment, carry on research, and profit from her own learning attempts. Unfortunately a teacher cannot always see all the results of her work, for there are many hidden treasures in teaching. All too soon she loses track of her pupils over the years and seldom knows how effective her brief educational contact with each one has been. Many educators "plug" along, creating more miracles than they ever know. Behavior cannot change overnight, nor can a tree bear fruit soon after planting; yet the true educator continues patiently to teach others as best she can. Some teaching methods may work wonderfully well with Johnny, but fail miserably with Mary. Consequently, the skilled instructor will not only know a wide variety of methods but she will also know how and when to use each of them most advantageously. A "method" is a carefully thought-out plan to achieve definite goals. As applied to health education, method refers to techniques used to provide the best kind of a learning environment possible wherein the pupil's behavior can be shaped and directed for the betterment of his own health and that of others.

The many methods for teaching health include:

Daily assignments
Lectures
Teacher questions and student answers
Special reports
Panel discussions
Teacher or student demonstrations
Class discussions
Workshops
Informal student to student discussions
Observation
Forums
School camping experiences
Debates
Projects
Role playing
Problem solving
Dramatizations
Arts, crafts, and other constructive projects
Analysis of current events
Recitation periods
Student-led class discussions
Surveys
Drills
Workbooks
Field trips
Supervised practice and guided study
Do-and-tell periods
Textbooks and supplementary reading assignments
Teacher-stimulated and directed discussions
Supervised study
Student reports
Small-group study
Creative dance and rhythms
Educational games
Individual or small-group counseling
Experience units
Small-group buzz sessions
Guest speakers
Storytelling
Research projects
Visual aids
Experiments

Fortunately, health education is rapidly gaining its long-deserved and righftul status in the school curriculum. Luckily, too, this subject is no longer included in the elementary school at the whim of a teacher, or taught by one forced to "volunteer" to do what she can with it, in spite of her lack of preparation and interest. There are also many new and wonderfully successful teaching departures now being made by creative instructors in this field from the old-fashioned, unproductive methods used yesterday, wherein students were made to memorize the parts of the body or repeat a list of hygiene rules. In modern health education learning activities are centered around helping students solve those important health problems which directly affect them.

Factors which determine the type of health teaching methods to be used include the teacher, the time allotment, equipment and supplies, and whether the pupils are homogeneous or heterogeneous in background.[1]

Those teachers who have had little training in health education unfortunately often teach the subject matter straight from the textbook, for they feel more secure in doing so. Actually, although the teacher's edition of most elementary textbooks does contain numerous suggestions for covering included materials effectively, all such books should be used primarily as an "idea springboard." Above all, they should not take initiative away from the teacher. Naturally, in those schools where adequate time is devoted to health education and an interested and skilled teacher is in charge of the class, most progress is being made. In such educational institutions the health curriculum has been carefully planned and made meaningful through the means of a well-selected and well-taught program from Grades 1 through 6. Although it is desirable to have a wide variety of well-selected visual and other teaching aids, these are not absolutely necessary for a successful program, because creative and skilled teachers are far more important than superior materials, equipment, or facilities. Ingenious instructors can succeed in getting students excited enough about learning to make their own posters, cardboard-box movie projectors, and

[1] Leslie Irwin, James Humphrey, and Warren Johnson, *Methods and Materials in School Health Education,* St. Louis, Mosby, 1956, p. 156.

illustrated health films rolled on a curtain rod, or to build a hamster cage for an experiment. Too many commercial gadgets and teaching guides in the classroom can rob teachers and pupils of their latent creative talents. In schools where health classes are alternated with those in physical education, pupils who were dumped into this latter "catchall" usually gain little from either experience, for there are often just too many pupils in the former class to teach health effectively, and therefore often too little opportunity to discover the real health education interests and needs of the class. Athletic coaches, who in some schools are saddled with teaching alternate physical education and health education classes as well as producing winning teams, cannot and usually do not do much except coach players who are already above average in ability. All health classes on the elementary level should be kept small enough for the teacher to know a great deal about each of the students enrolled in them. Our best-trained and most skillful teachers must be assigned to teach health before real progress can be made in the improvement of school health instruction programs.

METHODS FOR IMPROVING INSTRUCTION

The best methods for teaching health are the same as those used in the effective teaching of any other subject. The basic aim of any health education program should be to teach people to live healthfully, acquire health knowledge, and develop positive health attitudes. All educators with this aim well in mind will develop their own best teaching methods. Included below are some ways in which health teaching could become more meaningful and productive for each pupil:

Class Discussions. Class discussions are one of the most effective ways to teach health, but only if students are keenly interested and take part in the discussion, and if it is not dominated by a few bright students. Willgoose suggests the following ways in which class discussions can be made more meaningful:

1. An overnight assignment, which requires some study or searching for ideas at home, will provoke a number of good questions for the next day in class.

2. A list of questions, raised in earlier sessions and distributed prior to the discussion, helps the student who is a poor thinker. In studying teeth in the third grade, for example, questions such as these tend to generate curiosity: "How many teeth do I have?" "When will I have all my permanent teeth?" "Will baking soda and salt clean my teeth?"
3. A small group discussion or buzz session where the class is divided into small units is often productive.[2]

Although such a method can be used successfully, care must be taken to have the group help select discussion topics on *their* interest level. It is also wise to rotate student leaders and have each buzz-session subgroup select a pupil to give a brief report to the whole class on what the group discussed. The teacher or a student should summarize the main points presented by each discussion reporter. If the teacher is leading the discussion, she should avoid answering her own questions, for teaching is not a process of pouring in, *but rather it is one of drawing out.* Educators have a great fear of silence. Most teachers answer their own questions, sometimes less than seconds after posing them, thus stealing from children their educational right to discover logically the correct answers for themselves. One of the first things a child learns early in life is how to get around adults and thus free himself from pressure or work. He will give back to parents or other adults the "right" answers to such queries as "Do you love mommy?" or "What do you like most about school?," etc., in order to please the questioner and seldom to reveal what he really thinks or feels. Some children, according to psychologists, even refuse to talk, for they can get what they want from adults without making even that effort. Many soon learn in school how to get by with a minimum of effort, and are masters of this technique by the time they leave the elementary school.

Field Trips. Although field trips are increasingly being used as a means of teaching, they are often avoided because they are too much trouble. Some schools forbid groups to go on excursions because of the fear of accidents and the consequent legal liability. However, trips can be, and often are, the highlight of an entire elementary school experience. When teachers realize that neither they

[2] Carl Willgoose, *Health Education in the Elementary School,* Philadelphia, Saunders, 1959, pp. 295–296.

nor the school have a monopoly on teaching or education, and that learning for life can be accomplished without a teacher at school, more educators will find ways to provide out-of-school excursions for their groups. Education is more than reading, it is *doing*. Missing the next regularly scheduled class, if the field trip is to be extended, often is the best thing a teacher can do, for what the children might learn had they gone to class may be trivial in comparison with the gains possible from a carefully planned, purposeful tour. Although some parents become alarmed when children leave school for fear they are not learning anything, this attitude can be gradually overcome if such parents listen to the eager narration by their own child of the exciting out-of-class experience at the family dinner table, or if they hear guest speakers at the P.T.A. or elsewhere.

All field trips should be carefully planned, taken with a definite purpose in mind, cleared through the proper authorities, arranged with those in charge of the place to be visited, talked about beforehand, discussed as things are seen, related to materials being studied at school, be safely conducted, and summarized when the group returns to its classroom. Some exciting places to visit in a community are a:

Grocery store
Modern dairy
Health museums
Ice cream plants
Hospitals
Bakery
Farm
Canning and packing plant
City water and sewage-disposal plant
Farmers' vegetable market
Dentist's office
City health department
Large restaurant
Veterinarian's hospital
State health department
Fire station
Emergency rooms and first-aid stations
Children's court for bicycle offenders
Police station
Zoo
Drug laboratory
Slum area

A field trip can become a meaningful experience or a meaningless lark. To have educational value it must be an important adjunct to health problems currently being studied in the classroom. All out-of-school excursions should be taken for a definite purpose which is clearly understood by each teacher and pupil. It is imperative that trip plans be fully discussed and carefully drawn up before the group leaves the school. The classroom teacher should guide pupil committee groups to discuss and make trip plans carefully. Each committee chairman might well be asked to record on the blackboard the answers to such questions as these: "Why do we want to go on this trip?", "What do we want to learn?", "What is the relationship of the trip to what we are now studying?", and "How can we apply what we will learn to our daily lives?"

The following suggestions should prove helpful to those who plan and conduct excursions:

1. Make sure that this experience becomes a vital part of what is being studied in the classroom and that the children will learn many new things which they could not in the classroom at school.
2. Plan the trip carefully both with the pupils and host of the place to be visited so that both know what to expect when the group arrives and what can be learned from this experience.
3. Take safety precautions at all times throughout the trip; be prepared for accidents and emergencies.
4. Select and plan all trips according to the maturity and comprehension of the class.
5. Discuss the outing with the class upon returning to school and help each pupil link what has been learned outside of the school with what is being studied inside the school.
6. Clear all matters such as parental consent, conduct rules, rest-room stops, meals, and other necessary details before leaving the school. Be sure the principal knows when you are leaving, where you are going, how many pupils you are taking, and when the group will return.
7. Strive to increase the educational values of all future community visits by carefully evaluating each trip taken with the class.

The most fruitful educational excursions are those which enable pupils to learn from many kinds of first-hand experiences those things which cannot be learned elsewhere. Oberteuffer contends that field trips can become more valuable when they are built around surveys or studies in which relationships are stressed, such as visiting a slum area to learn more about the relation of poor housing to disease or delinquency, or evaluating a recreation area in relation to community and individual leisure-time.[3] Certainly

[3] Delbert Oberteuffer, *School Health Education,* 3rd ed., New York, Harper, 1960, p. 141.

such experiences can become a bridge between school experiences and community life. Some schools have developed guide books for the teacher which carefully outline trip procedures and also classify excursions which can be most suitable for each class grade. Such materials help eliminate duplication of trips through the child's entire school experience, and help the teacher select, from a list of possible places, those which are best suited to the maturity and intellectual background of her own particular grade.

A carefully planned and well-organized field trip can:[4]

1. Encourage explorations and interest.
2. Develop pupil curiosity.
3. Cultivate careful observation.
4. Provide careful, accurate, first-hand observation.
5. Clarify concepts and give additional meaning to previous classwork, especially for pupils whose experience backgrounds are limited.
6. Provide opportunities for vocational guidance through direct contact with various kinds of work.
7. Promote intelligent citizenship through experiences in social living.
8. Form new ties between the pupil and community.
9. Arouse the interests of parents and other citizens in what the schools are doing.

In spite of these worthy contributions, many school systems forbid teachers to take children on trips outside of the school. However, "where there is a will there is a way," as all teachers who are determined to give their pupils the richest kind of educational experiences possible well know. Such educators often contact the Girl Scouts or Boy Scouts, or other youth organizations in the community, and enlist their cooperation in helping children learn more about their community through Saturday excursions. Others assign older pupils to visit such places as a recreation center or health museum on their own time and write a paper which describes what has been learned from this experience. Regardless of what method is used to make education positive, purposeful, and functional to youth, the community, with all its rich resources for learning, should be fully utilized.

Experiments and Demonstrations. Although experiments often

[4] *Health Education,* National Education Association and American Medical Association, 5th ed., Washington, D.C., 1961, p. 285.

prove to be more valuable on the upper elementary level, primary children can learn an abundance of things from doing simple ones, too. Curiosity can easily be stimulated, for children are eager to find things out for themselves. Experiments should be kept simple, geared to help children discover their own answers to the problem around which the experiment has been built, planned under teacher guidance, and carried out by the pupils themselves. Care must be taken in using animal experiments, for although the pupil may learn that a mouse fed only on unhealthful foods will not grow as rapidly or be as healthy as one given a well-balanced diet, children know that they are not mice, and therefore what happened to the animal could not possibly happen to them. The teacher must help each pupil see a clear and definite relationship between any experiment or demonstration and his own life and those of others around him.[5]

Suggested experiments and demonstrations which pupils can profit from doing include:

Using balloons to demonstrate how the lungs work in breathing.
Using light meters in discovering which part of the room is best for reading purposes.
Simple food tests for starch, fat, protein, water, and carbohydrates.
Water-filtration experiments using layers of sand, gravel, and rock.
Treatment of stagnant water with chlorine.
Examination of bacteria on food and in water before and after they have been destroyed.
Food-intake experiments using colored water and plants.
Using mice, white rats, hamsters, guinea pigs, or chickens to show the effects of good and bad diet upon growth.
Making tooth powder.
Analysis of how bacteria works on bread, cheese, and vinegar.
Food canning.
Oxygen-consuming experiments.
Relaxation demonstrations.
Demonstrations of how muscles work and rest.
First-aid demonstrations, including artificial respiration, snake-bite treatment, stopping arterial bleeding at the pressure points, and bandaging.
Posture demonstrations showing how to use the body correctly while lifting, carrying heavy objects, sitting, and moving through space.

[5] See the splendid new book which shows how students can do many kinds of fun-to-do simple experiments without elaborate equipment, *Wading into Science*, by Mary Ellis, Elizabeth Fuller, and Robert Shipley, Minneapolis, Denison, 1960.

Demonstrations of how light and sun affect all growing things.
Reproduction demonstration using fish, insects, eggs, or small animals.
Safety demonstrations, including the conduction of electricity, extinguishing fires, riding bicycles, using hand signals, coming and going to school safely, combustibility of materials when improperly stored.

The scientific method used in experiments to prove or disprove a hypothesis embraces a number of other teaching methods, including discussion, problem-solving, demonstration, and investigation. Although planning and setting up equipment are time-consuming and tedious, properly performed experiments do have high educational value. Their correct use will help students develop (1) the ability to follow specific directions, (2) skills in using many new kinds of equipment, (3) an increased appreciation of the scientific method of research, and (4) the ability to see a project patiently through to its completion. Such techniques of discipline are especially valuable to children during their formative years. Likewise, nowadays when there is a marked emphasis placed upon science in our daily lives, youngsters can be guided through the use of the experimental method in the elementary school to gain an understanding and appreciation of its relationship to science. Nutrition experiments to show the value of a well-balanced diet are especially suited to children, as are those in safety, and those which show how the human body, or any of its systems or separate parts, works. The social sciences, geography, reading, and most other subjects taught in the school provide numerous opportunities for the use of the experimental and problem-solving methods. In schools in which the core curriculum is used, group teacher planning is necessary in order to discover and determine the many ways in which health problems can be incorporated and best used in the core content. Where a departmental organizational pattern exists, an important part of curriculum development should be given over to teacher planning based on pupil needs and interests and to allocation of health learning experiences to the various home rooms and departments.

Problem Solving. Elementary children have a natural interest in solving problems which directly affect them. They can be made increasingly aware that colds and other diseases should be avoided, that personal cleanliness is important, and of other aspects of health education through this method. Actually, the problem-solving method is not an isolated one, for it is used in almost all other methods. The teacher who summarizes the film shown in class by asking pupils questions about what they saw, or who motivates students' interest in conducting an experiment to find out why food decays, or what is the effect of the sun upon growing things, is using this method. The primary objective of the problem-solving approach is to develop the ability to think and to help pupils learn to appreciate the value of finding things out for themselves through thought instead of merely being told the answers to their questions. When a child learns to do this he often can better cope with and develop ways to solve his own health problems, as well as those of others.

Almost any area of health can be taught through this method. Ideally, the children should be stimulated and guided to set up their own problems and be motivated to find answers to questions they want to know about.

The problem-solving method may be used individually in health counseling, or by groups working on a specific project. Often a careful study can be made of the number of accidents which occur at school, or any other major concern which directly affects children. The steps to be taken by the group using the problem-solving method are:

1. Selecting a problem for study and clearly stating it.
2. Defining the problem by analyzing carefully its component parts.
3. Collecting pertinent facts from all sources, including surveys, interviews, reading, discussions, experiments, observations, and other methods.
4. Interpreting the data.
5. Drawing conclusions.
6. Applying the conclusions by drawing up a plan of action.
7. Evaluating the results of the steps taken to eradicate the problem.

As Grout points out, the use of the problem-solving method helps children think critically about information, and to collect, organize, apply, and evaluate data in relationship to their own health problems.[6] It also provides children with opportunities to think, plan,

[6] Ruth Grout, *Health Teaching in Schools,* 4th ed., Saunders, Philadelphia, 1963, p. 184.

participate, evaluate, draw conclusions, show initiative, cooperate, develop good social and group relationships, and develop the valued concepts of behavior so necessary for good growth and development. If the problem-solving method is to be used successfully, pupils should help select those problem areas which are important to them for study through teacher-pupil planning. Likewise, they will only become more skilled in using this method and applying it to their daily lives if they are given opportunities to develop skill, and are shown how to capitalize upon their previous attempts made in using this technique.

In one school recently, a small group of fourth graders became aroused (through the help of their teacher) over the lack of good manners among their peers using the lunchroom. Some gulped their food hurriedly in order to get out to the playground, others pushed and shoved in the cafeteria line, others talked at the table with food in their mouths, and some would even hold their noses or pretend to gag when they saw certain food being served. After considerable discussion in the classroom about this type of behavior, the group agreed that learning how to use the school lunchroom properly was a big problem which they themselves were causing, and they determined to find ways to solve it successfully for the sake of their own health and their reputation as pupils in that school. With the aid of the teacher, the class was able to define the problem clearly, which was that pupils did not fully understand or appreciate why they should eat well-balanced, carefully prepared hot lunches at school, nor the importance of eating slowly and using good manners. The class accepted the challenge this problem presented and decided to solve it. They drew up careful plans, which included committee assignments, personal interviews, on-the-spot lunchroom interviews, reading reference materials, class reports in which many kinds of visual aids on balanced diets in relation to growth were used, and other kinds of learning activities, including visiting the school kitchen and talking with the cooks and dietitian. When the class felt that they had gathered adequate data concerning their problem, they devised a possible solution to it, which was that the dietitian and two elected students from the class would check each tray of food selected by each pupil and announce daily the names of those who selected the best-balanced lunch and ate it while using the best manners. A student committee composed of two members also selected the pupil who was the most polite in the cafeteria line throughout the entire week. The group also voted upon and accepted the rule that no one could be excused from his assigned table until five minutes before the lunchroom period was over or until everyone else at his assigned table had finished eating. The class also chose a host and hostess for each table group to serve for one month before they were to be replaced by other elected pupils. A classroom honor roll was made which contained the names of those selected three consecutive times by the dietitian for having chosen the best-balanced lunch and having the best table manners. Committee groups gave reports on what they had found out through library and other assignments about the value of eating a balanced diet. One group acted out an original skit showing the difference between bad and good table manners. Periodically the pupils evaluated their solution to their lunchroom problem and behavior there, and made changes in their original plans several times during the term when they discovered these were needed in order to gain better results.

The teacher plays a major role in helping children become aware of important health problems. As Willgoose reports:

> She often leads the way in discovering such items as community health hazards, causes of accidents and illnesses in school, causes of school absences, difficulties in eating, personal unhappiness, etc. Sometimes the problem is demonstrated by the use of a film.[7]

Throughout each day, school children must make many decisions and choices. The problem-solving method of teaching and learning will, if it has been used well and is clearly understood by the pupils, enable them to make such decisions more wisely, thus increasing their own health, safety, and well-being. It will also help them develop desirable habits and attitudes concerning their personal responsibility for the development and protection of their own health as well as that of those in their own family. The wise teacher will utilize the possibilities to health education fully in her daily teach-

[7] Willgoose, *op. cit.*, p. 301.

ing in each class period. The use of the problem-solving method in health education should result in improved changes in thinking and in attitudes.

The Use of Textbooks and Assignments. Nothing can destroy interest in learning about health faster than merely reading what one is assigned in a textbook. The teacher who says to her group, "Tomorrow we will discuss the materials found on pages 61 to 68 in your text," or the one who spends precious class time having students read aloud to each other is not only a great time waster, but is being grossly overpaid for the little she accomplishes as an educator. Fortunately, health textbooks are becoming increasingly more fascinating to children, for they are beautifully illustrated and written by experts who know how to appeal to children's interests and can help them discover many new and exciting things.[8]

Effective assignments are those which help children discover the answers to their problems or to questions raised in class. The material in the book should be used both as a reference and an "idea springboard," and as such, need not be studied in the order presented in the book. All possible opportunities should be provided for children to bring to class things like magazine pictures, newspaper articles, or objects from their home or neighborhood which relate to the things they read about. Increasingly, publishers are printing textbooks in a graded series for children on the elementary level, and have done much to assure a logical, wisely selected progression of materials. Most teachers can obtain a sample copy of these books upon written request, as well as a teacher's edition for an entire series if the book is adopted by the school.

The library should be used in conjunction with outside assignments and as a means of stimulating interest in reading.[9] Children should be encouraged to read widely as well as to develop a scientific attitude about the things read. The school librarian and teacher must work together to help pupils gain skills in using available materials and to find new reference materials. Attractive health edu-

[8] See the Appendix for recommended health education textbook series for elementary schools.

[9] "Public Library Health Information Center," *Today's Health,* vol. 35, no. 4 (April, 1957), 15, 17.

cation library exhibits, arranged by a student committe assisted by the librarian, often stimulate pupil interest, as will displays of interesting books written for the entertainment as well as education of children in the area of health, such as Munro Leaf's splendid *Health Can Be Fun,* or Jean Augland's *A Friend Is Someone Who Likes You.*

The teacher should use a textbook in much the same way she does any other instructional teaching aid—namely, as a tool for helping children learn. Although it is common practice to have all pupils use the same textbook, the teacher might well use a variety of textbooks which can be assigned to individual pupils to read and then share additional information about any subject with others in the group. Teachers' manuals, which are usually available, should be modified in order to make them most suitable, for unless the suggestions found in such manuals are made to fit the needs and interests of each teacher's own class group, they are of no value. Pupils' workbooks should likewise be used with caution; too often such materials merely provide pupils with "busy work" which has no educational value, and can even encourage pupils to copy answers directly from textbooks rather than help them think about or discover their own answers. Although in some areas school administrators and state committees, rather than teachers, select textbooks, all instructors should have a voice in determining the books best suited for their needs. Those who are responsible for the selection of textbooks might well use the following criteria. The book must:

1. Contain scientific, accurate information.
2. Present graded materials in logical sequence.
3. Have high reader interest appeal, contain familiar as well as new materials, and be on the comprehension level of the pupils in the grade for which it will be used.
4. Motivate positive behavior and a desire for improved health.
5. Be attractive, easily read, and well illustrated.

Teachers must remember that, although textbooks have a real place in every classroom, there is no textbook which can replace an instructor who plans her teaching materials so that her pupils can have meaningful learning experiences. A text is only a starting point from which teachers and pupils can begin many new and exciting learning adventures together, but it is the teacher who makes such adventures become experiences of real value.

Exhibits and Museums. An exhibit is an excellent means of showing others what has been done by a class group, and of stimulating pride of accomplishment in each pupil.[10] Grown-ups who take their youngsters to visit the camp they went to as children often feel great pride and have real identification with that particular place, for it is here that *they* helped build the camp chapel or a swinging bridge across a deep ravine. School children need to develop such feelings of pride and to have close identification with *their* school. A well-planned temporary exhibit or a permanent display in a showcase in the school lobby can do much to produce such feelings, if the things collected for others to see and admire have been made by the children themselves.

All exhibits should convey a message and are best when built around a specific theme or fact, involve little reading, can be easily understood, and are eye-catching and hold the interest. The entire exhibit should be done by the pupils under the guidance of their teacher. Although she can plant ideas for the theme and the content of the exhibit, if the project is to be an educational one, the specific planning and execution of the project must be done by the class. Such exhibits should convey a special message to the viewers. Consequently, each pupil or committee group making each separate exhibit should determine what specific information they want to get across by means of their exhibit. This in turn, will make the development of each project a rich educational experience.

A visit to a health museum such as those in Dallas and in Cleveland, the Children's Museum in Fort Worth, the Museum of Natural History in New York, can do much to intrigue children in health. If the class group is taken on a visit to such places, the trip should be well planned, and the children not hurried along. The teacher, as well as a museum guide, should help the class understand the things at which they are looking, and make every attempt to broaden and increase each child's interest in and knowledge of health. Unfortunately, many localities do not have such museums,

[10] Dorothy Gilman, "An All-school Health Night Program," *The Grade Teacher,* vol. 62 (May, 1961), 31, 33.

Preparing projects for science fairs gives students opportunity to make practical application of knowledge gained through learning activities. (Courtesy, Nashville Public Schools.)

and many children are denied the rich learning adventure found from visiting them. Fortunately, the American Medical Association, the Cleveland Health Museum, and several commercial firms have traveling exhibits and miniature museums for loan or rent. The teacher should make every effort to visit outstanding health museums and bring back ideas to share with her group for making their own miniature museum. Ideally, each elementary school should have its own health education laboratory, health education room, or have a permanently assigned space for housing permanent health exhibits, displays, and current class projects.

Dramatizations. Many free health plays written for children are available from the American Theatre Wing Community Plays, 351 West 48th Street, New York; Human Relations Aids, 1790 Broadway, New York; National Safety Council, Chicago; Junior Red Cross, Washington, D.C.: National Boy Scout Headquarters, New York; National Girl Scout Headquarters, New York; and Campfire

Children gain many ideas for making their own visual aids for a school health museum from seeing examples such as this. (Courtesy, Dallas Health and Science Museum.)

Girls National Headquarters, New York. The best plays, however, are often those written, directed, and acted by the children themselves.

Children delight in dramatic activities. Their small world is largely one of make-believe and initiation. In order that they use this favorite pastime profitably while in school, however, the teacher should be cognizant of the following limitations of dramatics as a method of health teaching as pointed out by Irwin, Humphrey, and Johnson:

1. Unless the cast is frequently changed, all pupils will not receive the benefit of direct participation.
2. It is possible that entertainment will be substituted for education.
3. Certain forms of dramatization may not warrant the expenditure of time that it takes to prepare and present them.

4. Literary values may be overstressed, with little or no value for health and safety.
5. The lines may be largely "preachment" of health facts.
6. The dialogue might develop into the mere memorization of health facts.
7. There might be an insufficient amount of action and an overabundance of dialogue.
8. There is a possibility that pupils may be considered only as dramatis personae. Despite Shakespeare's immortal words, the play is *not* the thing; the learner should receive the greatest consideration when the dramatic method is used.[11]

Amateur shows in which original plays, songs, or poems can be presented to the class are exciting educational experiences for children. Health plays are more meaningful when written, acted in, and directed by the pupils themselves, as are their own miniature television series in which an individual or family can be shown solving a series of health problems. The use of puppets and shadowgraphs can also be an effective way to teach health to children. The very young enjoy simple finger plays and wall shadows that "talk" and can be made in the form of bears, rabbits, dogs, or other animals. Puppets made from discarded junk materials are far more fun for children to use than expensive store-bought marionettes. Those made of paper bags, socks, tennis balls, brushes of varying sizes, papier-mâché, vegetables, fruits, hedge apples, boxes, corks, spoons, or sawdust can be quickly made and cost nothing.[12]

Tableaus and pageants can be utilized well in elementary schools, for each grade group can be assigned a specific part in a production involving all the children in the school. A definite theme should be selected and attempts made to integrate materials from many subject areas. Role playing and sociodramatic activities are especially well suited to the upper elementary grades. Those using these media of expression should first show, through unrehearsed and spontaneous expression, how people *do* behave in certain situations, and then how they *should* behave. This second portrayal should reflect the reactions and suggestions of the actors and the class for improving behavior or eliminating problems which do arise in certain situations.

11 Leslie Irwin, James Humphrey, and Warren Johnson, *op. cit.*, p. 304.

12 Maryhelen Vannier, *Methods and Materials in Recreation Leadership*, Philadelphia, Saunders, 1956, pp. 54–57.

Oral Presentations. Discussions between the pupil and teacher should do more than merely exchange information, for when used correctly, this method has high educational value. Care must be taken that certain bright students do not gain and keep the limelight long enough to cause the already dull to become duller pupils. Carefully devised, concise teacher questions are most effective and yield the most fruitful results. Questions which require "yes" or "no" answers, or the repeating of memorized meaningless phrases should be avoided, for children are not slot machines or parrots, but human beings eager to learn and to solve hard as well as easy problems.

Some teachers can stimulate pupil interest in learning how the human eye works by describing to the class how birds, whales, or dogs see in contrast to how a person sees; others may motivate a class, when introducing a new unit on nutrition, by describing how bird mothers take care of their young. Regardless of whether the pupils are more stimulated by hearing about animals or about children of their own age or those living in other countries, oral presentation can work wonders in arousing pupil curiosity. Likewise, they can help children feel as though their questions are important and help them gain confidence in speaking before others. Through such class discussions children can also learn many other things, such as being kind and considerate to others, or how to express themselves well using good grammar. The instructor should carefully guide class discussions and help each child contribute something of value to this group activity.

Oral reports given by students also have great educational value, for children can learn much from accepting and carrying out responsibility for making such reports, and gain a feeling of pride that they are contributing something of value to the group. Some develop self-confidence and an interest in speaking before groups which has lasting value; many an politician or lawyer gained a strong desire to select a "talking type" of profession from these early experiences. Pupils giving special reports should be guided into interesting subject channels suited to their capabilities, yet challenging enough to help them develop new interests and knowledge. Each reporter should first give a brief statement of his topic, then report on it, and finally summarize briefly what he said. Experienced public speakers summarize this, "Tell them what you are going to say, then say it, and finally, tell them what you have just said."

The lecture method is considered by many to be the poorest of all methods of teaching, for man's attention span is short, and after a short time the listener tends to hear only snatches of what is said. However, this method, when used correctly, does have great merit. It can be used in the modified form of a story or brief description to motivate elementary children. Illustrated materials should be used and referred to as the teacher talks to the group, for what one both hears and sees can be a potent means of education. A discussion between the learners and teacher following the short talk will add to the effectiveness of this method, as will a summary at the end of the discussion, and a short résumé later, on the following day, or throughout the week. Such emphasis helps children remember longer the things they are learning. Pupils can become active listening participants, but the degree to which they can do so depends largely upon the skillfulness of the speaker and her ability to recapture wandering attention.

What children say and do when out on the playground, at home, or anywhere *away* from the classroom is the real test of the effectiveness of any educator or teaching method. Any teacher who is determined to help children learn things of value most effectively will experiment, keep trying, and finally, at last, find her own best methods for doing so.

PRINCIPLES OF TEACHING

Good teaching is based upon sound principles. Each instructor must make all class periods meaningful and purposeful, linking what is learned today with what was mastered yesterday. The following principles of teaching are suggested guides which will help eliminate wasting time and energy on the part of both the instructor and the learner:

1. The teacher and learner are working partners who must find purposes, devise plans, share experiences, see relationships in what they learn, and evaluate together what has been accomplished.
2. Individual differences must be taken into account and learners guided

toward accomplishments which bring them satisfaction, challenge, and new interests.
3. Each learning and teaching experience should be reality-centered.
4. The primary role of the teacher is to motivate pupils and guide them toward positive actions, attitudes, and values.
5. The teacher should place each student in a group in which he can make the most educational progress.
6. The teaching environment should be group-controlled, not teacher-dominated and be a friendly, encouraging one in which all pupils feel secure and are contributing members.
7. Teaching is helping others discover and develop their latent talents; the role of the teacher is to help the learner do better those things he finds he can do.
8. There can be no productive learning without productive teaching or productive self-motivation.
9. When we help others learn how to do certain things, we can usually do this best by showing how and then helping them analyze and do what we have done.
10. The teacher must discover the causes of slow learning or nonlearning, and relate herself to them in ways to improve learning.

Pitfalls to Be Avoided. It is not easy to teach health in schools. Teachers often make damaging and lasting mistakes in their zealous attempts to help children "grow up to be big and strong." Many, forgetting that they are only licensed to teach, not to preach, forecast destruction and doom to those children who do not brush their teeth every night, fail to bathe regularly, or do only a few of the many things they should. Still others overstress competition and rewards in the form of gold stars or other symbols to the extent that they fail to see that the child is washing behind his ears every day in order to have the class see his teacher paste another gold star on his chart, instead of doing so as a means of keeping clean. Other practices which should be avoided include:

1. Contests for the healthiest child.
2. Artificial rewards ("You do this, children, for me and I'll let you out early today," gold stars, and too frequent praise so that success comes too easily and without meaningful challenge).
3. The use of untrue, sadistic, or sensational materials in an effort to shock listeners to become concerned about health.
4. The use of ridicule, sarcasm, or projected frustration upon abnormal, unattractive children who become the adult's scapegoat as well as that of the class.

5. The use of senseless jingles or slogans that are cute and catchy, but educationally worthless.
6. Saying one thing and doing another in regard to health.
7. Making health instruction dull, thus destroying children's natural interest and curiosity to know about themselves and the world in which they live.
8. Causing pupils to become too health-conscious and hypochondriac.

Basic Guides for Teaching Health. Basic guides for teaching health to children in elementary schools include the following suggestions:

1. Place emphasis upon the positive approach toward health.
2. Teach to reach each individual and stimulate his own personal desire to improve his own health, and to value health as a way of life.
3. Teach each child how and why he must take ever-increasing responsibilities for his own health habits.
4. The goal of instruction should be the happy, well-adjusted and healthy child.
5. Base all lessons on the interests, needs, and capacities of children at each stage in their development, yet keep in mind that they will become adults who will be responsible for their own actions and those of others.
6. Relate what is learned in school to the reality in which the child lives.
7. Integrate and correlate learning experiences in health with as many other subjects taught in school as possible.
8. Stress that knowledge gained about health should be applied to one's daily life.
9. Scientific materials from the fields of anatomy, physiology, or other sciences are of value in health education only if they help the pupil understand his own body more and solve his own health problems better.
10. All materials which are taught must be related to helping pupils make right decisions concerning their own health.
11. Present health education as a means to an end, not as an end in itself.

SUGGESTED READINGS

Creating a Good Environment for Learning, 1954; *Instructional Leadership in Small Schools,* 1955; *Learning and the Teacher,* 1959; *Freeing the Capacity to Learn,* Association of Supervision and Curriculum Development, National Education Association, Washington, D.C., 1960.

Brown, James, Richard Lewis, and Fred Harcleroad, *Instruction Materials and Methods,* New York, McGraw-Hill, 1959.

Crow, L. D., and A. V. Crow, *Human Development and Learning,* New York, American Book, 1956.

Department of Classroom Teachers, American Educational Research Assoc., National Education Association: Trow, W. Clark, *The Learning Process,* 1954; Ojemann, Ralph H., *Personality Adjustment of Individual Children,* 1954; Gallagher, James J., *The Gifted Child in the Elementary School,* 1959; *Conditions of Work for Quality Teaching,* November, 1959; Washington, D.C.

Grout, Ruth, *Health Teaching in Schools,* 3rd ed., Philadelphia, Saunders, 1958.

Haag, Jessie, *School Health Program,* New York, Holt, 1958.

Harnett, Arthur, and John Shaw, *Effective School Health Education,* New York, Appleton-Century-Crofts, 1959.

Highet, Gilbert, *The Art of Teaching,* New York, Knopf, 1950.

Irwin, Leslie, James Humphrey, and Warren Johnson, *Methods and Materials in School Health Education,* St. Louis, Mosby, 1956.

Langton, Clair, Ross Allen, Phillip Wexler, *School Health,* New York, Ronald, 1961.

Macomber, Glen, *Principles of Teaching in the Elementary School,* American Book, 1954.

Moustakas, Clark, *The Teacher and the Child,* New York, McGraw-Hill, 1956.

Schneider, Robert, *Methods and Materials in Health Education,* Philadelphia, Saunders, 1958.

Simpson, R. H., *Improving the Teaching-Learning Process,* New York, Longmans Green, 1953.

Sharp, Louis, *Why Teach?,* New York, Holt, 1957.

Thomas, R. Murray, and Sherwin Swartout, *Integrated Teaching Materials,* New York, Longmans Green, 1960.

Turner, C. E., C. Morley Sellery, and Sara Louise Smith, *School Health and Health Education,* 4th ed., St. Louis, Mosby, 1961.

Wheat, H. G., *Foundations of School Learning,* New York, Knopf, 1955.

Willey, Roy DeVerl, *Guidance in Elementary Education,* rev. ed., New York, Harper, 1961.

Willgoose, Carl, *Health Education in the Elementary School,* Philadelphia, Saunders, 1959.

Zirbes, Laura, *Spurs to Creative Teaching,* New York, Putnam, 1959.

8 TEACHING AIDS

Learning experiences in health can be made more memorable through the use of supplementary teaching aids. Each teacher should have a variety of good instructional materials but should not use them as a crutch or substitute, with the idea that merely exposing the children to them will ensure learning. All such materials should assist in educating pupils, and should not be used merely as a means of entertaining them. Schools cannot and should not compete with the amusement world, nor were they ever meant to.

In a sense, all supplementary teaching materials are audio-visual. When properly used, these materials can:

Supply a concrete base for conceptual thinking and hence reduce meaningless word responses of students.
Have a high degree of interest for students.
Make learning more permanent.
Offer a reality of experience which stimulates self-activity on the part of students.
Develop continuity of thought; this is especially true of motion pictures.
Contribute to growth of understanding and hence to vocabulary development.
Provide experiences not easily obtained otherwise and contribute to the efficiency, depth, and variety of learning.[1]

All carefully selected visual aids should give a true picture of the ideas they present, contribute more meaningful materials to the

[1] Carl Willgoose, *Health Education in the Elementary Schools,* Philadelphia, Saunders, 1954, pp. 329–330.

unit in which they are used, be appropriate for the class, have good eye and ear appeal, and be well worth the time and effort spent in obtaining and using them.

There are many different kinds of teaching aids. Some of the best ones to use in health teaching include:

Chalkboards
Scrapbooks
Specimens (live and preserved)
Pamphlets
Bulletin boards
Flannel boards
Posters
Cartoons
Stick-figure drawings
Opaque projector
Spot and geographical maps
Visual materials and records
Mannikins
Diagrams
Charts
Graphs
Maps
Flashcards
Mobiles
Flat pictures
Newspaper clippings and magazines
Filmstrips
Photographs
Question boxes
Food samples, labels from cans, etc.
First-aid supplies
Mouth mirrors and other types of dental equipment
Microscopes
Mirrors
Comics
Collections
Radio
Television
Recordings
Models
Exhibits
Slides
Films
Puppets
Agar plates
Health records
Bicycles
Small toy or automobiles
Good grooming supplies, including a nail file, hairbrush, etc.

SOURCES OF MATERIAL

There is such an abundance of free and inexpensive materials in health that the problem for many teachers is to select, catalogue, and find ways to use those things she has obtained.[2] The wise educator starts her own collection while still a student in college, for such materials will help her feel more secure when she begins to teach. All teachers should subscribe to professional journals, daily newspapers, and several good popular magazines, as well as being ever on the lookout for supplementary materials and teaching aids which they might use in their classes. Going to local and national teachers' conventions will prove beneficial and keep a teacher up to

[2] See the Appendix for a list of sources of free and inexpensive health education materials.

date on new things in her field, as well as acquaint her with new teaching materials which are available.

The children should contribute even more than the teacher in the collection of materials, and will do so if encouraged to bring to class and share things they have found outside of school which pertain to what they are studying. Friends and parents can also contribute many materials but will need to be informed of the type of things needed, for although people are anxious to help others, they are often unaware of how to do so. Recently, the parents of one sixth grade class also learned a great deal about health when they were asked to help their children collect health education articles from the local newspaper and the magazines. In another school, a group of mothers helped pupils locate old snapshots taken of recreational activities they had enjoyed when they were children. These were used by a committee reporting on "How Our Parents Used Their Leisure Time When They Were Children." Family members of a third grade class in a school in Georgia recently helped youngsters gather their baby pictures, as well as those taken at yearly intervals. These were used in a written report made by each child entitled "I Am Growing Up."

The list of suggested readings, found at the end of this chapter, will prove helpful to the teacher who wishes to make her own supplementary materials with her students. Those who guide pupils in creating their own visual aids will share richer educational experiences with their children than those who collect such teaching aids because the children will profit much more from doing things for themselves.

RECOMMENDED MATERIALS

Each teacher should experiment and discover which type of supplementary materials could be used most profitably with her particular class. For most children, seeing the germs on their own hands under a microscope is a far more potent educational experience than seeing a cartoon entitled "Mr. Germ." Regardless of which type of aid is selected, its use should be made as personalized as possible. Seeing one's own teeth in a magnifying mirror may be excellent for most pupils, but may not be for all in the class. Gadgets to be manipulated, buttons to be pushed, and wooden flaps to be lifted in order to see what they hide are all fascinating to children and should be used in conjunction with their health education class.

Motion Pictures. When correctly used, motion pictures can be one of the finest ways to stimulate interest and motivate changes in behavior in the field of health education. Although it is no doubt true that one picture is worth a thousand words, it must be remembered that one direct, purposeful experience is far superior, educationally speaking, to many pictures. Most state departments of education have a wide variety of health films which are available upon request, and are increasingly developing audio-visual aid branch libraries strategically located throughout the state. The majority of our large school systems have their own film libraries and have stocked them with carefully selected pictures suitable for children on each grade level. State universities, private colleges, city, county, and state health departments, youth agencies, commercial organizations, and local libraries also have well-selected health films which are available upon request. The U.S. Office of Education Film Library Directory lists free films which can be obtained for use in the classroom.[3] Most schools request that films which contain advertising not be shown to pupils, and most of them have policies drawn up to guide in the selection of all films.

From research conducted by audio-visual educational specialists, there is no doubt that the use of well-selected films in the schools increases the whole climate of instruction, learning efficiency, and retention, as well as reading ability and comprehension. Certainly, all films should be carefully selected and shown for a definite purpose, whether this be to shape specific attitudes, increase interest in any given area, aid the pupils to gain a clearer understanding by seeing enlargements of things too small to see with the human eye, clarify and make clearer relationships of events in time, or help pupils gain a deeper appreciation of the wonder and beauty of life and living things.

[3] See the *Educator's Index of Free Films,* published annually by Educator's Progress Service, Randolph, Wis.

Factors to keep in mind when selecting a motion picture to show to a class are that it must:

1. Be suited to the age level of the group and have high educational value.
2. Contain accurate, authoritative information.
3. Give pupils a more complete understanding of the unit they are studying than they could get elsewhere.
4. Be well organized, clearly audible, and well photographed.
5. Fit the purposes, needs, and interests of the pupils.
6. Be of suitable length.

The teacher should know the correct time in the course of the unit to show the film, for the pupils should see it when they can most profit from the experience. It is important that the teacher preview the picture before showing it so she can best direct the pupils' attention to the important things in it. Likewise, she should give a brief resume of the content of the film in a manner which will excite the interest of the class. It is necessary to help children know what to look for in the film, so that they will remain alert and interested in what they are seeing. The teacher should summarize the important things learned from the film, or else members of the class may do so.

She should be a skilled projectionist; she should know what to do when the film jumps or breaks, or in any other kind of projection emergency. Nothing destroys the effectiveness of a film more than these irritating mishaps, which can become so uproariously funny to youngsters that the whole procedure becomes a farce and an educational waste. Certain pupils in the upper elementary grades will enjoy being taught to operate the projector. This is not only a good means of keeping truancy at a minimum on film days, but also can be a way to provide high-status jobs for those slower pupils who are attracted to machines and have a desire to master them. During the showing, the room should be well ventilated, darkened, and the viewers seated so that they can both see and hear well. The teacher should place herself in the best position to watch pupils' reactions to the picture.

After the film, the instructor should review its main points. This may be done by the teacher, by one pupil, by the entire group in response to her questions, or by a simple paper-and-pencil objective test. The film should initiate a wide variety of learning follow-up activities such as experiments, posters, bulletin boards, or creative activities devised around factual materials or concepts learned from the film. The film may be reshown, if necessary, to clarify certain points. Likewise, there are times when it is more advantageous to stop the film and involve the class in a discussion of probable solutions to problems being illustrated, and then, after continuing with the remainder of it, compare the shown solution with that devised by the class. An ingenious teacher will discover for herself effective ways to help pupils use what they have learned from seeing well-selected school health films. Teachers would be wise to make their own film-evaluation file for future planning and reference. Such a file, easily made on index cards, would have notes on each film shown, and information which should be given by the teacher in summarizing the main points of the film.

Filmstrips. These visual aids have many advantages over motion pictures in that they are less expensive, more easily shown, and often made to supplement a particular health education textbook series. Many commercial companies have free filmstrips for classroom use.[4] Suggestions given above about the best educational use of motion pictures also apply to the showing of filmstrips and slides.

Children can make their own filmstrips by cutting up old ones and rearranging the pictures. They can also create their own homemade cartoons by drawing pictures in a series on a long piece of paper, rolling it on a rod, and showing it by using a cardboard carton with a window cut in the front for a projector. Filmstrips allow the teacher more flexibility than movies, for she can more easily adapt the materials to the needs and interest of each class.[5]

Slides. Although there is an abundance of slides available, the best ones are often made by the pupils themselves. Many children have their own cameras and are fairly skilled at taking pictures by the time they are in the fourth grade. Biological supply houses and commercial companies also have slides either for sale or rental at a

[4] See the Appendix for a list of suggested ones.

[5] See *The Filmstrip Guide,* published yearly by the H. H. Wilson Company, 950 University Avenue, New York, N.Y., for a listing of 13,000 filmstrips suitable for schools.

nominal fee. Pupils will enjoy making their own pen-and-ink sketches on glass slides and seeing their work on a screen. An automatic slide changer is recommended for classroom use, since it can be timed perfectly with any comments the teacher wishes to make about the slide being seen, and frees the teacher from showing the pictures. Slides are ideal for classroom work, for they need not be shown in sequence, and only a few well-selected ones will help teachers get needed information over to children quickly. They are also ideal for presenting and magnifying graphs, charts, tables, or other similar types of information.

The Opaque Projector. Through these inexpensive machines newspaper clippings, charts, graphs, maps, examples of pupils' work, or any other type of written or printed material can be magnified and shown on a screen. Pupils respond quickly to having their own or a friend's best work shown to others in this manner.

As Haag suggests, in schools which cannot purchase human anatomy and physiology charts for health instruction, teacher-prepared slides of drawings from human anatomical and physiological texts can be used.[6] These same drawings can be shown enlarged so that younger pupils may more easily understand, and as a means of helping older children learn important details about the wonders of the human body. In a study of the bones of the body, the teacher might well have each pupil locate each bone shown on the screen in his own body, thus helping the learner grasp the relationship of what is being shown to himself.

The opaque projector has many different uses in the classroom. Pupils should help gather materials to be shown and can, through individual reports, help their classmates relate health and safety concepts to pictures. The teacher should take care that the pupils understand the significance of what is shown and that they do not read their own meaning into what they are seeing; must she always be aware that each pupil understands everything in light of his own past experience. The pupils should be given sufficient time to view each picture in order to gain full value from seeing it. The use of class discussions, question and answers, and asking pupils to

[6] Jessie Haag, *School Health Program,* New York, Holt, 1958, p. 412.

identify certain parts in the picture by pointing to it and giving its name are all recommended. This could be done especially well in showing a picture of a tooth and asking the class to identify the type of tooth shown, its parts, and care. Any body part and its care could be taught by using this same method. Pupils will especially enjoy learning how to operate the projector, and such experiences can help them build favorable attitudes toward contributing to the class. For some, this type of experience can be a means of gaining group status and helping them build self-confidence.

Television. No other communication medium has grown as rapidly as television. As an educational device, it is powerful and potent—whether for good or evil—for it can produce positive as well as negative results. Increasingly, schools are using television and children are being given opportunities to see as well as hear master teachers conduct lessons on regularly scheduled programs. The day of educational television is dawning, but meanwhile, teachers who work in schools without sets for classroom use can guide children to watch worthwhile and unique programs in their own homes and report to the group on things they have heard and seen that pertain to what they are studying in health at school.

School-planned television now exists in many of our larger cities. Such programs are planned and presented by experienced teachers; many show classroom experiences and situations well in advance of each telecast, and a copy of the program schedule and its contents, in the form of teacher and pupil guides, is sent to all teachers so that they can prepare their pupils to obtain full benefit from the program.[7] Educational telecasts vary from one lesson taken from a unit of several lessons on a subject to continued broadcasts of a complete unit shown daily for a week or longer, and to having the studio teacher give basic instruction on a subject to many children in a grade in all the schools in an area. Regardless of which method is used, it is imperative that the classroom teacher in each school "take it from there," and use what has been presented by the studio teacher as a foundation for her own teaching.

It is now possible, by closed circuit, for a class to view demonstra-

[7] *Health Education,* National Education Association and American Medical Association, 5th ed., Washington, D.C., 1961, p. 289.

tions and experiments in a faraway laboratory. Such experiences, which are less time-consuming than field trips, assure the teacher that all pupils are seeing the same thing, which is not usually the case when they are on an educational outing. Such viewing, however, should only be a supplementary part of the work the teacher is doing in her own classroom.

Since television is a one-way method of communication, its use in the school can only become effective if followed by classroom work such as discussions, questions and answers, written or oral examinations, or other teaching methods which will enable the child to contribute what he has learned and the teacher to gain insight upon what each child has learned and how he will apply it to his own life. Likewise, the teacher should summarize the main things seen, heard, and discussed at the end of the class period as well as give, or have a pupil or the class give, a review of these things the next day. Such summaries and reviews help children become aware of important things and help them retain this valuable information longer.

Radio Broadcasts. In order that children be guided to listen to worthwhile and educational radio broadcasts, the teacher should obtain as much advance information about specific programs as possible. Assigning students to do advance preparation before listening to any particular broadcast is highly recommended, as are follow-up assignments, and class discussions of programs heard either independently or in a group.

In order to retain their licenses, all radio stations must devote a certain percentage of their total broadcasting time to educational programs. Consequently, many local stations are now using school-sponsored broadcasts in which programs are planned and presented by the pupils themselves, assisted by their teachers. Such programs are not only an excellent means for maintaining a high level of pupil interest in health, but do much to arouse parental enthusiasm for the work their children are doing at school.

Like all other audio-visual tools, radio can be used advantageously at school by the teacher and pupils. However, it should be used to bring the world into the classroom and be regarded by the instructor primarily as a teaching aid instead of as an end in itself. The teacher must make every effort to integrate information from a broadcast with the course of study she is using in the classroom in order to help children gain the greatest value from listening to the radio, as well as to assist the pupils in becoming more critical and discriminating listeners. Carefully selected radio programs on such topics as events in history, stories about healthful living, or biographical sketches of health heroes can do wonders in vitalizing health teaching. Just as a reader of a textbook will get more out of his reading if he knows what he wants to accomplish, so the radio listener must also have his purpose well in mind. Consequently, before each class listening period, the teacher and group should discuss and write on the chalkboard their purposes in hearing the broadcast. Each child should then be encouraged to create and make a list of his own listening purposes. During the program, complete attention should be encouraged. By her own attitude the teacher can and should help create attentive listening among the group. Interruptions can be discouraged by cardboard signs, "Please—We Are Listening" or "Do Not Come In—We Are Listening," hung outside the classroom door.

The extent to which radio programs require follow-up activities in order that their maximum educational use be fulfilled is a good way to evaluate the effectiveness of a broadcast. Attempts to obtain more information about a subject, increased creative expression skills in language arts, student participation in their own actual or make-believe broadcasts, increased outside reading at home are only a few of the possible follow-up activities which can be utilized for excitingly valuable health teaching. When radio programs become important to children and they ask their mothers to tune in the same programs at home as those to which they listen in school, it helps to bridge the gap between home and school.

Children should learn to be self-motivated in their actions, and the teacher can help them learn how to become wisely discriminating and critical radio listeners who can select their own programs intelligently. Children should be guided to use their leisure time in and away from school, for this is an important part of their education, too. Teachers should discover what programs children listen to at home and help them select better ones by recommending certain outstanding future programs weekly in class. She can also assign homework listening and follow such assignments by classroom discussions. Older pupils can also learn much from analyzing radio commercials from the standpoint of misrepresentation.

Recordings. Phonograph records and tape recordings can provide learning experiences for children. Records are ideal for classroom work, for the teacher can stop them in order to discuss or repeat certain passages, and they can be played over and over again, can be preheard and evaluated, and can even be made by the pupils themselves, assisted by their instructor. Making a tape recording of a class discussion or panel can be enlightening and thrilling for children, especially when they hear their own voices and each becomes conscious of his need for improvement as a speaker and group member. Recording the talks given by visiting authorities or those heard on radio not only helps motivate pupil interest and makes them more aware of the high regard well-known adults have for the value of good health, but such recordings can be used for the benefit of future classes as well.

As in the case of the use of radio broadcasts or television, the teacher using these communication media should first prepare the listeners for the coming experience, later emphasize the important things that have been heard, and relate them to the actual life of each listening child. There are numerous helpful guides and manuals, issued by leading manufacturers of tape recordings, which the teacher should carefully study before using this type of equipment. Finding the best recording distances and positions in relation to the microphone, having all speak in a clear but natural conversational manner, eliminating background noise as much as possible by recording in rooms where echo can be reduced by drapes, screens, or acoustical tile, and taping the entire program without interruptions will all improve the quality of any recording made at school.

It is comparatively easy to provide elementary children with many kinds of learning experiences in which they can taste, touch, see, or hear, for youngsters in these early formative years are eager to find out everything by first-hand experiences. As they advance in school, such first-hand experiences are harder to find, for they will study history or learn about people in distant lands in geography. Educational recordings of such men as Presidents Franklin Roosevelt and Dwight Eisenhower have done much to bring realism into the classroom and to make history a study of events centering around outstanding, colorful people. Recordings of health heroes can do much to motivate individual desires to enter the medical profession, as well as to help children realize that because of the sacrifices of some people, they live in a healthier world. Such recordings can be taped by either the teacher or students. Excellent materials on health heroes can be obtained free of charge from the Health Education Department of the Metropolitan Life Insurance Company in New York, or from any of its branch offices.

Almost every teacher can make recordings of live events which happen in her classroom. The pupils of the fifth grade in the Horace Mann School recently wrote a play in conjunction with their unit in nutrition education. Although it was a simple, one-act version of imaginary conversations between a supermarket checker and various shoppers who went through her checkout line, the pupils delighted in hearing the tape recording made in class of "their play" and learned much from this experience. In still another school, a group of sixth graders recorded on tape four panel discussions given in class in a mental hygiene unit on "How to Be Popular," "How to Overcome Shyness," "When Should We Hide Our Feelings?", and "What Health Habits Can Help Make Us More Attractive?". These were played several times the following week and the pupils were then asked to select the best panel group according to criteria the class used for judging the work: accuracy of facts presented, ability of the panel to stimulate listener interest, and similar standards. In a second grade class in Texas, the teacher played a tape recording on "Our Eyes and How to Take Care of Them" which she had obtained from the Audio-Visual Aids Department of the Dallas Public Library. In order to help the group get the most out of listening to the recording, she told them briefly about its contents, saying that

> The doctor who made this recording will speak to us about how to take care of our eyes. He will first tell you how our eyes are like a camera, and then he will give you ten suggestions for taking good care of your own eyes.

Please write down each suggestion. Let's see which one of you can make the complete list of ten first. We will then divide up into groups of three to act out any of these ten suggestions. Listen carefully to what these suggestions are and decide which suggestion you would like to act out for the class.

The use of recordings in teaching can only be justified when they bring into the classroom greater pupil interest, and when faster and more meaningful learning can result from their use. The teacher's responsibilities for making such learning experiences valuable ones include prelistening, increasing the listener's vocabulary by teaching pupils the meaning and spelling of all new words, conducting well-thought-out class discussions, evaluating the results of this experience through testing (either verbal or written), and increasing and widening many other kinds of learning activities which revolve around each listening experience.

Pictures and Posters. Pictures and posters must be pleasant to see again and again, and should have aesthetic appeal and power. There is an abundance of free posters now available for classroom use. Even pupils who are unskilled in art can cut out pictures and use them for a poster, whereas those talented in this area can and should create an entire poster themselves. Traced figures, cut-out silhouettes, montages made from pictures, articles, or newspaper headlines, stenciled or free-hand lettering, the use of pipe-cleaner stick figures, cotton, or other materials pasted on to a poster all may be used effectively. Each child should make some kind of poster during a semester, working on it individually or with a classmate. Those who gain much from this type of experience should be encouraged to develop real skill in this medium of communication.

Commercial posters must be selected with care. Some schools prohibit the use of any visual aids or other supplementary materials which contain advertising. Many companies that supply free materials have obligingly printed their firm's name in small letters at the bottom so that, if necessary, it can easily be blocked out or covered over by an instructor.

Effective posters, whether they be pupil-created or obtained from other sources, are those which:

1. Contain a simplified idea or message.
2. Create a learning atmosphere.
3. Motivate action.

Many kinds of visual and other types of teaching aids are available free of charge. (Courtesy, American Institute of Baking.)

4. Give accurate, attention-getting information.
5. Emphasize the importance of doing a certain thing, or developing a good health habit.
6. Possess eye appeal.
7. Create a lasting impression.

Photographs taken either by the teacher or pupils can provide many meaningful educational experiences. A fourth grade teacher in Seattle recently discovered that the most effective way to motivate interest and desire to develop good posture among her students was to take individual snapshots of each child in her class as he stood before her facing first frontward and then sideways. A conference was held with each child, and each was asked to look closely at his own photograph as he and the teacher picked out his postural defects. Next, he was shown ways to correct his difficulties. The class later selected pictures of those in their group who had the best posture, and an elected committee group used the photograph for a bulletin board they made entitled "Good Posture for Boys and Girls." Many schools use posture pictures as a means of teaching children the value of having good posture, as well as to show each child what his defects are and how to correct them.

Cartoons, Comics, Sketches, and Stick Figures. Three kinds of simple drawings which can easily be made by most children are those which show faces, figures, and objects. Each should be drawn with the purpose of communicating an important message quickly and effectively. A cartoon should be used to exaggerate. It may show a food gulper instead of a slow and careful eater, or stress the value of drinking milk, or exaggerate what happens to one's body when one does not eat a balanced diet. In fact, any health concept can be illustrated with educational cartoons. Such pictures are especially fine to use with slow learners, especially when the teacher helps them get the point of the drawing. Carefully chosen comics or strip drawings which appear in newspapers or magazines can be used effectively with this group also, for often they can be strongly motivated to develop certain positive health habits because such heroes or heroines as Buck Rogers or Nancy, or animated creatures as Scampy or Donald Duck urge them to do so.

Creating cartoons, comics, sketches, and stick figures can also be a valuable classroom activity. The teacher should "draw out" each child as he shows and explains his pictures to others in the room in order to discover if he has clearly and correctly understood the fact or idea that he has drawn, and if he has made the drawing with a definite purpose in mind. The class might well devise criteria for selecting those creations which were the most meaningful. Since cartoons are associated with entertainment, care must be taken by the teacher to assure their use for educational purposes. Although many valuable cartoons can be obtained from commercial companies, the most effective ones are those which they make themselves. Those with a good aptitude for drawing and a poor aptitude for reading can be motivated to develop skill in the latter through their interest in cartoons and sketching.

Charts. A chart is a diagrammatic visual rearrangement of materials which is made so that one can see relationships or a sequence of events more clearly and easily. The types of charts used most frequently are *time charts* (a traveler's itinerary), *tree or flow charts* (a genealogical tree), *organizational charts* (a personnel chart), and *comparison or contrast charts* (height and weight tables). For classroom use, a chart should be simple, easily read, and clearly labeled. Upper elementary children can make their own charts and show them on an opaque projector. To use charts effectively in teaching, it is vitally important that the instructor help the child see the meaning of the chart in relationship to himself. A fourth grader who looks carefully at the height and weight chart on page 176 can find how much he weighs and should weigh and how tall he is and should be.

Teachers should file and catalogue all charts so that they are easily accessible. Care should also be taken that only scientifically accurate charts be used in the classroom, and that those which are selected for showing be displayed well so their use be educational, whether this be to motivate interest, stimulate thinking or action, show factual or comparative data, influence pupils' opinions, or help boys and girls develop desirable attitudes and behavior in relationship to their own health.

Pupil-made charts are a valuable means of helping youngsters grasp an understanding of the relationship and impact of figures to themselves. A *data* chart is the most commonly used type of chart in health education. For example, a fifth grade teacher recently motivated her class to conduct a survey among 100 children from Grades 3 through 6, who were selected at random, on whether or not they ate breakfast every day. After the data were compiled, she

TABLE 3. Height and Weight of Children

	Boys													
Height, Inches	5 Yrs.	6 Yrs.	7 Yrs.	8 Yrs.	9 Yrs.	10 Yrs.	11 Yrs.	12 Yrs.	13 Yrs.	14 Yrs.	15 Yrs.	16 Yrs.	17 Yrs.	18 Yrs.
39	35	36	37											
40	37	38	39											
41	39	40	41											
42	41	42	43	44										
43	43	44	45	46										
44	45	46	46	47										
45	47	47	48	48	49									
46	48	49	50	50	51									
47	...	51	52	52	53	54								
48	...	53	54	55	55	56	57							
49	...	55	56	57	58	58	59							
50	...	...	58	59	60	60	61	62						
51	...	...	60	61	62	63	64	65						
52	...	...	62	63	64	65	67	68						
53	...	...	...	66	67	68	69	70	71					
54	...	...	...	69	70	71	72	73	74					
55	...	...	...	...	73	74	75	76	77	78				
56	...	...	...	...	77	78	79	80	81	82				
57	...	...	...	...	...	81	82	83	84	85	86			
58	...	...	...	...	...	84	85	86	87	88	90	91		
59	...	...	...	...	...	87	88	89	90	92	94	96	97	
60	...	...	...	...	...	91	92	93	94	97	99	101	102	
61	...	...	...	...	...	...	95	97	99	102	104	106	108	110
62	...	...	...	...	...	...	100	102	104	106	109	111	113	116
63	...	...	...	...	...	...	105	107	109	111	114	115	117	119
64	...	...	...	...	...	...	...	113	115	117	118	119	120	122
65	...	...	...	...	...	...	...	...	120	122	123	124	125	126
66	...	...	...	...	...	...	...	...	125	126	127	128	129	130
67	...	...	...	...	...	...	...	...	130	131	132	133	134	135
68	...	...	...	...	...	...	...	...	134	135	136	137	138	139
69	...	...	...	...	...	...	...	...	138	139	140	141	142	143
70	...	...	...	...	...	...	...	...	...	142	144	145	146	147

helped the class make a chart of their findings so that they could not only "see" the facts but could draw their own conclusions from them. Found below is the type of chart the group made:

BREAKFAST INFORMATION CHART

Number of pupils who usually did or did not eat breakfast

	Boys		Girls		Total	
Grade	Did	Did not	Did	Did not	Did	Did not
3	6	5	6	7	12	13
4	5	3	5	12	10	15
5	5	4	4	12	9	16
6	4	4	4	13	8	17

Table 3 (*Continued*)

	Girls													
Height, Inches	5 Yrs.	6 Yrs.	7 Yrs.	8 Yrs.	9 Yrs.	10 Yrs.	11 Yrs.	12 Yrs.	13 Yrs.	14 Yrs.	15 Yrs.	16 Yrs.	17 Yrs.	18 Yrs.
39	34	35	36											
40	36	37	38											
41	38	39	40											
42	40	41	42	43										
43	42	42	43	44										
44	44	45	45	46										
45	46	47	47	48	49									
46	48	48	49	50	51									
47	...	49	50	51	52	53								
48	...	51	52	53	54	55	56							
49	...	53	54	55	56	57	58							
50	...	...	56	57	58	59	60	61						
51	...	...	59	60	61	62	63	64						
52	...	...	62	63	64	65	66	67						
53	...	...	...	66	67	68	68	69	70					
54	...	...	...	68	69	70	71	72	73					
55	...	...	...	...	72	73	74	75	76	77				
56	...	...	...	...	76	77	78	79	80	81				
57	...	...	...	...	...	81	82	83	84	85	86			
58	...	...	...	...	...	85	86	87	88	89	90	91		
59	...	...	...	...	...	89	90	91	93	94	95	96	98	
60	...	...	...	...	...	...	94	95	97	99	100	102	104	106
61	...	...	...	...	...	...	99	101	102	104	106	108	109	111
62	...	...	...	...	...	...	104	106	107	109	111	113	114	115
63	...	...	...	...	...	...	109	111	112	113	115	117	118	119
64	...	...	...	...	...	...	...	115	117	118	119	120	121	122
65	...	...	...	...	...	...	...	117	119	120	122	123	124	125
66	...	...	...	...	...	...	...	119	121	122	124	126	127	128
67	...	...	...	...	...	...	...	...	124	126	127	128	129	130
68	...	...	...	...	...	...	...	...	126	128	130	132	133	134
69	...	...	...	...	...	...	...	...	129	131	133	135	136	137
70	...	...	...	...	...	...	...	...	...	134	136	138	139	140

Source: Jesse Feiring Williams and G. G. Wetherill, *Personal and Community Hygiene Applied*, Philadelphia, Saunders, 1950, p. 28. (Reprinted by permission.)

After this study was completed, the children then made another survey to find out what children in Grades 1 and 2 usually ate for breakfast and how many of them usually had a good breakfast before coming to school. Such activities were part of a unit on nutrition and the value of eating three well-balanced meals daily. Projects of this type are especially well suited to the field of health education for they offer many opportunities for a teacher and class to correlate arithmetic, art, and other subjects with health education.

A skilled instructor in a sixth grade class recently showed her group a commercial flow chart to help the youngsters gain a better understanding of the step-by-step process by which flour is made from wheat. Later, she asked the children to choose partners and assigned each couple to bring to class a well-illustrated flow chart they had made which would show how blood circulates into, around, and out of the heart. She was amazed at and proud of the work the children brought and shared with the class. Once again she realized how much more the group and each individual pupil in it learned from making their own charts than they did from seeing the flour and wheat chart she had previously shown them. Consequently, when shortly afterward the class was studying the organization of the local health department, she asked each pupil to select a new partner and make an organizational chart of the local department of health. Such endeavors not only helped children learn about health coworkers in their own community, but helped them also to gain a new appreciation of the work of their own fellow classmates, as well as encouraged each child to widen his circle of friends.

Graphs. Although often confused with tables, graphs are diagrammatic methods of showing *numerical* data which show quantitative comparisons in forms of bars, geometric shapes, or pictorial symbols so that one viewing them can quickly see relationships between figures. There are various ways to help children grasp the significance of numbers when comparing things. These include *bar graphs; figure graphs* containing pictures of human beings, animals, birds, or fish with each one representing a certain number of the same kind; *pie charts;* and *line or curve graphs.* These can be obtained commercially, collected from books or other printed sources, or better still, be made by the pupils.

Dale gives the following suggestions to teachers for the best use of statistical data when showing it in graph form.[8]

1. Each symbol should be self-explanatory.
2. Large quantities should be shown by a larger number of symbols and not by an enlarged symbol.
3. Only approximate quantities should be compared, not minute details.
4. Only comparisons should be charted, not isolated elements.

Elementary children should be carefully taught how to read and interpret graphs correctly, and be taught that these materials can be used effectively to show statistical data, comparisons, and relation-

[8] Edgar Dale, *Audio-Visual Methods in Teaching,* rev. ed., New York, Dryden, 1954, p. 334.

ships. One of the best ways to do this is to have them make their own graphs using simple stick figures, squares, or lines. Giving each one an assigned task, such as making a series of stick-figure drawings to show how many persons there were in his grandmother's family, in each of his parents' families, and his own family is often a good beginning, and can be used in units on family education, heredity, and for other purposes. Others will find pleasure in keeping careful records of how many hours of play or sleep they had each day for a week and then showing this on a bar graph to the rest of the class, when the class is learning the value of exercise, sleep, and rest in relationship to growth. As Irwin, Humphrey, and Johnson point out, area graphs give pupils on the upper elementary level an opportunity to integrate health and safety with arithmetic because a circle graph can be used effectively in the study of simple fractions.[9] Such graphs are also effective ways to help students see how much time they actually spend daily in sleeping, going to school, watching television, or at play. To make such a circle graph, the pupils should divide the circle horizontally in the center, and in the lower half of the circle number from 1 to 12, going around the circle right to left. The upper part of the circle should be numbered 12 to 1, from right to left. The circle should then be cut like a pie, showing the hours which a pupil actually spends at this or that activity daily. Such experiences are revelations to many pupils. They often can become more concerned and profit more from this type of an experience than from hearing a teacher "preach" to them about going to bed earlier, or playing outdoors more. All will enjoy making pie charts or other types of graphs and experimenting with different kinds of colors and materials, in order best to present accurate information. Such graphs are especially well suited for cost studies, such as how much of the family budget is spent for clothing, rent, food, or medical care.

Maps. Maps can also be used effectively in health education, whether they be commercial ones purchased by the school or those made by the children themselves, for they help children understand special relationships. Maps of the route followed by each pupil as he comes to school, locating playground hazards on a map drawn

[9] Leslie Irwin, James Humphrey, and Warren Johnson, *Methods and Materials in School Health Education,* St. Louis, Mosby, 1956, p. 215.

of the playground, showing railroad crossings, national highways, and city streets in one's own town or within a mile radius of one's home can be both an interesting and profitable experience for children who are studying safety education. Such endeavors will help each see his school, town, or city as a whole, gain a concept of where he lives in relationship to hospitals or fire stations, and become more cognizant of hazards or dangers at school or on the way there. The use of maps can provide many opportunities to integrate a study of nutrition as pupils are studying the states of their nation, their own particular state, or the nations of the world. It is important for children to know where the food products they eat come from, how they are raised and transported, as well as the nutritive values of food.

Bulletin and Other Boards. Modern classrooms have large, colorful bulletin boards on which examples of children's work are attractively displayed. Such boards can be used as a means of bringing new or current things to the attention of the class, showing parents and other adults what pupils are doing in school, and giving children a place in the classroom which is their primary responsibility to use creatively and well. Class bulletin-board projects, which are carefully planned around a health unit, such as "Safety at School" or "The Muscles of the Body," may take several days and much class work by many pupils assigned to various committees. Such an educational adventure should be carefully thought through and the class should have definite objectives in mind as it determines how it can find out what it wants to know. Wide reading, visits to places of importance to that particular project, interviews, and many other kinds of experiences can become vital parts of any well-planned health education unit. A bulletin-board committee should become responsible for displaying new materials or the final work of the class on any such project. Naturally, the success of any such learning experience depends largely on the teacher and her ability to spark student interest. The pupils will need as much guidance and encouragement as possible. Likewise, the teacher should assist them by showing how the bulletin board can be used most effectively in order to reach general and specific learning objectives the group has devised. Shared evaluation, often called

Cardboard cutout figures can be used in many ways to help children gain needed health information. (Courtesy, Dallas Health and Science Museum.)

"action research," should be used throughout such projects and be viewed as a means of learning where one is now in relationship to where he wants to go. Some educators refer to a well-arranged, well-displayed bulletin board as a "silent but an effective teacher."

Any bulletin board can become a potently effective communicative device if it can

1. Get an important message across through the means of well-selected and well-displayed materials.
2. Attract and hold attention in such a way that it becomes a living and frequently-changed medium for reaching others.
3. Stimulate thought and motivate action.

Bulletin boards, or "tack boards" as they are sometimes called, can serve several purposes, including that of displaying announcements, student work, posters, short-term projects, and art work.

Here again, since children learn mostly from their own direct experiences, they should keep their class bulletin boards up to date and full of interesting and worthwhile materials which have aesthetic, cultural, and educational value.

A well-planned bulletin board is one that contains information and pictures which can be seen from a distance, has a title to indicate its purpose, well-arranged educational materials, and brief but pertinent informative statements which communicate what it is intended that the viewer learn or do. Such a teaching aid can arouse curiosity, quicken interest, motivate action, and inform.

A cooperatively created bulletin board can provide many kinds of stimulating and satisfying educational experiences to children. As Wittich and Schuller point out:

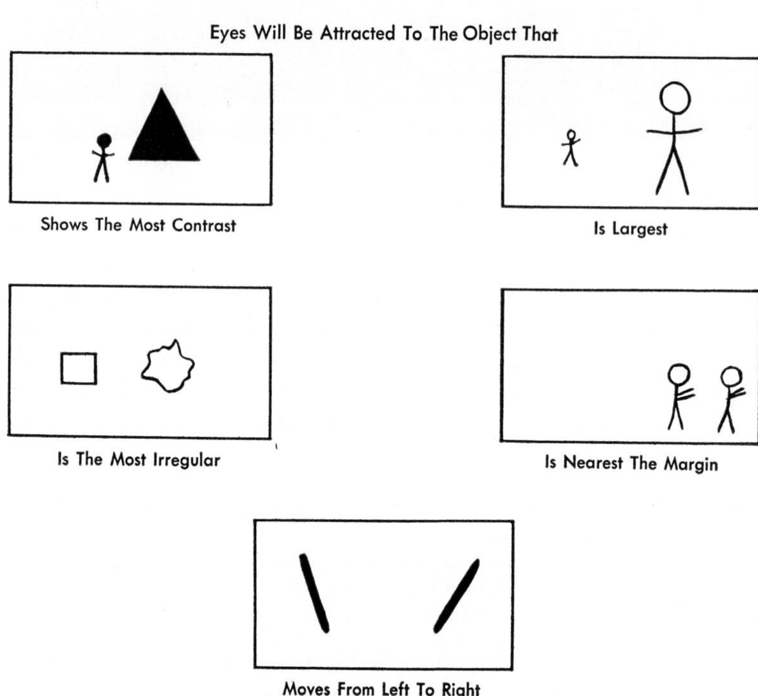

FIGURE 2. Techniques for Making Meaningful Posters.

It can be used to illustrate steps or phases of a unit as they are developed by the class and teacher together. It can be important as a summary or review device. It can be a versatile and valuable teaching tool.[10]

Suggested ways to make attractive eye-catching bulletin boards for health education purposes are to:

1. Use a few well-selected pictures rather than a large number.
2. Capture, center, and focus viewer attention; this can sometimes be done best by providing contrast through a generous use of space, having an irregular shape in a group of similar ones, placing the most important materials nearest the margin of the board, using both large and small pictures, and moving viewer attention from left to right.
3. Use color, remembering that red and browns or their combinations (warm colors) attract attention better than do blues and greens and their combinations (cool colors).

Regardless of what type of health information is used on a bulletin board, and whether the display is homemade or commercially made, created by the teacher, a pupil, or a committee, the instructor must keep in mind that merely exposing learners to a picture does not by any means ensure that they will gain anything of educational value from this experience. The teacher must bring to the attention of the class the specific importance of each picture or item of information displayed on the board, alert the pupils to definite things to look for, and make sure that the viewers understand and appreciate what they see. Likewise, she should help the pupils develop habits of making a careful scrutiny of all pictures they see, as well as teach them how to gather quickly the general impression a picture gives, and help them develop an aesthetic appreciation of the materials as a whole.

Learning how to set up and utilize a health education bulletin board effectively can be a part of any unit on any level in health education. Suggested activities for a class bulletin-board committee of any one of the five grades studying safety and first aid might well include the following:

1. Have each pupil on the committee bring in several pictures in this area of concern which have been taken from magazines or local newspapers.

[10] Walter Wittich and Charles Schuller, *Audio-Visual Materials, Their Nature and Their Use,* New York, Harper, 1953, p. 81.

2. Help the group select a bulletin-board theme and determine the information they want to get across to the viewers.
3. Guide the committee in their final selection of the best pictures, and help them learn why some pictures are better than others for their purposes of communicating a message or information to others.
4. Have the group mount the best pictures, stressing the value of different shapes and colors.
5. Teach the committee how to focus viewer attention by using contrast in color and size, regular and irregular shapes, moving the best pictures closest to the margin of the board, and moving the viewer's attention from left to right of the board.
6. Help the group set up and evaluate their display.
7. Evaluate the work of the committee and the display on the board by means of a full class discussion.
8. Assign the committee to prepare a file of future pictures which might be used on another bulletin board later in the year for any other aspect of safety education, such as "Safety on the Playground," or "Safety in the Home."

Since pupils will soon lose interest in bulletin boards which are unattractive, dull, and lack eye appeal, the wise instructor will make every endeavor to learn, either by her own trial and error or from specialists in audio-visual education, how to make attractive displays for the purpose of helping children appreciate health as a valued concept. Such an educator will soon learn the necessity of displaying pertinent, up-to-date materials which have eye and interest appeal plus the power to stimulate thought, understanding, action, and appreciation. In short, then, a bulletin board can only be as effective as the teacher who will use it creatively to help children learn better about health.

The Chalkboard. The classroom chalkboard is fascinating to young children. They are attracted to its magic, for on it writing and drawings can come and go, and can be whisked away by a sweep of the hand. It is a vehicle on which things can become *real,* where visual symbols become important. Today it is most often green in color and when the teacher puts "something on the board," children sense immediately that this is going to be important. It is a big day in every child's life when *he* finally gets to write on the board.

The chalkboard can be used fully as a means of helping children learn if one keeps the following suggestions well in mind:

1. Keep the board clean.
2. Be sure that all can see what is written or drawn on it.
3. Avoid standing in front of it, thus blocking the full view of the pupils.
4. Use class time to the fullest extent; do not waste it by using half of a period making a chart, but rather do this before the class begins.
5. Get an idea or fact over to the students quickly. Accurate, time-consuming drawings done to scale can be a waste of time if a quickly drawn stick figure can accomplish the same purpose.
6. Prepare an entire board in advance, cover it, and remove parts of the cover as a means of stimulating interest. Use such a trick sparingly, however.
7. Avoid putting too much on the board at one time.
8. Write key words, new ones, or key phrases on the board as you discuss things in class.
9. Have your pupils use the board often and encourage them to discuss what they have written or drawn there for the benefit of the group.

The use of colored chalk will add to the effectiveness of drawings made on the chalkboard, such as a sketch of the body or a diagram of the eye. Since one of the purposes of the teacher is to help children build a vocabulary in order that they can communicate effectively with others, she should clearly print all new words which will be introduced in each day's health lesson, such as "digestion" or "retina." It will help the pupils learn the meaning, spelling, and use of each new word, or slogan such as "Play Safely," if the instructor takes the time to point out how each new word is pronounced and then have the class repeat it with her several times, have the group spell and write the word, and encourage through praise each pupil who does use a new word or slogan that day in class discussion, written work, or in question-and-answer period.

Collections and Specimens. Children are pack rats! Their pockets are full of magical things which range all the way from an old key to a lucky rock. Many future world authorities on insects, plants, butterflies, birds, or health now sit in an elementary school classroom somewhere in this nation. Still more future amateur hobbyists and collectors of all manner of strange things are found there, too. Seemingly an interest to gather things together, catalogue them, and label them is found in most human beings, but it bursts into bloom as children grow older. Teachers should do their utmost to encourage pupils to become experts in their chosen field of interest, even though this may frequently change, for in so doing they can spur on the desire to learn and encourage an awakening interest. Likewise, they can help children develop lifelong hobby interests for wise, positive leisure-time use.

Making a collection of specimens is both an interesting and valuable experience in health education for children. They will enjoy bringing to class real objects to supplement pictures found in their textbooks. Since most of our learning comes through the senses, it is important that children touch and feel, as well as see and hear about the many wonders of creation in their world, such as a baby duck, or a milkweed. An understanding of any part of the human body can be quickened through this method of teaching.

It is important that any collection be more than a gathering of dead things, for children can be helped by their teacher, through a fresh and creative approach, to see life and meaning even in a mounted fish or a stuffed owl. As Whitehead points out, a pupil should never be taught more than he can think and wonder about. This implies that the teacher must guide children to well-presented and carefully selected learning aids, which she has tailored to fit their short interest span and comprehension level. Consequently, this instructor, aided by a committee of pupils, should sort through, select, and arrange well those collections and specimens children bring to class which can best serve as an educational aid.

The field of health education provides many opportunities for children to bring to class and share with others things they have collected in relationship to their work in health and safety on every grade level. One sixth grade class recently made a collection of all the kinds of animal teeth they could find (either in actual or picture form) for a comparative study of human teeth. Next, they examined each specimen for evidence of decay. Finally, they discussed what causes tooth decay and how they could prevent it happening to their own teeth. The group also studied the parts of a tooth and the relationship of a well-balanced diet to the prevention of decay. A fifth grade class studying food buying in a nutrition unit at a school in Florida last year made an extensive collection of empty food containers. The class spent the next two weeks discussing the Pure Food and Drug Law and its application as shown on food-packaging labels. They then learned how to stretch each food dollar further by discovering how much more good nutritive food could be purchased by knowing what constitutes a good diet and why one should read and know the declared weight or other vital information found printed on each packaged food product. Still another group of second graders who were studying "Happy Families" brought to class pictures they had found in magazines of family groups enjoying themselves together. Even "bad" specimens can be used, as Willgoose illustrates by describing an interesting assignment once given to a group of fourth graders.[11] This class was studying food spoilage and proper food storage. Each pupil was asked to bring to class one good and one spoiled piece of food, such as a good and bad orange, a sound and unsound potato, or a fresh and spoiled tomato. Through the use of the vivid contrasts between healthful and harmful food, the class saw for themselves enough evidence to make up their own minds about the value of proper food storage. They were then highly motivated to learn how to store food in safe and sanitary ways. Such vivid experiences help make learning about health and safety exciting and meaningful and long-lasting experiences to boys and girls.

Models. Models are imitations of real things, and usually are made on a smaller or larger scale than the actual object they represent. A miniature grocery store used in a nutrition unit is a model, as is an enlarged replica of the human heart made of plaster of Paris. Models can be used for teaching pupils many things in the area of health education. They serve chiefly, however, as a means of motivating pupil interest so that they can gain a clearer understanding and appreciation of the things they are studying.

Some pupils can learn quickly about traffic safety through "dry runs" using miniature toy cars on a table, or by three-dimensional representations of a highway and potential hazards a pedestrian or driver might encounter. This type of visual aid is called a diorama and has great possibilities for enriching health instruction. Others grasp the meaning of the red, green, or yellow stop-light signals from seeing these colors flash through a milk carton in which three windows have been cut; a light is turned off and on to shine

11 Willgoose, *op. cit.*, p. 374.

through at each color. Still others can create many kinds of models which test their ingenuity and creativity. Thus, balloons and plastic tubes might be used to demonstrate how food is digested, or a water gun squeezed and a faucet turned on to show the difference between arterial and venous bleeding.

Many commercial firms now have splendid models available which show various parts of the human body. Some of these are available in cross-sectional form, or in parts which fit together and can be separated so that each piece may be examined singly and relationships clearly seen. Cutaway models, or those which show what "the inside" of any body part looks like are also available at small cost.

Children love to make their own models and experiment with clay, papier-mâché, soap carving, wooden blocks, plasticine, flour-and-water paste, plastics, and an abundance of other materials. The teacher must encourage them as much as possible in their attempts to gain a clearer, better understanding of health and its importance in their lives, and, if the use of models can assist them to learn this faster and better, they should be used accordingly. Caution must be exercised, however, for the mere making of a teaching aid can become an end to itself, and "making things for health class" can all too quickly become meaningless busy work. Likewise, the teacher must be sure that the children's attention is directed from the model to the actual thing it was meant to represent, and that they see the relationship of that object to their own lives and general well-being. Many children have learned how to count money and work together, and about the values of eating well-balanced meals by using miniature box models of food and a toy cash register. Pupils should have increased opportunities to make things and learn from their own creative efforts as they progress in school. Far too often such experiences are limited to the first grade, and as the children move upward on the academic ladder, they are given fewer opportunities to do and make things in the classroom. Often, too, they are provided with fewer opportunities to talk in class or plan their approach toward learning and mastering assigned materials. In haste there can be much waste, for it is not a question of how much a child learns but how meaningful his learning experiences become to him and are expressed in what he does and how he feels.

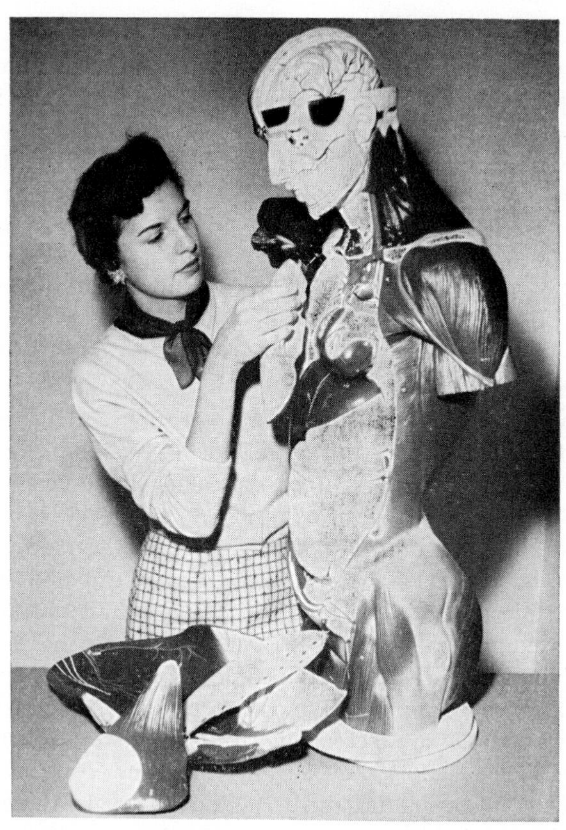

A pupil displays her understanding of the body and location of its parts by using a cutaway model. (Courtesy, Dallas Health and Science Museum.)

IMPLICATIONS FOR HEALTH TEACHING

Learning is a teacher-pupil responsibility. One of the major tasks of the modern school is to help students in any age group to gain an understanding of good health and its importance to the individual and society, along with the skills necessary for developing and maintaining it. As a subject in the school curriculum, health is not easily taught, nor is it generally taught well. Consequently, teachers on all levels must first develop a great and deeply felt desire to become efficient and effective instructors in this important field. Supplementary teaching aids, created mostly by the learners themselves, can and will add much to the worth of any health education program, but only if they are used intelligently for a definite purpose always kept well in mind. Supplementary teaching materials are effective and worthwhile only to the degree that they can motivate behavior and learning. The greatest motivator of all, it should be stressed, is an enthusiastic, capable, and skilled teacher.

As Love has pointed out, a teacher's way of life is her greatest source of inspiration for teaching, because everything she sees and does is viewed through the very special eyes of an educator. These eyes are trained to analyze quickly any situation and take from it that which is meaningful and applicable to teaching.[12] She tells how she used some materials from the comic strip "Peanuts" concerning Charlie Brown's posture problem for the bulletin board, as an illustration in a unit on posture. When she read *The Hidden Persuaders,* by Vance Packard, she gained many valuable ideas on how to sell ideas to others which helped her in all phases of her work as an educator. Although the life of every teacher is a busy one, involving contact with many people of varying ages and backgrounds, plus keeping up a wide range of reading, the best educators are those who always are seeking and utilizing new and better ways to improve their teaching skill. Such inspired and inspiring leaders help children discover the thrill of learning new things every moment of every day in the school year, and at home as well as at school.

SUGGESTED READINGS

A List of Sources of Films on the Subject of Health, American Medical Association, Chicago.

Babcock, Chester, "The Teacher, TV, and Teaching Machines," *NEA Journal,* vol. 412 (May, 1960), 36.

Burton, W. H., *The Guidance of Learning Activities,* New York, Appleton-Century-Crofts, 1952.

12 Alice Love, "Look into Your Daily Living to Find That Extra Something for Your Teaching," *Journal of Health, Physical Education and Recreation,* vol. 322 (April, 1961), 21.

Dale, Edgar, *Audio-Visual Methods of Teaching,* rev. ed., New York, Dryden, 1954.

East, Marjorie, *Display for Learning; Making and Using Visual Aids,* New York, Dryden, 1952.

Educators Index of Free Films, latest ed., Randolph, Wis., Educators' Progress Service.

Filmstrip Guide, H. W. Wilson Company, 950 University Avenue, New York, N.Y.

Gladston, I., "Motivation in Health Education," *American Journal of Public Health,* vol. 39 (1949), 1276.

Haag, Jessie, *School Health Program,* New York, Holt, 1958.

Hass, Kenneth, and Harry Packer, *The Preparation and Use of Audio-Visual Aids,* Englewood Cliffs, N.J., Prentice-Hall, 1955.

Hornkeimer, Patricia, and John Diffor, *Educators' Guide to Free Slide Films,* latest ed., Randolph, Wis., Educators' Progress Service.

Koritz, G. T., "Motive to Learn," *Elementary School Journal,* vol. 59 (April, 1959), 380–385.

Learning and the Teacher, Association for Supervision and Curriculum Development, Washington, D.C., 1959.

Miller, Marion, "A Radio Project Teaches Your Class," *Journal of Health, Physical Education and Recreation,* vol. 23, no. 9 (November, 1952), 41–46.

Murray, Thomas R., and Sherwin Swarthout, *Integrated Teaching Methods,* New York, Longmans, Green, 1960.

Prescott, Daniel, *The Child in the Educative Process,* New York, McGraw-Hill, 1957.

Sands, Lester, *Audio-Visual Procedures in Teaching,* New York, Ronald, 1956.

Sneider, Robert, *Methods and Materials of Health Education,* Philadelphia, Saunders, 1958.

Steinhaus, Arthur, *More Firepower for Health Education,* Washington, D.C., U.S. Office of Education, Bulletin No. 2, 1958.

Wittich, Walter, and Charles Schuller, *Audiovisual Materials, Their Nature and Their Use,* 3rd ed., New York, Harper, 1962.

Woelfel, Norman, *How to Reach Your Teaching Goals with Teaching Aids,* Teaching Aids Laboratory Pamphlet no. 2, Columbus: Ohio State University, Bureau of Educational Research and Service, 1955.

THREE

THE PROGRAM

"FACTS ARE NOT ENOUGH TO CHANGE BEHAVIOR. EMOTIONS MUST BE TAPPED TO THE END THAT MORE HEALTH KNOWLEDGE WILL BE TRANSLATED INTO PRACTICE IN EVERYDAY LIVING."

ARTHUR STEINHAUS

OVERVIEW TO PART THREE

Included in this part of the book is a suggested graded program in health education for Grades 1 through 6. It is a pattern which should be tailored to fit into any specific elementary school curriculum. Such a recommended program teaches health from the concept of total well-being, consisting of physical, mental, emotional, and spiritual fitness. It has been based on the typical needs, interests, and characteristics of children in each school grade. A wide variety of learning activities is suggested which will help make health education become an alive, exciting, and important learning adventure for children. It shows how the curricular patterns described in Chapter 6 and the teaching methods discussed in Chapter 7, as well as all other previous materials, can best be used for an improved health instruction in all elementary grades.

9 DENTAL HEALTH

Dental decay and loss of teeth are major health problems among people of all ages in America. It is estimated that nine out of every ten people have carious teeth or more serious dental difficulties. It is the chief health problem among school-age children. In a survey of the health problems of 78,448 pupils in the Philadelphia Public Schools, the number of pupils with dental caries was six times as large as those with the next leading health difficulty![1] Like all pressing health issues, the solution to this problem lies in prevention, education, and proper care. The school must assume real and increased responsibility in helping to eliminate this vast problem, for dental disease is a public health responsibility. As Oberteuffer has pointed out, the school is in a strategic position to formulate a complete program in dental health education and to assume leadership in organizing community resources for dental care of all children.[2]

Specific responsibilities of the school lies in health protection, correction of defects, health conservation, and health promotion. In an effort to promote improved dental health, some schools have assumed the following responsibilities:

1. Provide periodic dental health examinations.
2. Inform parents of dental disabilities in children.

[1] Jessie Haag, *School Health Program,* New York, Holt, 1958, p. 68.
[2] Delbert Oberteuffer, *School Health Education,* New York, Harper, 1960, p. 389.

3. Refer children for dental treatment to appropriate sources.
4. Recheck for correction of dental defects.
5. Provide a continuous program of instruction in dental health.
6. Give individual dental health guidance.
7. Provide special services where indicated.
8. Establish interest among parents through a program of education and participation in the dental health of school children.
9. Give adequate financial support to provide a complete dental health education program.
10. Provide sufficient professional personnel to staff the program of service and instruction adequately.[3]

School administrators should work closely with local dentists in order to establish policies which outline the role of the school in dental health and follow these up with a well-planned educational program and dental service for all children. Any periodic school dental examination is worthless unless it is coupled with a remedial program, and unless those needing special attention receive it. Parental cooperation is necessary on all educational levels if health problems among children are to be solved, but it is particularly imperative in the elementary grades, for these pupils by themselves can do little, if anything, to correct existing dental or other difficulties.

A complete dental health program should include:

1. Dental health service—including periodic dental checkups, informing the parents of dental defects, rechecking for corrections, compiling and evaluating findings.
2. Dental health instruction—including the presentations of authentic factual information in understandable units in a graded program through the entire school curriculum from Grade 1 through senior high school. Such a program should stress the development of proper knowledge, attitudes, and habits which will promote good dental care.
3. Dental care—although this responsibility rests with the family, if it cannot assume it, this falls upon the community, the school, the state, and the nation.

The role of the elementary teacher in the area of dental health education is of major importance. Children should not only be taught the essential facts about teeth and their care but be motivated

[3] Frances Stoll, *Dental Health Education,* Philadelphia, Lea & Febiger, 1960, p. 64.

The school dentist is an important resource person in a dental health education program. (Courtesy, Los Angeles Public Schools.)

and encouraged to put in practice what they have learned, for only then will the development of good habits formed in school be carried out at home. Without the cooperation of parents, little can be done to help solve the great problem of dental disease among primary children, for this disease is caused largely by improper diet and lack of proper mouth hygiene. The content of the dental health program must be timely and carefully planned. Readiness for learning about teeth begins when the child starts losing his deciduous, or baby, teeth. Likewise, when the permanent teeth begin to appear, most youngsters become increasingly curious to know what is happening and thus can be easily motivated to receive favorably information concerning proper mouth hygiene. As children grow older they become more conscious of their appearance and are ready to learn how to be good looking and popular, as well as the importance of having the good teeth necessary for an attractive smile. Children can be motivated to want to learn more about dental health if they are provided with meaningful experiences coupled to an increasing awareness of their own health needs and changing selves. All should be taught that the care of the teeth is a lifelong responsibility.

SUGGESTED GRADED TOPICS

There is no doubt that in far too many schools, instruction in dental health has suffered from lack of continuity, along with any subject area usually included in the health program. There will always be omission and repetition, as teachers come and go, and not enough of them really care about the physical well-being of their pupils. One way to ensure a meaningful graded program in health education is to have a group of representative teachers from each grade meet to:

1. Prepare an outlined recorded plan stating the objectives and desired educational outcomes for each health topic for each grade.
2. Prepare a complete list of facts and concepts to be included on each grade level.
3. Devise a list of reference materials for the pupils and the teacher in the range of classes to be taught.
4. Make a list of supplementary teaching aids such as films and other audio-visual aids.
5. Revise these materials yearly.

Any teacher worth her salt knows the needs and interests of her class group and of each child in it. This knowledge is invaluable in gaining insight into the degree of readiness of the group. Just as it would be foolish to teach first graders who are losing their baby teeth about the whole set of teeth, including wisdom teeth, so it would be to teach any group a "canned," prepared lesson found in a textbook which is supposed to be suitable for any class studying any aspect of health. Unless units of instruction represent the joint planning of the teacher and the class, or are made in a flexible outline form, they cannot help children reach the desired educational goal. As Stoll points out, the desire for good dental health should originate within the child, rather than from a demand made by outside influences or forces.[4]

[4] Stoll, *op. cit.*, p. 178.

Suggested graded topics and outlines for dental health instruction in each elementary grade are:

GRADE 1

1. Regular good tooth care, and how to brush the teeth properly.
2. Eating a well-balanced diet three times daily.
3. Why sweets are harmful to the teeth.
4. How many teeth a first grader usually has.
5. The dentist as a friend; a visit to a dentist's office.
6. How teeth can be safely protected in play, at home, and at school.

GRADE 2

1. Review of tooth-brushing methods.
2. Why we lose our baby teeth.
3. The importance and care of the six-year molars.
4. What causes tooth decay and how it can be prevented.

GRADE 3

1. Review of proper dental-care techniques.
2. How to make and use our own dentifrice.
3. What is the best type of a toothbrush to use.
4. Proper care of a toothbrush.
5. Why we should go to a dentist.

GRADE 4

1. The structure and function of the tooth.
2. How human teeth work like scissors and grinders.
3. A comparison of human and animal teeth.
4. How second teeth form and appear.
5. The best kinds of food to eat in order to have well-fed teeth.
6. The value of chewing food properly.
7. Review of how teeth can best be cared for daily.

GRADE 5

1. Study of the basic foods needed daily for a balanced diet.
2. Why sweets are harmful to the teeth.
3. Function of vitamins, minerals, phosphorus, and calcium in the teeth.
4. How poor nutrition affects the teeth.
5. Fluoridation and its effect upon the prevention of decay.
6. Review of the techniques of proper oral hygiene.

GRADE 6

1. Review of the role nutrition plays in dental care.
2. Accident prevention in competitive games, with special reference to injuries of the mouth and teeth.

3. Malocclusion, its cause, prevention, and correction.
4. Analysis of advertising and consumer education in the purchase of dental care products.
5. Detailed study of tooth structures.
6. The causes of diseases of the mouth and protection from them.
7. The importance of periodic dental examinations.
8. The use of a dental X ray in dental examinations.
9. The use of mouth protectors in competitive sports.

CURRICULUM PLACEMENT

It is the obligation of all teachers to provide those educational experiences in the school curriculum which will enable children to learn how to develop and maintain good health, for it is in the formative years that lifelong habits, upon which the foundation of health and happiness rests, can best be built. Opportunities arise every day for the integration and correlation of health with most subjects included in the elementary school curriculum. In the broad-fields, core, or experience curricular patterns dental health education can be interwoven into larger areas of study such as the communicative arts, science, mathematics, and creative expression. In those schools wherein health, safety, and science are integrated with one broad field, numerous opportunities arise for direct health teaching in all health areas.

The Communicative Arts—reading, writing, and speaking, as well as seeing and hearing—enable children to learn much on their own about dental health when carefully guided by a teacher. Stories about initial dental experiences, such as Burchheimer's *Let's Go to the Dentist,* the reading of scientific facts in library reference materials assigned to the older pupils, and other reading materials can all contribute to the improvement of reading speed and comprehension, as well as serve as a means of dental health education. Increased understanding and use of new words can aid pupils to build a good vocabulary for increased communicative purposes. When each new word is introduced, it should be written on the chalkboard, and the pupils taught how to spell, pronounce, and use it correctly. Skills in writing can be practiced and developed through the correlation of dental health instruction and the communicative arts by having the pupils write about their first experiences at the dentist, how the selection of good foods helps prevent decay, or writing for a make-believe dental appointment or to the American Dental Association for bulletin-board materials or information. Group discussions not only help bring to light how much or how little children really know about dental hygiene, but such experiences can help them learn the value of talking over and logically thinking through a problem, as well as assist them develop skill in expressing themselves verbally. Discussions among primary children might well revolve around such topics as why we have teeth, what happens when we lose a tooth, or in what ways a dentist can be a good friend. Among the older pupils, interest in the improvement of oral hygiene can be stimulated through panels as well as group discussions around such topics as evaluating a dental film seen in class, or modern dental treatment in contrast to that found throughout history. For these older pupils, individual research reports can do much to help them learn to speak well before groups as well as to develop research skills. Younger children, through their "do-and-tell" periods, might well demonstrate the correct way to brush the teeth, how a dentist examines the teeth, and many other kinds of similar experiences. Visiting speakers, such as the local dentist, dental hygienist, or a school dietitian, can all add much to the effectiveness of the program, especially if each pupil is asked to make a list of the most important things he learned, or if there is a class discussion following the speaker's presentation.

Social studies provide rich opportunities for the correlation and integration of dental health, and can increase an understanding and appreciation of the fact that dental disease is a community and national problem. Through the study of history, children can learn that ancient people also had this problem, as well as learn how it was handled. The effects of food upon health in our own as well as in other lands is one of many areas in which dental health, nutrition, social studies, and geography can be combined into an integrated learning experience. Visits to places of interest in the community in a unit entitled "Getting to Know Our Health Coworkers in Our Community" might well include a trip to a dentist's office, as well as to the local health department or local dog pound. Listed below are some other suggested activities for correlating dental health with social science:

1. Make a comparative study of the incidence of dental caries on a state-by-state and nation-by-nation basis.
2. Learn the role the state and national government plays in the prevention of dental disease.
3. Study superstitions and fallacies regarding dental care throughout the history of America.
4. Learn about dental care among the ancient peoples in contrast to practices of today.
5. Find out how industry helps promote good dental hygiene.
6. Write a research paper on the value of fluoridation in the prevention of tooth decay. Compare what your city and state are doing in this area with those elsewhere.
7. Debate the pros and cons of socialized medicine, including free dental care.

Science and dental health are closely related, for science provides much of the facts necessary to help pupils learn more about any part of themselves. Units on nutrition and dental health have frequently been successfully combined. In such units children should learn about the necessity of chewing food well, as well as of eating a balanced daily diet. Science fairs, which can be the work of a school science class or club, are increasing in popularity throughout the nation. Experiments, collections, and projects made by the pupils, either in class or as extracurricular activities, are usually open for the public to see. Although dental health materials made by children can only be a part of such a fair, they can do much to motivate both pupil and parent interest in obtaining better health, as well as help both learn more about how it can be accomplished.

Specific activities which can be used to correlate dental health with science include:

Experiments

1. Make tooth powder composed of one-third salt and two-thirds baking soda.
2. Bite an apple and leave it in the classroom overnight. Show it to the class the next day, and have them discuss the cause and prevention of decay in food as well as in teeth.
3. Examine a decayed tooth under a microscope.

4. Conduct an annual feeding experiment to learn the relationship between a poor diet and decay and unhealthy gums.
5. Teeth are fed by blood. Of what is blood made? How does it look under the microscope?
6. Examine the teeth under a magnifying glass, and with a dentist's hand mirror. Discuss.
7. Test for starch. To one-half teaspoonful of cornstarch add a little water and a drop of iodine. The blue color that appears shows that starch is present. Learn how starches and sugars affect teeth.
8. Examine the saliva, or materials from your tongue under a microscope. Learn how mouth wash destroys bacteria.

Mathematics also offers good opportunities for the correlation of dental health. However, care must be taken to select topics with the purpose of teaching children about dental health instead of just numbers. For example, if the problem given pupils to solve is to discover how much ten toothbrushes and two tubes of toothpaste costs if the former costs 30¢ and the latter 38¢, often the group will think of toothbrushing in terms of expense instead of as a good habit. When numbers enter naturally into a class discussion is the best time for mathematics to be used. Simple addition and subtraction problems, such as finding out how many have ever been to a dentist or how many teeth are missing from the number children should have at a certain age, enable both the class and the teacher to learn, for the group will gain an understanding of a dental health problem and the teacher will find out another significant fact about each child. Problems which can help children gain a deeper understanding of percentages can be based upon discovering the total number in the class who need dental care, according to the school dental examination, in relation to the total number in each class or grade, or to the total number of students in the school. In the upper grades, graphs and tables can be used to show such things as a comparison of the number of people needing dental care in one state with those in another, the amount of money from the family budget which should be spent on health care and protection and the percentage which should be spent on dental care. Finding needed information for such problems will also help youngsters learn how to use the library. Dental health also provides many opportunities for drill in learning numbers. However, care must be taken to individualize the meaning of figures; if the children find out that 350 pupils in their school have unfilled cavities in their teeth, there is no direct relationship to each pupil unless each cares for his own teeth properly, and knows and practices ways to prevent decay.

Dramatic and art activities, when used as a means of helping children learn more about dental health, has great educational value. The use of puppets, one-act plays, mime, mock radio and television broadcasts, etc., can also be successfully integrated and correlated with both the creative and communicative arts. Merely coloring outlined pictures of teeth, however, has questionable value other than giving the young child a chance to improve his hand-eye coordination. Likewise, making dental care posters from pictures cut out of magazines will have no value in teaching dental health unless this experience motivates the postermaker to take better care of his own teeth and mouth, as well as eat the proper kind of foods necessary for maintaining good overall well-being. Free-hand drawings, color choice, the use of finger paints can all help children express pent-up emotions and tensions about going to the dentist or losing their own teeth. Clay, plaster of Paris, and other materials can be used successfully in helping older pupils make their own models of teeth. Such experiences are often more meaningful than merely showing the class a slide or three-dimensional model, for they provide avenues for youngsters to use their own hands in creative ways to express what they know and have learned.

Suggested art and dramatic activities which can be used for dental health education purposes include:

1. Divide the class into committees. Let each group make a poster or present a skit on any aspect of a unit on dental health.
2. Make clay models of teeth, dental instruments, etc.
3. Demonstrate the proper way to brush the teeth by using a large model of teeth and a brush. Have each child brush his own teeth, preferably with a brush, or with his pencil or forefinger, or by using a paper model of a set of teeth and a pencil.[5]
4. Have each pupil draw a picture of a happy person with pretty teeth. Let each make up and tell a story about his picture.

[5] Such models and other free dental teaching aids are available from The Bristol-Myers Company, Educational Department, New York.

5. Dramatize going to the dentist, getting ready for school, buying a toothbrush and toothpaste.
6. Make a dental health exhibit of clay models, posters, and other creative media.
7. Study drawings and pictures of malocclusion. Discuss the prevention and treatment necessary to avoid disfiguration of the mouth and face.
8. Present mock or real radio or television programs built around any work done in class in dental health.
9. Make a toothbrush rack for the family bathroom or for a tent group at camp.
10. Black out certain teeth. Examine yourself in the mirror. Explain your reactions to what you see there.
11. Discuss the dental films seen in class.
12. Make your own movie or cartoon about any character and his experiences in learning any aspect of dental health. Show this to the class. Use a curtain roll and a cardboard carton for the film and camera.

Safety implications for dental health education are many. Safety education should teach children to take chances wisely in order to avoid accidents by knowing what the risks are and instilling in them a desire to eliminate them. Children should learn the danger of putting foreign objects in their mouths or biting on them. Stress should also be placed upon playing safely at school and at home, drinking from water fountains correctly, and using other precautions in order to prevent having broken teeth or jaws. On the playground, care should be taken to use the swings, jungle gym, monkey bars, and other equipment correctly, for this type of play can be especially hazardous to young children. Head-on collisions, which often occur in chasing and fleeing games such as "Run, Sheepie, Run" can also be prevented, and injuries to teeth be avoided. It would be foolish to eradicate all hazards from children's play areas; wise instructors utilize dangerous and adventuresome playground games for some of their most fruitful lessons in safety education. Teaching youngsters, who seemingly are ever on the go, the value of taking time out to perform routine health and safety practices should be promoted and praised at every possible occasion. Drinking fountains are especially hazardous to primary children. Consequently, rules regarding pushing and shoving when someone is drinking should be enforced, and those whose horseplay causes a classmate to suffer broken front teeth, should be punished. Children should also be taught the dangers of running with sharp or pointed articles in their mouths and biting hard objects such as pebbles or cracking nuts with their teeth. Those who have been taught well, and have gained an understanding of the relationship between continued thumb sucking or grinding the teeth and malocclusion, are most likely to discontinue these appearance-damaging habits.

TEACHING METHODS

There is little doubt that reading materials and the lecture method of instruction have been used excessively in dental health instruction. Reading a pamphlet on how to brush the teeth correctly has little educational value unless this experience motivates the reader to brush his own teeth properly. There are many teaching methods which can be used successfully for helping children gain needed dental health information and motivating positive and healthful behavior. Such methods might well include the following:

The problem-solving method is especially well suited to dental health education. However, problems which are selected by the teacher and pupil should be of real and vital concern to them, and more than mere busy work. These may well be problems concerning community health, of which dental health is but a part, but they can also be specific ones, such as studying why and how the community should educate its voters to establish water fluoridation for the protection of its citizens.

A sixth grade class in Florida recently made an intensive study of their community's health problem. The class was divided into committees and each group chose an area for intensive study—dental health, mental health, etc. The pupils interviewed people, did library research, visited clinics and other places in order to collect as much information as possible. Daily committee discussions brought many interesting facts to light. After the class had studied this problem for almost a month, each committee group reported its findings, and the class as a whole came up with some excellent recommendations of ways in which the health of all the people in the community might be improved. Such projects have lasting value, for those children who were so enthusiastically involved in this type of learning experience gained a new outlook on their own city, as well as learned to use successfully the problem-solving method, and became better-informed future voters and citizens.

Class discussions depend largely upon the skill of the leader to get each pupil to contribute and become an active participant in discussions of a selected topic. The interchange of information during such periods should stimulate thinking which should lead to action and to change. Consequently, the pupils who take part in this type of health education should, through their actions, affect their families and help bring about improved health practices in their own household. A good discussion leader sets the stage for thinking, brings everyone in the group into the discussion without allowing any one person to dominate or dictate group action, helps the group set goals, and finds a feasible solution for the problem at hand. Likewise, such a leader should be skilled in keeping the discussion on the right path and avoiding time-consuming and needless digressions which have no bearing upon the problem at hand. Skill in uniting individual efforts for the attainment of group goals can only be mastered through trial and error. The elementary school should be the place wherein such skills can be developed. Each group member must be an informed participant if the group discussion is to be a learning experience. Topics suitable for class discussions in dental health might well include the following:

1. How serious is the problem of tooth decay and improper dental care in our school? How can we help this problem?
2. Discuss how to prepare young children for the periodic school dental examination.
3. The relationship between good teeth and good health.
4. The harmful effects of food containing sugars to dental disease.
5. The food habits and dental problems of the peoples in the countries studied about in social science.
6. The cost of early dental treatment versus neglect.
7. Changing concepts in dental health procedures.

Guidance opportunities are prevalent in the area of dental health education. Often these are individual in nature and involve working directly or indirectly with adults, as well as with pupils.

Although most parents want the best for their children, there are many who do not know how to go about getting it; there are some too, unfortunately, who simply do not care. It is then the task of the school administrator and school health authorities to reach these few adults in order to convince them of the value of obtaining corrections of defects. Sometimes this becomes the task of the teacher, or she may be asked to work in cooperation with the school nurse to help reach the parents. In such cases, informal home visits can sometimes accomplish more than having the parents come to the school, although this often has advantages as well. Regardless of where the conference is held or which school representative is involved, it is vitally important that rapport be established and a feeling of mutual concern for the child in question be present. The counselor or teacher should inform the parents of the findings of the school dental inspection, help them understand what these mean, and explain to them why the defects should be corrected. Suggestions of sources of care, unknown to them, will often prove helpful. Through encouragement, patience, and good guidance, the cooperation of these difficult-to-reach parents can often be gained and, in turn, the child concerned is aided. Teachers, then, should often do more than "just teach children."

Individual and group guidance can also be used effectively to help children find solutions to their own health problems, whether these be uncared-for and dirty teeth or halitosis. Many problems revolving around oral hygiene are delicate and require skillful handling. Since children are often unknowingly cruel in their frankness, the teacher should guide class discussion periods if this is the approach she thinks best to use in any particular situation. In some cases it is wiser to talk over with the class problems which might be delicate or embarrassing, thus controlling what is said.

Drills can be used effectively for teaching primary children how and when to brush their teeth. Some schools have a tooth-brushing time after lunch, and the children are taught the importance of brushing the teeth within five minutes after eating. Vocabulary drills can also assist these children in learning the meaning of all new words introduced in a dental health unit. No kind of drill can be effective, however, if the children taking part in such an experience merely go through meaningless, routinized motions which have no value to them. Movement does not always mean progress, whether in life or in learning.

Field trips can teach children many things about dental health that they can learn best from direct experiences. Ideal places to visit in the community include a dentist's office, a firm that specializes in the making or repair of dentures, or a local health museum. The teacher can prepare the group for such trips by drawing from them a list of specific things they want to learn while there, and the purpose of their visit. Likewise, she should ask leading questions of the host in the place visited, for this will, in turn, encourage the pupils to ask also about specific things they want to know. Upon returning to the classroom, she should discuss the trip with the group and have a pupil write on the chalkboard the specific things the class has learned from this experience, for the summary will cause important items to remain in the memory for a longer time. Frequently, trips to such places as a bakery, ice cream or milk pasteurization plant, or farmers' market can teach the youngsters about food, as well as provide the instructor with an opportunity to review or reemphasize facts concerning the relationship between a well-balanced diet and the prevention of dental decay.

Role playing can be an especially valuable method of teaching primary pupils facts and shaping proper attitudes towards dental experiences. They will both enjoy and profit from dramatizing "going to the dentist," "buying a toothbrush and toothpaste," or "how the dentist cleans our teeth." Such experiences will prove to be far more valuable than taking part in professionally written plays, for children find their own skits, which express their own knowledge and experience, far more interesting. Youth needs opportunities to gain legitimate recognition, such as taking part in many kinds of positive learning experiences in their own classroom, or being in an all-school assembly program. Such activities also give them added opportunities to express themselves. In one school recently, a group of first graders made up their own skit which revolved around using a giant toothbrush. They chose certain of their classmates to act out the story their class made up, and after it was all over, they talked about this experience many times throughout the year. Role playing can also be used to demonstrate the importance of brushing after meals, good dental habits, balanced diets, the work of each type of tooth, safety in play, or other related topics. These little dramatizations and skits can also be used to show visiting parents what their youngsters are learning in school. Following the class presentations, a pupil, the school dental hygienist, the teacher, or the health coordinator might well explain the school dental health program in order to enlist the parents' cooperation. On such occasions, pupils can also prepare simple instruction sheets on the techniques of proper toothbrushing and a list of the food needed daily to build and maintain a strong, healthy body and teeth. Such activities can do more than entertain adults, for they can be especially fruitful in getting the message across to parents that their help is needed in providing good home care for those in their family, as well as for obtaining needed dental treatment for all children.

Surveys are more suitable for the upper elementary grades. The best ones are those which are part of the child's own world, such as a study made in his own class, school, home, or block, to find out facts such as how many have missing teeth, brush their teeth three times daily, etc. When all these data have been collected, the pupil or committee involved should draw conclusions from the findings, as well as determine how the problem can be remedied or eliminated. The important thing for the teacher who is guiding pupils in such projects to remember is to determine what can be done with the knowledge gained from making such a survey, as well as helping each pupil see the relationship between what he discovers and his own life and well being.

INSTRUCTIONAL MATERIALS

Audio-visual materials can help pupils learn faster, more, and retain information longer, but only when properly used. They are not meant to take the place of the teacher, but instead can add to her effectiveness. If the viewer of such materials becomes merely a spectator, nothing of educational value can result. The formation of a critical attitude, the development of proper habits of thinking and action, an increased vocabulary and better understanding of words, and other enriching educational results can accrue from the proper use of any or all of the following supplementay teaching aids.

Feltboards and chalkboards should be used mainly to show symbols, words, numbers, and charts. All materials displayed should be neat and legible. Script writing should be used in the upper grades, and manuscript writing for the primary children. The pegboard, a variation of the feltboard, is best for showing three-dimensional materials; these can be obtained from educational supply houses at a nominal cost. Like the feltboard, it should be used during class discussions or in simplified "lectures" to illustrate important facts or points. The best flannelboards or feltboards are portable and lightweight. Such boards can be easily made by stretching and nailing flannel or felt over a large square of heavy cardboard or plywood. A piece of similar material or a rough grade of sandpaper should be placed on the back of pictures which are to be put on the board as the speaker tells the class a story involving illustrated objects or pictures. Children will delight in making up their own stories about animated characters such as a tooth, brush, or types of food, and making their own feltboard illustrations to use as they share various kinds of health education information with their classmates. Games involving choosing a balanced lunch or snack, word games, sentence completion, and word drills can all be used by a creative leader in all areas of health teaching. A whole "library" of feltboard dental educational materials can be made by the pupils, used, and then stored away for later use.

Models and specimens are available from local dentists, the American Dental Association, and toothpaste companies, and all can help enrich dental health education. These are ideal for showing the parts of the tooth, how the teeth fit into the gums, and the kinds of teeth, for such visual materials can help children gain an increased understanding of what they are studying about teeth. A class, through assigned committee projects, can also make their own models out of clay, papier-mâché, or other materials. Such created objects can range from a set of teeth, a single tooth, and the parts of a tooth, to a giant toothbrush and tube of toothpaste.

Since these materials often exaggerate size, care must be taken in using them with primary pupils, so that the children know that the large things they are seeing and touching are like the "little" things in their own mouths or environment.

Bulletin boards and posters are excellent materials to use in teaching dental health. Although many health agencies and commercial firms have an abundance of free posters which are available for educational purposes, those which children make themselves become more meaningful to them. The best posters and bulletin-board materials are those which concentrate upon a positive idea, thought, or message, are colorful, and motivate the viewer to do or reflect upon something. Suggested posters which the children might make in connection with a unit on dental health are:

1. Pictures of various teeth, or tooth decay germs.
2. How to have an attractive smile.
3. How to brush the teeth properly.
4. Why we should see our dentist regularly.
5. The different teeth and their functions.
6. Name and parts of a tooth.
7. The role that chewing plays in digestion.
8. How decay spreads from the enamel to the pulp of a tooth.
9. The best kind of toothbrush to buy and how to care for it properly.
10. The value of an X-ray examination.
11. Safety in play as a means of avoiding broken teeth.
12. Safety at the drinking fountain.
13. The relationship of good teeth to good health.
14. How to avoid malocclusion; how it can be corrected.
15. Snack foods which are good for teeth.
16. What sweets do to the teeth; those which cause the most damage.
17. The dentist as a friend.

Although bulletin boards can be one of the most effective means of visual education, they too should be used with care. They can be an excellent way, however, of informing pupils about proper tooth care, increasing interest in this activity, as well as the latest news in the field of oral hygiene. Here again, the best boards are those which are planned and arranged by the pupils themselves. This can be done by committees, or by several interested individuals guided by the teacher. The boards can also be used to advise pupils when the school dental examination will be given, remind them of the necessity of regular dental care given by their own family dentist, or even contain the name of an honor roll of pupils who had seen their dentist twice a year, or of those in a class or grade who have not had a single cavity. Such techniques often serve as strong motivational forces.

Radio and television programs used in relationship with dental health are of two types: (1) those which are purely informative, and (2) those which have been prepared and presented by the learners themselves. The former is a one-way type of communication, and the latter, two-way, and therefore of richer educational value. Increasingly schools are installing public address systems. These can be used for spot announcements and brief presentations on a wide variety of health topics including dental health, or for a solid week of concentrated effort in any one area. Dental Health Week in February would be an ideal time for such brief daily programs.

In the upper elementary grades stress can be placed upon consumer education, and children taught to purchase dentifrices wisely. Each child could be assigned to listen to and report on toothpaste advertising claims, and the class as a whole determine the differences between true and false advertising. Such projects might well be a part of a larger unit based upon the problem of self-medication and health protective measures, or they can be used in a single unit on dental health.

Mock or real radio and television broadcasts, whether these be pupil-created plays or panel discussions, might well cover informative program materials which all enable the listeners and viewers to learn how to maintain and retain their own teeth throughout life.

Photographs and cartoons can be used effectively as a means of motivating interest and action for good dental health. The former are especially well suited for educational use with older children. These can be photographs of the pupils themselves, showing each child at various stages of his development in each grade in the elementary school. Pictures showing malocclusion, taken from books and shown on the opaque projector, and the stages and measures used for its correction, are especially helpful in teaching youngsters about the damages which can be done to the formation of teeth, mouth, and face by bad habits.

Cartoons appeal more to younger pupils. Those which show animated figures such as "Mr. Germ" or a talking carrot, however, should be used with caution, for often the children will merely be entertained by the antics of these characters, and learn little from watching such films unless the teacher draws "meaning" out of the pictures and helps them understand it. Commercially sponsored cartoon programs which appear regularly on television can also be utilized for dental health education. These may be watched by the class at school, in their own homes, or at a neighborhood recreation center after school, and discussed by the group later. Needless to say, the best use of cartoons can be made in the classroom, for the discussion which follows the showing can then best be guided and summarized by the class and teacher.

DESIRABLE OUTCOMES

If the materials presented in dental health education have been effective, the following desirable outcomes should result in the areas of knowledge, attitudes, and practices:

In the primary grades, the pupils will:

1. Know that there are different kinds of teeth.
2. Become alerted to what happens when they have unhealthy teeth.
3. Realize the importance of having and keeping sound teeth.
4. Develop a strong desire to maintain mouth cleanliness.
5. Understand the relationship between eating a balanced diet and having good teeth.
6. Be prepared for and get periodic dental examinations.
7. Take good care of their own teeth, have their own toothbrush, know how to use it properly, and to keep it hanging separately in a holder and dry.
8. Know that they have twenty baby teeth (ten above, like their ten fingers, and ten below, like their ten toes) and that the new teeth which appeared around the age of six are permanent and will last a lifetime, if cared for properly.
9. Know that "grown-up teeth" are behind baby ones and that if a baby tooth becomes loose it will not hurt much to pull it out.
10. Be aware that foods eaten when they have baby teeth and the good care taken of these will help make permanent teeth stronger and better.

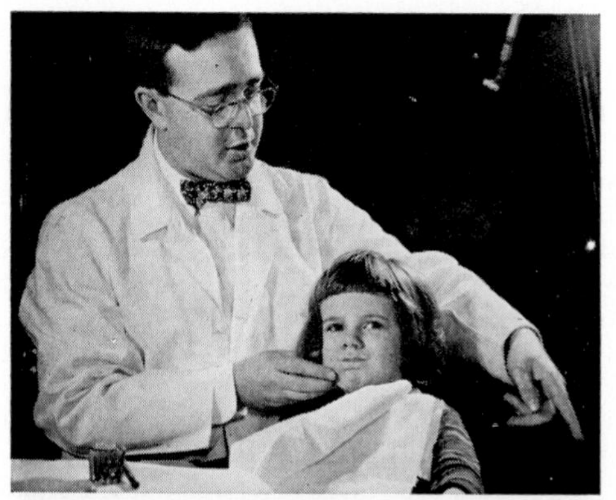

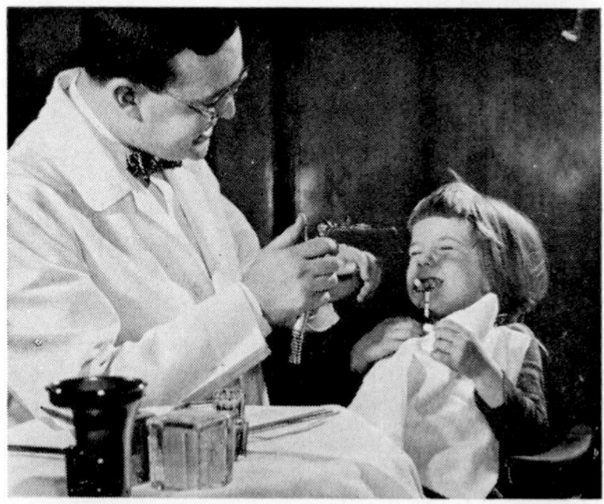

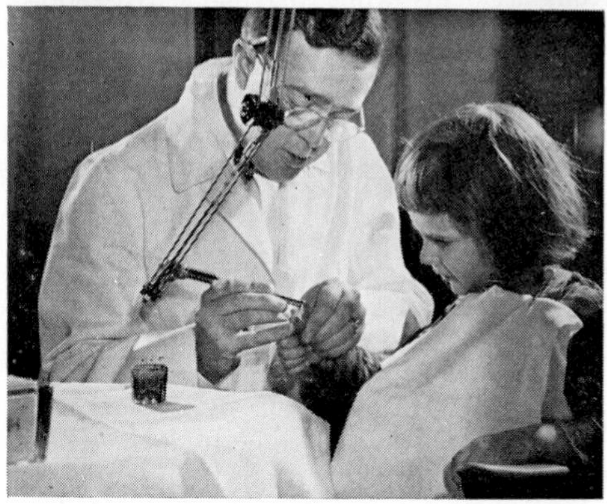

A visit to the dentist can become an educational experience of lasting importance to a child. (Courtesy, Robert Yoho, Indiana State Department of Health.)

11. Know that little, unfilled cavities will become bigger and cause pain.
12. Recognize that the dentist is a friend who can help make one's teeth last longer.
13. Avoid thumb sucking or other harmful habits which will cause the teeth to protrude or be crooked.
14. Know the danger of biting hard objects or cracking nuts with the teeth.
15. Become aware of the importance of brushing the teeth within five minutes after eating.
16. Eat apples, carrots, bread crusts, and other foods which require lots of chewing.
17. Guard against having or causing accidents which will break or injure the teeth, especially when drinking from a water fountain.
18. Make their own dental appointment or remind their parents to do so by the end of the third grade.

In the upper elementary grades, the pupils will:

1. Take good care of their teeth.
2. Know that human beings have two sets of teeth in a lifetime.
3. Know the names and functions of permanent teeth.
4. Be aware of the importance of and eat a balanced diet daily.
5. Know that major factors in causing dental decay are improper care of the teeth and the consumption of sugar or other sweets.
6. Be aware that dental decay is more prevalent in the preadolescent and adolescent years than during any other time in life.
7. Know the diseases of the mouth and gums and how to prevent them.
8. Be aware of the causes and treatment for malocclusion, and that one with malformed teeth should consult an orthodontist.
9. Carefully avoid accidents while playing active sports and games or when drinking from water fountains.
10. Understand the use of fluoridation in preventing tooth decay.
11. Know that by the age of 12 or 13 they should have 28 permanent teeth and will get 4 wisdom teeth between the ages of 16 and 25.
12. Know that teeth have different functions—that incisors cut, cuspids tear, and molars grind.
13. Be able to name the parts of a tooth.
14. Understand the role teeth and chewing play in digestion.
15. Be aware that a sound tooth is a well-fed tooth and know that gums can be kept healthy through diet.
16. Know that sweets produce tooth decay and that mouth bacteria turn sugar into acids which destroy enamel.
17. Be able to illustrate and describe how tooth decay spreads from the enamel to the pulp of a tooth.
18. Know the importance of and follow correct tooth brushing practices and be aware that teeth should be brushed soon after eating.

19. Know the best kind of toothbrush and how to care for it properly.
20. Go to the dentist regularly.
21. Take pride in the appearance of their teeth and of themselves.
22. Be aware of the value of an X-ray examination given by a dentist in discovering between-the-teeth cavities and abscesses at the root of the tooth.

SUGGESTED READINGS

Learning Aids

The following recommended materials will help children learn valuable materials, help shape desirable attitudes, and behavior in the area of dental health:

IN THE PRIMARY GRADES

Buchheimer, Neomi, *Let's Go to the Dentist,* New York, Putnam, 1959.
My Toothbrushing Book, Bristol-Myers.
Schloat, Junior, *Your Wonderful Teeth,* New York, Scribner, 1954.
Free materials from the American Dental Association (posters and pamphlets); Bristol-Myers Company (charts, pamphlets, and paper models of teeth).
Highlights for Children (a magazine), Box 269, Columbus, Ohio.
Leaf, Munro, *Health Can Be Fun,* New York, Lippincott, 1940.
Don't Be a Dental Space Man, Proctor and Gamble, Cincinnati, Box 687.
Book Club for Beginning Readers, Humpty Dumpty Magazine for Little Children, Children's Digest, Education Division, Parents' Magazine Press, Bergenfield, N.J.

Health Readers
Bobbs-Merrill Health for Young America Series—*Health at School; Health Day by Day; Health and Fun.*
Scott, Foresman Health Series—*Five in the Family; The Girl Next Door; Three Friends.*
Scott, Foresman Basic Health and Safety Program—*Just like Me; Seven or So; From Eight to Nine.*
Ginn—Healthful Living Series—*Spic and Span; The Health Parade; Growing Up Big and Strong.*
Laidlaw Road to Health Series—*My First Health Book; My Second Health Book; Easy Steps to Health.*
Lyons and Carnahan Health Series—*First Steps to Health; Awake and Away; Keeping Fit for Fun.*
Macmillan, New Health and Growth Series, *All through the Day; Through the Year; Health Secrets.*

IN THE UPPER ELEMENTARY GRADES

Basic Seven Chart, American Institute of Baking.

Bobbs-Merrill, Health for Young America Series, *Health and Growth; Health and Living; Health and Happiness.*

Chart Showing First and Second Teeth, Division of Oral Hygiene, State Board of Health, Raleigh, N.C.

Ginn, Health for Better Living Series, *Going Your Way; Keeping Healthy and Strong; Teamwork for Health.*

Mother Hubbard's Cupboard (Chart of the 7 basic foods), General Mills.

Who—Me? (self-evaluation chart), National Dairy Council.

Health Readers

Ginn, Safe and Healthy Living Series—*Doing Your Best for Health; Building Good Health.*

Lyons and Carnahan, Health Happiness Series—*The Girl Next Door; You; You and Others; You're Growing Up.*

Scott, Foresman, Basic Health and Safety Program—*Going on Ten; About Yourself; You.*

Teaching Aids

The following recommended teaching aids will assist children in the elementary grades learn much about dental health:

IN THE PRIMARY GRADES

Books and Pamphlets

Bryd, Oliver, *Health,* 3rd ed., Philadelphia, Saunders, 1961.

Dental Caries Survey, Who, What, and How, California State Department of Public Health, Division of Dental Health, San Francisco, 1955.

Dental Health Teaching Units, Bristol-Myers Company.

Dental Caries Prevention and Control, American Dental Association.

Healthy Teeth, John Hancock Life Insurance Company.

Diehl, Harold, *Elements of Healthful Living,* 5th ed., New York, McGraw-Hill, 1955.

Working Together for Healthier Children, New York State Department of Health, Albany, N.Y., 1954.

Schifferes, Justin, *Essentials of Healthier Living,* New York, Wiley, 1959.

Films and Other Visual Aids

Teeth (10 minutes), *Save Those Teeth* (10 minutes), Encyclopedia Britannica Films.

For Health and Happiness, U.S. Department of Agriculture (Motion Picture Service Division) (10 minutes).

A Drop in the Bucket (water fluoridation), U.S. Public Health Service (Communicable Disease Center) (15 minutes).

IN THE UPPER ELEMENTARY GRADES

Books and Pamphlets

Aids in Teaching Health in the Elementary Grades, Webster Groves, Mo., Webster Groves Public Schools, 1948.

Compilation of Lesson Material in Dental Health, Department of Health and Welfare, Augusta, Me., 1956.

Dental health Guide for Teachers, Ohio Department of Health, Columbus, Ohio, 1960.

Dental Health Program, A Two Year Plan, Tennessee Department of Public Health, Division of Dental Health, Nashville, 1960.

Dental Health Teaching Units, Minneapolis Public Schools, Minneapolis, 1954.

Foster, Julia, *Health Activities,* Philadelphia, Lippincott, 1950.

Good Teeth, The Borden Milk Company, 1960.

Handbook of Dental Health Education for the Elementary School, Bureau of Dental Hygiene, Iowa City, State University of Iowa, 1955.

Patty, Willard, *Teaching Health and Safety in the Elementary Grades,* Englewood Cliffs, N.J., Prentice-Hall, 1951.

Schwebel, Robert, *Health Counseling,* New York, Chartwell, 1951.

Stoll, Frances, *Dental Health Education,* 2nd ed., Philadelphia, Lea & Febiger, 1960.

Teaching Dental Health to Elementary School Children; The Care of Children's Teeth; Your Guide to Dental Health; Dental Health Facts for Teachers, American Dental Association, 222 E. Superior St., Chicago,

Wheatley, George, and Grace Hallock, *Health Observation of School Children,* New York, McGraw-Hill, 1956.

Films and Other Visual Aids

Teeth, Their Structure and Care, Coronet Films (13 minutes).

You're on Parade; Let's Get Ready for School; Tale of a Toothache (Filmstrips), Society for Visual Education.

Irwin, Leslie, *Ditto Lessons in Health and Safety,* Chicago, Owen Publishing, 1950.

10 NUTRITION

Although Americans are considered by many to be the best-fed people in the entire world, there is an abundance of evidence that many in our land have faulty food habits, are undernourished or obese, tire too easily, are the victims of false advertising, food fads, and starvation diets. Nutrition experts estimate that nine out of every ten Americans are not eating properly. Some are all but starving in our land of plenty. Education in nutrition can do much to improve the food habits of children. In a two-year study, conducted among sixth and seventh graders in Kansas City in 1956, the food habits of pupils in five schools were appraised. Children in all schools were found to be eating unbalanced diets and to fall below daily nutritional standards by not eating enough milk, eggs, citrus fruits, butter or margarine, potatoes, and green, leafy vegetables. An intensified nutritional education program was established and by the end of two years noticeable differences were made in food-selection patterns of the pupils as well as their scores on standardized hygiene tests.[1]

Far too many pupils come to school without eating breakfast, in spite of the fact that medical authorities say that this is the most important meal in the entire day for human beings. Some family dinner tables are miniature battlefields, where children are trying their best to eat in a tension-filled, hostile environment, and yet pediatricians and nutritional experts agree that how a person feels *while* he is eating is as important as *what* he is eating. Children

[1] Jessie Haag, *School Health Program,* New York, Holt, 1958, p. 204.

with emotional problems often use food as a weapon—some by refusing to eat, others by gorging themselves. Some educators say that we have a "grab-me-gulp" type of educational program in America on all academic levels that is similar to the 15- or 30-minute school lunch program conducted in any noisy, packed school cafeteria, from which children emerge dissatisfied, confused, and miseducated. Surgeon-General Thomas Parran has warned that as taxpayers we are wasting our time trying to educate children with half-starved bodies, for they cannot absorb teaching, they hold back classes, and they require extra time of teachers and repeat grades, all of which he claims is pure, expensive stupidity.

The total school nutritional program should and can be an important educational experience for children, so that as they grow older they will become increasingly concerned about maintaining a diet that meets high nutritional standards. Such a program should consist of nutrition education, school lunch and midmorning feeding, nutritional appraisal, guidance for individuals with specific food problems, and the adjustment of the school day for those who are below par physically and mentally.

The general objectives of any program in nutrition education in the elementary grades might well include the following:

1. Help children develop and practice good eating habits.
2. Develop in each child an understanding and interest in foods necessary for growth.
3. Build favorable attitudes toward eating a wide variety of foods, regularity of eating times, and possessing good table manners.
4. Develop school and home cooperation in relation to good nutrition as well as in all other aspects of the health instruction program.
5. Provide for integration and correlation of nutrition and all other aspects of the health instruction program with other teachers and in all school subjects.

The program must be based upon the needs and interests of the pupils. These can be determined by observation of what the child chooses to eat in the school cafeteria or brings from home for lunch, the results of a periodic weighing and measuring program, postural tests, detection of growth deviation by the use of the Wetzel Grid, observation of facial skin and hair, health records to check for recurrence of colds, results of dental and physical examinations, attitude and knowledge tests, and conferences and question boxes from parents, as well as other sources.

Nutrition can be a fascinating subject to learn about, for everyone has a need and interest in food in some degree. It can be studied as a part of other units such as growth, or be an integral part of units such as dental health or good grooming. It is imperative that home cooperation be secured if the educational program in nutrition is to become as effective as it might be, especially in the primary grades. Lunchroom experiences can be used to provide teachers with much valuable information regarding how much or how little pupils really know and apply about eating balanced diets. Consequently, they should eat with their pupils frequently.

SUGGESTED GRADED TOPICS

Suggested graded topics in nutrition education include the following:

GRADE 1

1. The necessity for eating three well-balanced meals.
2. What is a good breakfast, lunch, and supper.
3. Why children should drink milk.
4. Washing before eating.
5. Why too many sweets are harmful.
6. Food, sleep, play, and rest, and their effects upon growth.

GRADE 2

1. The Basic Seven.
2. Why raw fruits and vegetables are good for you.
3. What sweets are best for health and when they should be eaten.
4. Why you should drink water.
5. Eating new kinds of foods.
6. The best kinds of between-meal snacks for young children.
7. The difference between white and whole-wheat bread.

GRADE 3

1. How food affects growth.
2. What each pupil should and does weigh; how tall each is and should be.
3. The necessity of eating a good breakfast.

4. What are three well-balanced meals a day.
5. How to plan and prepare a simple, nutritious lunch.

Grade 4

1. The Basic Seven food groups.
2. The six classifications and function of foods.
3. Foods which best aid growth and digestion.
4. Grading and pasteurization of milk.
5. Milk products and their values.

Grade 5

1. How to plan and choose three well-balanced daily meals.
2. Foods essential for growth and good health.
3. Comparative study of milk and carbonated beverages.
4. Sources and functions of vitamins and minerals.
5. Normal and abnormal weight.
6. Advertising and food fallacies.
7. Food allergies.

Grade 6

1. Foods in relationship to health, attractiveness, fatigue, growth, strength, and the emotions.
2. Interrelationship of weight to health.
3. The digestion and absorption of food.
4. The effects of coffee, tea, and alcohol upon the human body.
5. Sanitation in the preparation and serving of foods.
6. The Pure Food and Drug Act.
7. Social customs and etiquette.
8. A weekly food budget and food selection for a family.

CURRICULUM PLACEMENT

Teachers who work in self-contained classrooms should be aided by the school health coordinator in planning ways in which nutrition education can be correlated and integrated into all subject areas in the school curriculum, as well as what topics in this field should be stressed at each grade. In those schools which are not fortunate enough to have such a specialized person to guide and direct the total school health program, or the health instructional part of such a program, all elementary teachers (or chosen representatives from each grade in large school systems) should draw up plans and suggested ways in which nutrition education can be interwoven into the entire elementary school curriculum. Even the teachers in those institutions where the subject curriculum is used and health education is either a separate subject area or one combined with safety education or science should use and be guided in their teaching by graded, outlined teaching units. Likewise, each instructor should utilize every available opportunity to correlate and integrate nutrition education with all other subjects she teaches. Regardless of the type of curriculum used in the school, there are certain pitfalls to be avoided when teaching nutrition to children. These include "preaching," or predicting doom for those who fail to eat a well-balanced diet *every* day, accepting food fads and fallacies as facts, becoming the victim of faulty and inaccurate advertising, placing too much stress upon the often dry facts of physiology (such as requiring older pupils to memorize the name and function of each digestive enzyme), or stressing one's own food likes and dislikes ("*My* favorite food is cottage cheese" or "I cannot *stand* liver!").

Nutrition education can best be correlated and become an integrated part of the subject areas given below, in the following suggested ways.

Arithmetic: Have the pupils:

1. Make height and weight charts for recording the monthly weighing and measuring of each child.
2. Calculate daily caloric intake; make a list of those foods which are the highest and lowest in calories.
3. Make graphs showing the results of animal and plant feeding experiments.
4. Add food costs.
5. Show in percentages and pie graphs the part of the family budget which should be spent on food, rent, medical care, insurance, clothing, and recreation.
6. Determine the food cost per person in a family of two adults and two grade-school children, aged 6 and 9, for one day, one week, and one month.
7. Show with measured string the length of an average large and small intestine of a child and adult; make a model from clay or papier-mâché showing the exact size of the stomach, liver, heart, or other organs of the body used in the digestion of food and circulation of blood.

8. Discover the difference between the cost of three well-balanced daily meals for one person or a family of four and the price of a doctor's home visit and medication for treating a cold for one person or all four family members for one week.
9. Determine which foods are the cheapest and most nutritious to buy in three of the six main food groups (fats, proteins, carbohydrates).
10. Study food bargains as advertised in the local paper and show how much can be saved by buying the groceries for one week for a family of four by planning well-balanced daily and weekly meals.
11. Prove on paper that advertised "real" bargains which might be available in another part of your city are not money-savers after all.
12. Observe and estimate on paper how much money is lost weekly in one's own home by food waste, spoilage, and improper storage.
13. Discover and prove which is cheaper—eating a well-balanced diet or medical and dental care.
14. Plan and give a party in your home for ten friends for one dollar, or do so for your class. Determine the cost of the refreshments per pupil. Make a list of foods which you could have served for this same amount of money, a dollar more, and for half a dollar.

Social studies are especially well suited for the correlation of nutrition education. Suggested activities which will enable the pupils to learn much about both areas include:

1. Study local, state, and national food and drug laws. Bring illustrations to class showing how these laws are obeyed on can labels or other ways.
2. Compare the food eaten in other countries with that eaten in America.
3. Learn of the discovery of vitamins and their role in the prevention of such conditions as scurvy, pellagra, etc.
4. Study the geographical areas of the United States which produce certain foods, such as the cornbelt, and the areas where citrus fruits, sugar cane, etc., are raised.
5. Discover the ways in which foods are transported, packaged, and marketed.
6. Learn of the laws regarding the pasteurization of milk and the fortification of margarine or other food products.
7. Compare the diet of our early pioneers with that of the Indians and of people living today.
8. Study the role diet plays in longevity today as well as in the past.
9. Learn of local coworkers in the health protection of the people in your community in the foods they eat.
10. Compare the methods of cooking used by the pioneers with those of today.

11. Study the varieties of frozen food on the market today and compare these with methods of canning and preserving foods used by the early American settlers.
12. Bring to class current-events clippings which pertain to nutrition.
13. Prepare and give a class party based upon the theme, "The Gold Rush Days."
14. Study the life of the pioneers, their problems, government, music, type of clothing worn and food eaten, games they played, and their work. Illustrate what you learn from this experience by writing and presenting a play or pageant using scenery, props, and costumes made in class.
15. Learn about some of the great health heroes, such as Louis Pasteur or Clara Barton.
16. Study fallacies and fads about food.
17. Learn to what extent the United States "feeds the hungry people of the world." Have a debate on the pros and cons of this action.
18. Study about epidemics and plagues in Europe and America.
19. Have a "tasting" party of each favorite vegetable or fruit brought to class.
20. Have each class or grade plan the school cafeteria luncheon menu for one week or for a special holiday such as Thanksgiving, assisted by the school dietitian. Divide the class into committees, such as publicity, table decorations, etc.
21. Divide the class into groups, giving each the responsibility to plan, prepare, and serve one foreign dish for an all-school International Night party. Have each group present a folk dance or song typical of that nation for entertainment.

Science presents abundant opportunities for correlation and integration of nutrition. Suggested ways in which this can best be accomplished include having the pupils:

1. Learn how foods grow, and the effect soil conditions and the weather have upon their growth.
2. Conduct animal and plant feeding experiments.
3. Test foods for chemical content, such as potatoes for starch, or beets for sugar.
4. Make a chemical analysis of milk.
5. Study the influence of the endocrine glands, emotions, and fatigue upon diet.
6. Learn how animals are government-inspected for human consumption.
7. Study about food spoilage and its prevention.
8. Learn the relationship of sugar to tooth decay.
9. Study how foods such as prunes or apricots are dehydrated.
10. Study the claims of certain "health foods" and health faddists.

11. Learn the relationship of a good diet to good health and to the prevention of colds, food poisoning, etc.
12. Study the effect of a poor diet upon the skin, hair, and body.
13. Learn of the dangers of being overweight and underweight.
14. Learn how food-allergy skin tests are made.
15. Study the hazards of food additives.
16. Learn how exercise helps in body growth and the digestion of food.
17. Study the effects of coffee, tea, alcohol, and cola drinks.
18. Learn how diet can prevent night blindness or other vision defects.

The communicative arts, especially reading, writing, and speaking can be correlated well with nutrition education. The following suggestions for doing so include having the pupils:

1. Report verbally or in writing on places they have visited which were connected in some way with food.
2. Suggest ways to learn to like new foods.
3. Locate foods in the Basic Seven Food Chart. Tell something important about each food.
4. Discuss ways foods are sold, such as meat by the pound, eggs by the dozen, milk by the quart. Correlate this with the units of measure in arithmetic.
5. Discuss the daily school lunch menu served in the cafeteria, which one pupil can copy on the board. Guide each child in making a wise food selection. Send the weekly menu home and enlist the cooperation of parents in helping their children choose a wisely selected daily lunch. Also send the Basic Seven Food Chart home to parents who prepare their child's school lunch, and help them plan this meal according to good nutritional standards.[2]
6. Discuss and list on the chalkboard the relationship of good food to growth and good teeth.
7. Tell how to care for a pet, or a baby sister or brother, or how wild animals seek food and what they eat.
8. Make a list of new foods seen or heard about on radio or television, and of new foods each has tasted or would like to taste.
9. Talk about ways to improve eating habits at school, at home, and in a restaurant.
10. Plan a class visit to a grocery store, giving each group a definite assignment, such as having them visit the meat section and find out all they can about it, another the frozen-food section, etc. Have each group compile a written, illustrated report on what they learned.
11. Have individual students report on their experiences in eating at a

[2] See the Appendix for a suggested letter to send to parents enlisting their cooperation.

Pupils might well be encouraged to bring real food into the classroom during a study of nutrition. (Courtesy, Los Angeles Public Schools.)

Chinese, French, or Italian restaurant; invite foreign adults to visit the school and describe or serve a typical meal or type of food from their homeland.

12. Teach the class to prepare simple menus in the school kitchen or out of doors. Experiment with different kinds of cooking such as boiling, frying, baking in pans or in foil. Have the group discuss what they learned from these experiences.
13. Demonstrate correct table setting and experiment with flower arranging. Discuss the importance of atmosphere to good eating.
14. Devise a miniature cafeteria or grocery store. Figure out how much a well-balanced meal costs, or "buy" the groceries for a family of two, four, six, or eight persons for a week on a preconceived budget. Have each pupil write a paragraph on what he learned from doing this.
15. Clip weekly food ads from the newspaper. Discuss how to shop well and get the most from every food dollar.
16. Tape-record skits, special reports, or other types of pupil work.
17. Write and give a playlet, puppet show, or skit to a local P.T.A. group on any aspect of nutrition.
18. Give an oral report on a book, such as Mabel Robinson's *Pioneer*

Panorama (Denison), or *Swift Arrow* by Alice Pendergast (Denison). Describe a typical day in the life of the main character of either book.

Dramatic and art activities which are suitable for correlating with nutrition are numerous. Have the pupils:

1. Do dramatizations of good manners at the table; a "mother" buying, preparing, and serving a meal; eating out at a large restaurant.
2. Visit a farm, bakery, dairy, or ice cream plant. Have the class make a list of things they would like to find out about, and make an illustrated poster of their visit.
3. Color pictures of fruits, vegetables, and other types of food, cut them out, and arrange a balanced meal on a desk or flannelboard.
4. Make a clock, learn how to tell time, and show the best time for eating each meal, going to bed, getting up, and resting.
5. Play cafeteria, store, or going shopping.
6. Display in the school lunchroom or lobby, children's posters of three balanced, well-planned meals.
7. Make posters showing "Foods I Take in a Lunch Box," "Foods for a Birthday Party," "Cold Weather or Summer Foods," "Foods for Thanksgiving," etc.
8. Create and give a puppet show or playlet revolving around any aspect of how to select a balanced diet.
9. Discuss and list on the board the relationship of good food to growth and teeth.
10. Dramatize the correct way to chew and eat food properly; exaggerate the incorrect ways to do so.
11. Bring magazine pictures of people eating food. Make up and tell a story about the pictures.
12. Make jigsaw puzzles out of colored pictures of food.
13. Present in charade form any activity done in the preparation of food, such as rolling dough or shelling peas. Have the class guess what is being done and select the best charade.
14. Make models of different kinds of foods such as oranges, corn, steak, pie, etc., out of clay or heavy cardboard. Have each pupil make up a story about any one of these which will stress its nutritional value.

Physical education, like science, can be more easily and naturally used for correlating and integrating nutrition education than certain other subjects included in the elementary school curriculum. Suggestions for doing so include having the pupils:

1. Learn the relationship of exercise to growth.
2. Become aware of the dangers of stimulants, alcohol, tea, tobacco, and soft drinks to athletic performance.

3. Learn which are the quick-energy foods, and the best foods to eat before playing in strenuous or competitive games.
4. Study the caloric intake of athletes.
5. Learn how to keep well and be in top physical condition.
6. Learn the cause and relationship of fatigue to accidents.
7. Learn the role that poor nutrition plays in poor posture.
8. Know their own body type, proper height, and proper weight according to age.
9. Learn how diet affects the rate and speed of recovery from sprains, broken bones, and other injuries.
10. Know the value of eating a good breakfast as a means of avoiding fatigue and becoming a top performer.

USE OF TEACHING METHODS

Planned instruction in nutrition should grow out of the problems of the daily living experiences of the pupils at home as well as at school, and include many of those of the community in which they live. As Haag points out, each teacher should receive in-service educational programs which will help them to do a better job of teaching nutrition. Such a program might well include:

1. Informing the teachers of the incidence of nutritional deficiencies among their own pupils.
2. Discovering the causes of these problems.
3. Helping teachers realize and understand the interrelationship of nutrition with human growth at all ages of the school-age child.
4. Recognizing the signs of nutritional problems.
5. Emphasizing the role of nutrition in the total school health program.
6. Helping the teachers correct their own food habits.
7. Understanding the benefits of supplementary school feeding programs, and becoming aware that the school lunch can supply one-third of the daily food intake.
8. Giving each teacher a comprehensive set of facts on the elements of nutrition.
9. Encouraging teachers to attend extension courses and workshops in nutrition education offered by departments of home economics or foods and nutrition in teachers' colleges, universities, and schools of public health.
10. Stimulating parent education in nutrition.[3]

[3] Haag, *op. cit.*, pp. 208–209.

It is the task of the elementary teacher to help children: (1) develop the attitude that health is important for growth, fun, and appearance, (2) accept increased responsibility for their own health, (3) understand their own health problems in the areas of nutrition, emotional health, safety, promotion of health habits, and prevention of infection, (4) develop desirable practices for healthful living in the areas of physical, social, and emotional health, (5) learn the ways in which they can solve their own health problems. Nutrition education plays a foundational role in the school health education program, for it touches every subject area which should be included in it either directly (as in dental health and growth) or indirectly (as in social adjustment and first aid). Consequently, expert teaching in this important area is necessary. The following suggestions for using various teaching methods successfully in nutrition education include:

Problem Solving. Teachers using this method must be skilled in discovering nutritional problems which are real to pupils. Often much class discussion and observation is required before an existing problem can be isolated and defined.[4] Recently, a group of third graders in a school in Atlanta, Georgia, selected a nutrition problem for further study when they realized (with the help of their teacher) that too many of them were not eating all the food on their plates served at the school cafeteria. The class discussed such things as why they should eat a balanced lunch and of what such a meal should consist, what caused likes and dislikes in food choice, how three well-balanced daily meals stimulated growth, and other related topics. The teacher, who noticed that most of the group avoided eating a variety of fresh and cooked vegetables, helped the group plan a visit to the fresh vegetable counter in a large supermarket. There they talked with the manager of the store, who showed and told them about the many kinds of food displayed, where they came from, how they were shipped across the country or state, and many other interesting things. The pupils decided later to divide up into committees and each group chose a specific area to find more information on, and others volunteered to make special reports in

[4] Ruth Strang, *Helping Children Solve Problems,* Chicago, Science Research Associates, 1953.

class or informative posters on good nutrition. Within a few days the class, as one of their proposed solutions to the problems, suggested that a "Clean Plate Club" be formed and all children who ate all the food on their plates be listed on the chalkboard as members. They also decided to have another honorary list made up of those who ate a new kind of vegetable served in the cafeteria. These learning experiences helped the pupils not only to learn to like many new kinds of foods and motivated them to eat all the food on their plates, but also helped them recognize a problem which existed which they could solve collectively through the improved actions of each individual.

Group interest in many kinds of nutritional problems may arise from current news items, such as a mass attack of food poisoning at a church picnic, reported in the daily newspaper, or the occurrence of floods throughout the nation and the problem of how homeless people can be housed and their daily dietary and other health needs met. Studying such problems provides many kinds of rewarding learning experiences for boys and girls, and they can be made to feel an important part of our ever-changing world.

Guidance. Individual health counseling can help many pupils successfully solve their own dietary and nutritional problems. It can assist the boy who is worried about being the class "runt," or the one who knows he should have more calcium in his diet but is allergic to milk products, or the sixth grade girl who is concerned about her oily skin and pimply face, or the third grader who always brings a jelly sandwich, candy bar, and drinks a Coke for lunch. These are real pupils with real nutritional problems. These children should be helped to solve their own problems with the assistance of professionally trained adults, including their own teacher, and by the things they and their classmates guide them to find out and learn more about at school.

Class discussions in nutrition education can be a valuable means for helping the teacher find out what the pupils know about the subject, as well as provide her with opportunities to clear up misconceptions, and to learn how the children are applying what they have learned. Care must be taken, however, not to "pry" into the private lives of the pupils or putting them in situations which prove embarrassing. She should not ask direct questions such as "Johnny, what did you have for breakfast?" and then, after hearing his report ask Billy what he had, for the latter, even though he has not even had breakfast that morning, will be most apt to tell her that he had even a better breakfast than Johnny's. Children feel that they cannot afford to "lose face," especially those in elementary schools, to whom the teacher's approval means so much.

Discussion in the area of nutrition might well revolve around the following topics:

1. The importance of eating three well-balanced daily meals.
2. How food helps us grow.
3. Why we should chew our food well.
4. Where does food come from?
5. How can we prevent illness by eating certain kinds of food?
6. How our bodies use food.
7. The importance of good manners.
8. The role of public health in nutrition.
9. Food preservation.
10. Each individual's height and weight chart; his weekly food consumption chart.
11. Eating in a restaurant or cafeteria.
12. The use of color in food serving; table decorations.
13. The emotions and food.
14. Dangers of being overweight or underweight and how this can be avoided.
15. How to count calories.
16. Self-medication and vitamins.
17. Food allergies.
18. Growing up.
19. Consumer protection and education.
20. Foreign foods.
21. Others.

Special reports assigned to certain pupils who have specific health problems related to nutrition, such as diabetes, food dislikes, or bad table manners often will help them gain new insight into their own difficulty. Some teachers prefer to have pupils volunteer to make class reports on certain phases of a unit which especially interest them. They should remember, however, that often those needing practice in speaking before groups rarely volunteer or want to take advantage of such an opportunity. Certainly no good teacher would want to make the already good become better at the expense of the already weak becoming weaker, and yet this too frequently happens.

Special reports in the area of nutrition suitable for older pupils might well include:

1. Signs of malnutrition.
2. Restored cereals.
3. Menu planning.
4. Religious customs.
5. Trends in American dietary habits.
6. Effects of cola drinks upon dental health.
7. Diets for those who are ill.
8. Foods as disease carriers.
9. How animals are tuberculin-tested.
10. Infections spread by food handlers.
11. How foods are contaminated by rodents and insects.
12. The diets of athletes.
13. Food buying.
14. Vitamin therapy.
15. The use of color and food selection.

Demonstrations children will enjoy and profit from doing in this area might include:

1. How to prepare uncooked vegetables for storage in the refrigerator, such as lettuce, celery.
2. Buying food at the class "grocery store."
3. How to cook simple foods, such as frying eggs.
4. How to use a microscope to see germs and bacteria.
5. Good and poor posture and its relationship to diet.
6. Animal experiment results.
7. The effect of lighting upon food, such as blue lights upon milk, green ones on meat, etc.
8. Relaxation techniques and their relationship to relieving tensions before meals.
9. Food tests for the presence of water content in vegetables, fruits, etc.
10. The dehydration of foods such as grapes, plums, etc.
11. Table setting and decorations.
12. Good and bad table manners.

Field trips to places within the community which have a direct relationship to nutrition education can often be a more valuable means of educating pupils than many hours of class time spent reading or studying about food and related topics. Suggested places to visit are a farm, bakery, ice cream plant, food packaging firm, grocery store, food storage or locker plant, community or farmer's outdoor market, garbage disposal plant, city water department, meat market, fish market, and a flour mill.

Experiments can be used effectively for getting the message of the dangers of eating an unbalanced diet across to growing boys and girls. When they see for themselves that one mouse which had been fed only tea or coffee looks and acts sick in comparison to one which had eaten a balanced diet, this experience becomes far more meaningful than merely hearing the teacher warn them against eating unwisely, especially when they realize that what happened to the mouse could also happen to them. Rabbits, hamsters, baby chickens, and birds are especially well suited for such experiments.

Simple food tests such as those mentioned below can be used to help children learn to identify the content of various foods, as well as motivate interest in learning about the classification and function of the six types of foods:

Tests for starch. Crush and soften with water one soda cracker. Place this in a test tube. Add one drop of well-diluted iodine. The material will turn blue, indicating that starch is present.

Test for fats. Place fried bacon, a pat of butter, or pastry on a piece of paper. Remove the food and put the paper on a radiator to heat. Observe the oily marks left on the paper. Compare the amount of fat in whole milk and skimmed milk in the same way.

Test for proteins. Burn raw lean meat, cheese, dried milk, or dried beans over the direct flame of a Bunsen burner. Since proteins are present, the food will give off a smell of burned feathers.

Test for minerals. Place peas, dried milk, or egg yolk on an asbestos metal plate. Burn it over the direct flame of a Bunsen burner. A gray ash will remain, showing that the food contains minerals. Nonmineral foods such as sugar will burn up quickly and leave no ash.

Test for water content. Cut an apple in two. Leave it exposed to the sun for one week. Note how it dries out.

Role playing and storytelling are best suited for younger children. Taking the part of a father, mother, or family member doing the weekly grocery shopping can also help them gain a better understanding of the duties and functions of each of these persons. Such experiences can be used to integrate nutrition with that of family life education. Playing grocery store, enacting the part of the ice cream man, etc., can also help the youngsters develop creativity, as well as give their teacher insight into their knowledge of nutrition, behavior, problems, and family background.

Older pupils will profit from making up and telling stories about what happens to vegetables or fruits from the time they are ripe until ready for market, along with their "adventures" while being shipped to market and at the canning factory. Stories can also be written about people who work on farms or elsewhere and are engaged in the production and transportation of food. Sixth graders can learn much from their outside reading either for special reports or for pleasure. Such books as Edna Ferber's *So Big,* or Mark Twain's *Huckleberry Finn,* are especially well suited for this purpose.

Surveys made by the pupils of the actual eating habits of people in their own community will help them gain insight upon the scope of nutrition problems and the role each might play in finding solutions to them. Suggested surveys might discover:

1. The number of pupils in each grade who eat their lunch daily in the school cafeteria or bring it from home.
2. The amount of milk drunk daily by each pupil in each grade.
3. Favorite foods of boys in contrast to those of girls.
4. How much a family of four spends, on the average, for groceries weekly.
5. How many food buyers go to market with a shopping list; how many buy impulsively.
6. How many adults in a city block eat breakfast regularly.
7. Favorite between-meal snacks among children, teenagers, and adults.
8. Family rules regarding the amount of candy children can have daily or weekly.
9. How many in the community or a city block have refrigerators and home freezers.
10. How many mothers bake their own cakes, bread, cookies, etc.
11. How often does an average family in a city block eat in a restaurant.
12. How much pupils help with the preparation and serving of food at home; how many have regular dishwashing duties.
13. How many in the community or a city block have their own kitchen sewage disposals, and electric dishwashers.
14. Which is used most frequently, canned, fresh, or frozen orange juice by the people living in a community or a city block.

Regardless of which type of a survey is used, the gathering of data must be of educational value. Likewise, the findings and results of such surveys must become important in the lives of the children.

USE OF INSTRUCTIONAL MATERIALS

Many different kinds of instructional materials and supplementary teaching aids can be used in nutrition education. These include:

Specimens of the different kinds of food in the six food classifications, examples of home canning in contrast to commercial, food packaging and the labeling of contents, food decay, "best" food buys for a given amount of money, carious teeth, improperly and properly cooked vegetables and meats, as well as many others. The pupils will profit most from bringing to class things they have collected, and explaining what they are and why each brought in what he did. All kinds of displays can be set up as a result, such as one showing the many kinds of vegetables which are good for growing children. Such experiences not only help certain youngsters to belong and contribute to a group endeavor, but also help to personalize education and gives each pupil tangible things to see and do, as a result of factual materials he has learned at school.

The chalk and bulletin boards should be fully utilized when teaching nutrition. Suggested "idea springboards" for doing so include showing:

1. New vocabulary words by making a weekly list and adding to it daily.
2. A list of new words seen or heard on television or radio.
3. The names of new foods told about or tasted by classmates.
4. Showing on a big map of the state or nation where certain foods are grown.
5. Questions requiring yes or no or short answers to discover what has been learned.
6. Restaurant menus collected by the class.
7. Illustrated lists or reports of a field trip made by the class showing the main things learned from it.
8. Posters made by individuals or small committees on any phase or subject regarding food or nutrition education.
9. Drawings of the digestive and circulatory systems of the body.

10. Current events pertinent to the subjects being studied in nutrition.
11. Pictures of families enjoying Thanksgiving dinner together, or other family tradition.
12. Illustrated evidence that good food affects good health.

Films, either seen in the classroom, at home on television, or in a movie theatre should be fully utilized by an alert teacher. There is an abundance of free films on nutrition available from many sources.[5] Likewise, many television programs can be used, including the morning foodmaking shows in most areas, and favorite weekly serials such as "One Man's Family" or "Lassie." Older pupils can profit from learning to distinguish between true and false advertising, as well as from watching more grown-up programs built around central characters, different times in history, or current and historical events. It is not enough, however, merely to have a class view such programs. They should be given opportunities to discuss what they have learned, as well as be guided to understand fully the meaningful facts and "messages" which have been presented.

Photographs collected by the pupils of colorful recipes can be used for outdoor cookouts and picnics. Pictures of how to cook on a large coffee can which can be used as a stove can motivate pupils to try frying hamburgers or eggs on the top of such stoves. These can be made by cutting off one end, making a hole for smoke to come out of near the opposite end, and setting the whole can over a small wood fire.[6] Pupils who are members of the Campfire Girls, Boy Scouts, or Girl Scouts will be eager to share their outdoor campcraft and cooking skills with their classmates. The class going on such an adventure should plan, purchase, and prepare the food they are to have.

The pupils can also bring and display photographs taken of themselves when they were babies and each year thereafter to show others how much they have grown, and describe the role good health habits played in their own development. They can each also make a poster showing what they want to be when grown up, whether this

[5] See the Appendix for specific listings.

[6] See Maryhelen Vannier, *Methods and Materials in Recreation Leadership,* Philadelphia, Saunders, 1956, p. 137, for directions for making these tin-can stoves as well as outdoor cooking recipes.

be a fashion model or spaceman, and list below the picture things they should do to be able to reach this grown-up ambition.

DESIRABLE OUTCOMES

A well-planned and well-taught unit in nutrition education should yield the following results by obtaining desirable knowledge, attitudes, and practices.

In the primary grades the pupils will:

1. Eat three well-balanced meals daily.
2. Wash before eating.
3. Avoid eating many sweets.
4. Know the relationship of good food to growth and good health.
5. Know what the Basic Seven Foods are.
6. Eat slowly.
7. Drink at least three glasses of milk and eight of water daily.
8. Help prepare the food and table at home according to skills suitable to their age.
9. Recognize that each parent has a unique contribution to make in the family, and that the father usually works to buy food and the mother works to prepare it.
10. Not talk with food in their mouths.
11. Know the names of and eat a wide variety of fruits and vegetables.
12. Know what unwise food selections will do to their teeth.

In the upper elementary grades, the pupils will:

1. Continue to eat a balanced diet and to try new foods.
2. Wash their hands before eating.
3. Become more cognizant of good table manners, the social graces, and practice them.
4. Know and appreciate that pleasant surroundings are desirable at meal time, and that one should eat slowly.
5. Assist in planning the family meals and in their preparation.
6. Become aware of food nutrients and the functions of growth, energy, and repair.
7. Understand how the body digests food.
8. Understand more in detail the specific values of each type of food to the body.
9. Practice cleanliness when handling food.
10. Know about vitamins and the specific function of each one.

11. Become aware of how food values can be diminished or destroyed by improper storage or preparation, and know that a balanced, nourishing diet need not be expensive.
12. Know how food patterns and social customs differ throughout the world; become aware of the many types of food eaten in America and the countries from which these come.

SUGGESTED READINGS

Learning Aids

Suggested materials in nutrition which will assist the pupils to learn valuable information and develop favorable attitudes and behavior in relationship to this subject include the following:

IN THE PRIMARY GRADES:

Free materials from the American Dry Milk Institute, American Institute of Baking, American Meat Institute, National Dairy Council, and the Metropolitan Life Insurance Company.

Make a Meal Picture Book, Wheat Flour Institute.

Health Readers

O'Keefe, Maxwell Health Series—*How We Grow.*

Baruch, Montgomery, Bauer, Health Series—*Three Friends, Happy Days, The Girl Next Door, Five in the Family.*

Jones, Morgan, Landis, Health Series—*My School Health Book, My Second Health Book, Easy Steps to Health.*

IN THE UPPER ELEMENTARY GRADES:

Books

Adams, Fay, *Educating America's Children: Elementary School Curriculum and Methods,* New York, Ronald, 1954.

An Experience in Health Education. Battle Creek, Mich., W. K. Kellogg Foundation, 1950.

Health in the Elementary School. Twenty-ninth Yearbook. The National Elementary Principal—Bulletin of the Department of Elementary School Principals, National Education Association, vol. 30, no. 1, September, 1950.

Walker, Herbert, *Health in the Elementary School,* New York, Ronald, 1955.

Films and Other Visual Aids

And One to Grow On, Social Science Films (12 minutes).

Food as Children See It, General Mills (18 minutes).
Why Won't Tommy Eat?, National Film Board of Canada (19 minutes).
"Why Nutritive Values" (six posters), Evaporated Milk Association.
"Wheel of Good Eating" (chart), American Institute of Baking.

Teaching Aids

Suggested teaching aids are:

IN THE PRIMARY GRADES:

Books and Pamphlets

A Nutrition Guide, General Mills, Inc.

A Teacher's Guide to Classroom Food Facts and Fun, Wheat Flour Institute.

Health Education for Elementary Schools, Utah State Department of Public Instruction, Salt Lake City, 1949.

Martin, Ethel, *Roberts Nutrition Work with Children,* Chicago, University of Chicago Press 1954.

A Science Course of Study for the Elementary Grades, Shoreline Public Schools, Seattle, 1954.

Free materials from The Cereal Institute, Evaporated Milk Association, General Mills, Kellogg Company, Metropolitan Life Insurance Company, Ralston Purina Company, and Swift and Company.

Health readers

Scott, Foresman Health Series, *Happy Days with Our Friends; Good Times with Our Friends; Three Friends.*

Jones, Morgan, Landis, Health Series, *Keeping Healthy.*

Laidlaw Road to Health Series, *My First Health Book; My Second Health Book; Easy Steps to Health.*

Food Makes a Difference in These Twin Rats (poster), U.S. Department of Agriculture, Bureau of Human Nutrition and Home Economics.

Fisher, Helen, and R. Van Allen, *Independent Activities for Creative Learning,* New York, Teachers College, 1961.

Sheckles, Mary, *Building Children's Science Concepts through Experience,* New York, Teachers College, 1961.

IN THE UPPER ELEMENTARY GRADES:

Books and Pamphlets

Nutrition Aids, Grades 1 through 8, Kellogg Company.

Good Foods: A Tentative Program for Learning Experiences in Foods in the Elementary School, Grades 1–6, Washington State Nutrition Council, distributed by the U.S. Office of Education, Washington, D.C.

Arey, Charles, *Science Experiences for Elementary Schools,* New York, Teachers College, 1960.

Clark, John, and Laura Eads, *Guiding Arithmetic Learning,* New York, Harcourt, Brace, 1954.

Bogart, Jean, *Nutrition and Physical Fitness,* 7th ed., Philadelphia, Saunders, 1961.

Health Aspects of the School Lunch Program, Washington, D.C., American Association of Health, Physical Education and Recreation, 1961.

What to Eat and Why, John Hancock Mutual Life Insurance Company.

Godshall, Frances, *Nutrition in the Elementary School,* New York, Harper, 1958.

Health Education, Grades 1–7, Virginia State Board of Education, Division of Purchasing and Printing, 1956.

How to Conduct a Rat Feeding Experiment, Wheat Flour Institute, 1960.

Kilander, H. F., *Nutrition for Health,* New York, McGraw-Hill, 1951.

Keys, Ancel, and Margaret Keys, *Eat Well and Stay Well,* New York, Doubleday, 1959.

Preston, Ralph, *Teaching Social Studies in the Elementary Grades,* New York, Rinehart, 1958.

McHenry, E. W., *Foods Without Fads,* Philadelphia, Lippincott, 1960.

Films and Other Visual Aids

Guide to Good Eating, National Dairy Council (10 minutes).

The School That Learned to Eat, General Mills (22 minutes).

Food That Builds Good Health, Coronet Films (10 minutes).

"Food Value Charts," National Livestock and Meat Board.

To Your Health, Columbia University Press (10 minutes).

11 BODY CARE, STRUCTURE, AND FUNCTION

A functional health education program is one which will aid each pupil to gain a clear understanding of and real appreciation for his own body, as well as assist him to develop the knowledge and desire for taking good care of it throughout life. Consequently, all materials included in this area should be directed toward learning the best ways to protect oneself and others from hazards and disease. In the primary grades a minimum amount of time should be spent in studying the names of various parts of human anatomy, for such facts as the parts of the teeth or names of bones mean little, if anything, to a child. Rather, emphasis should be placed upon developing good health habits which will ensure the protection of eyes, ears, and all other body parts as well as ways to increase their functional use. In the upper elementary grades, pupils should see their body as a whole, and know the relationship that exists between what they do and how they look, act, or feel. It is essential that all youngsters, regardless of which school grade they are in, gain a lasting appreciation for the wonder, beauty, and miracle of his own life and the body in which it is housed. A visit to a health museum to see a transparent man or woman, or the use of models, or pictures of the entire human body in the classroom will be of great value in helping children see the unity of man—a masterpiece created by

God. As the child progresses in school, he should be taught simple facts of the physiology and anatomy of the many organs and structure of the body. However, learning the scientific name of any body part is an educational waste if the child cannot or does not apply what he has learned. Teachers working in this area should primarily be concerned with helping children live healthfully.

SUGGESTED GRADED TOPICS

Units of study in this area might well include noncommunicable and contagious diseases, good grooming, and the care of the senses, as well as the structure and function of the various parts of the body. Suggested graded topics include the following:

GRADE 1

1. Keeping clean.
2. How to avoid colds and sickness.
3. Having good teeth.
4. How to have good posture.
5. Suitable clothing.
6. Play, rest, and sleep.
7. How we grow.
8. Why we should, and how we can, avoid accidents.

GRADE 2

1. Reasons for using personal toilet articles.
2. How to drink from the fountain without touching it; how not to spread germs at home and school.
3. Staying home when we are sick.
4. The body as a machine.
5. Protecting ourselves from accidents.
6. Common contagious diseases of children.
7. Exercise, nutrition, and sleep in relationship to growth.

GRADE 3

1. The framework of the body.
2. Care of the eyes, ears, and nose.
3. The skin and its care.
4. The systems of the body.
5. How disease germs get into the body.
6. Periodic health examinations.

7. Heart and circulation.
8. Dental health.

Grade 4

1. Mechanics of movement.
2. Body care and grooming.
3. The value and need for good health habits in relationship to growth.
4. Effect of bacteria and viruses.
5. Diseases of the respiratory and digestive systems.
6. How the body protects and heals itself.
7. The effect of accidents and illness.
8. Structure and care of teeth.
9. The skeletal system.

Grade 5

1. Our senses and how they work.
2. The brain and mental hygiene.
3. Skin, hair, nails, and good grooming.
4. Bones and muscles.
5. How the stomach works; the digestion of food.
6. Safeguarding the body at work and play.
7. Immunization.
8. Disease carriers and communicable diseases.

Grade 6

1. The heart and lungs, their structure, function, and care.
2. The effects of alcohol, smoking, and drugs upon the body.
3. How we use food.
4. Problems of growing up.
5. The glands and growth.
6. Feet and their care.
7. How the body protects and heals itself.
8. The noncommunicable diseases of diabetes, heart disease, cancer, rheumatic fever.

CURRICULUM PLACEMENT

Instruction in the structure, care, and function of the human body should be included in the curriculum for every grade level from the first through high school. There are numerous ways which this may be done, and often these are through the means of a separate health and safety program, or integrating and correlating this subject with science, home economics, or physical education. However, there are other subject areas which can be used most successfully for correlating and integrating these health education foundational materials. These areas are:

The social sciences, by providing opportunities for children to see the relationship between good health and good living throughout the entire history of mankind. Older pupils will profit from finding out about a number of health devices, such as how eyeglasses have changed from those first bifocals invented by Benjamin Franklin to modern contact lenses or from learning of the serious health problems among primitive peoples in contrast to our own. Special reports can be given when the class is studying about wars and determining whether or not the advancement of scientific knowledge is a positive result of such struggles, or on how seeing-eye dogs are trained and how dogs are used in warfare or in apprehending criminals. They can also profit from learning how blind people read Braille and by listening to talking books in order to increase their understanding of the many problems sightless people have. Units on good grooming and boy-and-girl relationships will help older children gain needed social and physical skills which may have lasting effects upon them as high school and college students and adult members of society. The older pupils will also profit from learning about some of the famous historical medical experiments, such as that conducted by Dr. William Beaumont, who was the first person to look into the stomach of a living person, as well as becoming acquainted with medicine, nursing, or related fields as a profession. Heart disease and cancer might well be discussed from both social and economic aspects, and children be taught ways to protect themselves from these dreaded illnesses. Actually, the possibilities for intermeshing this phase of health education with the social sciences are as abundant as an alert and skilled teacher can make them.

Science is the foundation upon which study in this area rests. Children can become fascinated by learning more about themselves and what makes them the way they are. The class group on every grade level need not be kept together and all pupils required to study the same things, for some will be naturally more eager and interested to learn more scientific details than others. This is especially true of those even in the elementary grades who have decided that they want to become nurses, doctors, or scientists. Many dreaming of becoming spacemen can develop great interest in the physical hazards and effects of outer space upon the body, or the physical training program of the famous astronauts. In this scientific age, children tend to be more science-minded than their parents were and often, consequently, are all the more eager to learn many of the more scientific facts about human beings.

Conducting simple experiments and learning how to use such equipment as a microscope, stethoscope, dental mirror, height and weight scales, etc., are exciting experiences for growing children and should be a part of the skills taught in this area. Simple scientific experiments which can also help the pupils learn many new fascinating things about the body and how it works are:

1. Blindfolded, taste pieces of raw onion, apple, and potato in order to learn how the senses of taste and sight work together.
2. Blow through two sheets of thin paper to discover how quickly the ears pick up vibrating sounds.
3. Use an ordinary fork or a tuning fork. Observe how sound travels.
4. Strike a spoon against several glasses filled with various amounts of water. Note that sound has musical qualities.
5. Taste a fresh lemon, a piece of candy, and sugar in that order, then taste the lemon again. Note how the sense of taste is deceiving, for on the second taste the lemon seems sourer than before.
6. Blindfolded, touch a wide variety of objects such as a ball, bowl, etc. Note the connection between the sense of touch and that of sight.
7. Experiment blindfolded with hot and cold objects. Note the quickness with which the hands respond to these two temperatures.
8. Observe a small bird closely. Do birds have ears? If so, where are they, in the feet or head?
9. Rub a piece of cleansing tissue over your face. Note that the skin has its own natural oil.
10. Look at a hair pulled out of your own head under a magnifying glass. Find the root and discuss how hair grows and if cutting or shaving it makes it grow faster.
11. Show how perspiration cools the skin as it evaporates by placing a bit of cotton which has been dipped in warm water on your forehead.
12. Examine an uncooked meat bone under a magnifying glass. See its spongy tissue, outer covering, and marrow.
13. Make a stethoscope out of a cardboard mailing tube. Listen to the heartbeat of a classmate through it.

14. Locate and feel the pulse of a classmate at his wrist, in front of the ear, along the jawbone line. Record your finding. Have your partner do vigorous exercise for one minute, such as run in place. Count his pulse again. Have him rest for one minute. Count his pulse rate and compare it to the first reading. Know that if the first and last rates correspond within five counts, your partner is physically fit.
15. Examine blood cells under a microscope.
16. Compare the skin on your hands and face, using a magnifying glass.
17. Make your own fingerprints, using ink and paper. Compare yours with anyone else's in class.
18. Observe a healing cut on your hand under a magnifying glass. Note how the body heals itself.
19. Place milk and four spoonsful of vinegar in a quart jar. Shake it up. Observe what happens to the milk. Discuss how the stomach, enzymes, and digestive juices churn and change food into liquid.
20. Examine unclean food and eating and drinking utensils under a microscope. Experiment with various ways to destroy germs. Review state and local laws for food handlers and restaurant inspection standards which must be met in public dining places.
21. Invite a local druggist to talk to the class about his work and show how pills are made. Have him list things which should be in every first-aid cabinet.

The communicative arts of reading, writing, and speaking can be used in this area in the following suggested ways:

1. Read stories, talk about good nutritional habits, and supervise school lunchroom experiences; conduct play activities in the class at regular intervals.
2. Teach new vocabulary words and play quiz games built around them.
3. Divide the class into groups and assign each tasks, including room responsibilities. Discuss the value of work in life, stressing that it is a privilege, not a drudgery, and that everyone must share responsibility for the benefit of the group as well as himself.
4. Bring a book written in Braille to class. Demonstrate how blind people read. Discuss how blindness is caused, how seeing-eye dogs are used, etc. Stress why the eyes must be protected and well cared for at all times.
5. Have the class make a survey and report their findings of sanitary conditions found in the school toilets and public restrooms throughout their city. Discuss in detail local sanitation laws and how they could be better enforced.
6. Have the class bring pictures or tell about handicapped victims. Stress that in one way or another, all human beings are "handicapped." Dis-

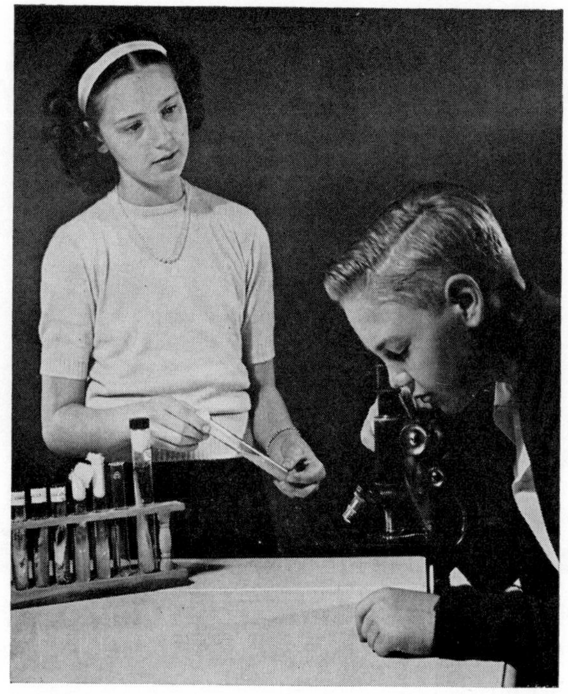

These pupils are learning to use a microscope and are looking at germs taken from their own bodies. (Courtesy, AAHPER.)

cuss ways an exceptional person should be treated; how such a person can learn to help himself; great leaders or artistic geniuses who were handicapped, such as Franklin D. Roosevelt or Lord Byron.

7. Study the big muscles of the body by looking closely at charts or book illustrations. Discuss sprains, muscle soreness, and the recommended first-aid treatment for both.
8. Have each pupil keep a record of his activities for each 24-hour period in a week. Look at this report carefully as an adult friend and educator who desires to help each child become an increasingly independent citizen who is "health" educated.
9. Have a committee give a report and demonstrate safety measures taken in sports by showing many kinds of recommended equipment, such as a catcher's mask, float board for a nonswimmer, archery finger tab, football shoulder pads, etc.
10. Have each pupil write a summary of the findings of his yearly physical and dental checkup. Discuss the report with each individually.

The use of live models is a good way to teach growth and development. (Courtesy, N.E.A.)

11. Listen to several class panel discussions on "Why I Know I Am Growing Up."
12. Play a game "Guess How I Feel" in charade form, with one child having only his back toward the group. Have that child act out being angry, etc., and the class guess which emotion is being acted out according to the position of the spine, head, body. Discuss how posture reveals emotions.
13. Write letters to the American Medical Association, 535 N. Dearborn Street, Chicago, asking for free health literature on any subject included in this unit. Use this in an oral or written report given in class.
14. Tell your own version of the life and work of any of the health heroes, such as Dr. Harvey, Dr. Salk, or others. Look into such books as *The Story behind Great Medical Discoveries* by Elizabeth Montgomery (Dodd, Mead) or *How Man Discovered His Body* by Sarah Reidman (International).
15. Write in your own words the story of how food is digested.
16. Make up and write health slogans and rhymes, such as "See Your Dentist Twice a Year" or "When Riding a Bicycle to School (Ride Safely, Don't Be a Fool)."

17. Have a speaking contest, choose the best oral talk given on "The Human Body, the Greatest Wonder of Them All."
18. Consult the encyclopedia to gather material for a written report on any topic covered in this unit such as "How the Eyes See," or "A Bone Bank."
19. Invite an admired older boy and girl to talk to the class about the importance of having good health and grooming habits.

Mathematics is especially suited for correlation with materials on structure, function, and care. Many kinds of learning experiences can be devised which will help pupils gather and apply increased knowledge in both areas. Topics might include discovering the costs of medical, accident, and hospital insurance policies; life-expectancy predictions in relationship to obesity or lung cancer; height and weight tables for a variety of ages; advertising costs in relationship to increased sales in food and grooming products; hidden costs in drugs; yearly expenditures for patent medicines; costs for rehabilitating drug addicts or mental patients, etc.; or making graphs of temperature and barometer changes; reading and recording outdoor temperature; learning how to forecast the weather; making weather flags. Care must be taken that the pupils see the relationship of such mathematical problems to themselves and their own well-being. Knowing how much it costs to rehabilitate a mentally ill person is just another fact unless this knowledge motivates the learner to practice good mental hygiene in order to prevent him from becoming emotionally and mentally ill.

Dramatic and art activities can be used successfully with each age group. Suggested ways for doing so are:

1. Have the group divide up into couples and have each give a demonstration of the many aspects of good grooming, care of the feet, etc.
2. Have the class draw pictures showing the effects of measles, scarlet fever, mumps, and other diseases of the body. Discuss the signs and symptoms of each of these.
3. Study anatomical charts or view models of all parts of the human body. Reproduce models of any body part or system for the class health museum made out of clay, papier-mâché, or plaster of Paris.
4. Make models or other types of visual aids to show how blood circulates; digestion; how the respiratory system functions; parts of the skin, or any other information gained from the library or other assignments. "Pool" gleaned information with the class.

5. See a film on the harmful effects of tobacco, alcohol, or narcotics upon the body. Assign the class a library reference project on this topic, and have each write a paper or make an illustrated poster or cartoon on his findings.
6. Bring a camera to class. Make a poster to show its similarity to the human eye.
7. Discuss the reasons the school requires immunizations before entrance, and what vaccinations each has had.
8. Make posters illustrating why wet clothing should be changed, how colds are spread through sneezing, etc.
9. Bring pictures of animals to school. Discuss how animals protect themselves; what is rabies; the importance of avoiding strange animals or reporting an animal bite immediately.
10. Visit the zoo and learn how animals are protected from illness. Illustrate by labeled drawings things learned from this experience.
11. Discuss cleanliness in public places. Write a letter to city officials suggesting ways these places can be made more attractive and sanitary.
12. Paint pictures of the activities of city employees who protect community health, such as the garbage collector, dog catcher, etc.
13. Visit the city water department or the waste disposal plant. Write a short report or tape-record a class discussion on important things learned from this experience. Make a poster on such topics as "Keep Our City Clean."
14. Give a puppet show to show health practices such as getting ready for bed, coming home from school, getting ready to go sledding, etc.
15. Paint or draw and color an illustrated panel showing ways food is handled from its source to the consumer. Explain each step in this process to the group.
16. Plan and make a window display on what the community is doing to protect the health of its citizens.
17. Give a puppet show, playlet, or make a cartoon motion picture on the life of any health hero or a large scale epidemic, such as the Black Plague.
18. Make a water color, oil, or illustrated poster the Red Cross might use for one of its financial drives. Select the best five made and display them in the school lobby.
19. Make a skeletal model of the human body, using cardboard, paste, and string.
20. Carve a human figure out of any kind of wood or soap. Have the class select the best one.

Physical education presents many opportunities for correlating and integrating health instruction in this area, both through direct and incidental teaching. The conscientious physical educator and athletic coach will capitalize upon moments for health education from situations which arise naturally out of class activity, on the playground, or athletic field. The following are suggested opportunities for relating this area of health education with that of physical education:

1. Emphasizing the relationship between exercise and physical activities to organic vigor and physical fitness.
2. Discussing the opportunities provided by taking part in play for widened social contacts and improved mental health.
3. Showing the carry-over value of activities and stressing the need for some kind of physical activities throughout life.
4. Stressing that physical activities provide chances to work out feelings of hostility and aggression in positive ways.
5. Discussing the values of physical activity in modern, sedentary life.
6. Showing how the body recovers from fatigue.
7. Emphasizing the necessity of well-balanced diets for energy and growth.
8. Showing how bones, muscles, and joints work, and helping pupils learn the joy of well-coordinated body movements.
9. Discussing what causes muscle cramps, strains, and tears, and how these should be cared for and can be prevented.
10. Explaining the values of conditioning the body before strenuous activity and teaching basic exercises for doing so.

Safety education can also help pupils put in practice knowledge gained in this area, as well as help them shape favorable attitudes toward the value of safety as a means of protecting themselves from injury and avoiding needless and costly accidents. Ways in which the importance of teaching safety can be stressed in this area include:

1. Teaching the proper use of equipment, showing how misuse can bring about injury.
2. Emphasizing common-sense rules and good techniques in and around swimming pools and other bodies of water.
3. Pointing out the reasons for matching competitors for weight, size, maturity in some activities.
4. Emphasizing safe conduct in shower and locker rooms.
5. Teaching first aid and the recognition of emergency situations.[1]

Guidance and counseling, whether done in groups or through individual conferences, can do much to help children find ways to find

[1] *Health Education,* National Education Association and American Medical Association, 5th ed., Washington, D.C., 1961, p. 256.

solutions to their own health problems and answers to questions concerning their everchanging and fast-developing bodies. Some will need to be referred to the school doctor or specialists within the community because of their own unique problems, such as a too rapid increase in weight or the onset of acute nervousness. Others will need special encouragement and parental help to have remedial defects corrected, such as a crossed eye or protruding teeth.

Every teacher in the school, through the help of specially trained guidance personnel, should capitalize upon opportunities for integrating health with counseling and guidance, for this is essential if pupils are to be helped and reached as individuals in a large group to solve their own unique health problems. In the elementary school it is imperative that such health guidance and counseling include the parents.

USE OF TEACHING METHODS

Problem solving. Group problem solving in this area can be done informally by day-by-day activities or by extensive problem units. Grout has reported that in one school there was too much fighting on the playground and too many children were being hurt. These problem incidents were discussed, and the children figured out ways of having just as much fun with less risk.[2]

Problem areas suitable for study in this area can be any aspect of physical, mental, or emotional health. In general these pertain to:

- Nutrition and diet
- Exercise and diet
- Rest, relaxation, and sleep
- Physical defects
- Chronic diseases
- Growth and development
- Mental and emotional problems

Older pupils will be interested in studying not only the problems which occur in their own school in this area, but also in their community and in the world. One group of sixth graders in a school in Indiana recently became concerned about the fact that, although

[2] Ruth Grout, *Health Teaching in Schools,* 3rd. ed., Philadelphia, Saunders, 1958, p. 103.

polio vaccine is available and is a known preventive, relatively few of the school-age children in their state had been inoculated. They determined to discover why this was true and what could be done about the problem. The group began by studying the cause, types, and effects of polio. Next they learned about the development of the Salk vaccine and how it works. One committee studied the polio problem on a world-wide scale, still another made a class-by-class survey first of the pupils in their own school and then in all of their city's schools in order to learn just how many had been protected, another committee interviewed one hundred adults from all walks of life in an attempt to discover how they felt about requiring by law that all school-age children be inoculated as a requirement for entrance and re-entrance to public schools. The class invited a leading pediatrician to talk to them about this subject. They saw three films, *The Magic Touch* (Avis Films, New York), *What Is Disease?* (Institute of Inter-American Affairs, New York), and *The Control of Communicable Disease in Man* (American Public Health Association, New York). After spending two weeks on this problem, the class drew up a list of specific things which could be done in their community to eradicate polio. Through the efforts of their school principal, the class planned and gave a 30-minute televised program on this subject over a local station. The newspaper publicity received from this endeavor, the amount of education each pupil obtained, and pride among the parents for what the children had done, did much to increase the appreciation of the citizens in that community for the teacher who had skillfully guided the whole project, as well as for their own school system.

Every daily newspaper and many periodicals such as *Time*, *Life*, *Reader's Digest*, *Today's Health*, and *National Geographic* contain materials which can be used to motivate pupil interest in any area of health education, including those which revolve around the human body, its structure, care, and protection.

Class discussions which will help the pupils gain better understanding concerning their own bodies might include the following topics and activities:

1. Play several types of quiet games in the classroom often; talk about the value of doing tapering-off activities before bedtime.

2. Teach relaxation exercises to the class, such as playing at being a rag doll, floating like a big log lazily down a quiet stream, etc. Play soft music to the children as they stretch out on the floor and listen to it with their eyes closed. Discuss with them how the heart and other body parts rest.
3. Teach the group a wide variety of large-muscle activities, exercises, and games which require twisting, hanging, crawling, skipping, running, etc. Discuss with the group why they need vigorous exercise every day in order to grow and develop good posture.
4. Conduct vision and hearing tests and encourage the pupils to adjust their own seating arrangements according to the test results. Discuss the value of good sitting posture.
5. Elect or appoint a class health committee or inspector to check washing hands properly, drinking from fountains, or keeping objects out of the mouth. Change membership in these often enough to give each child an opportunity to serve. Discuss how children can prevent illness by being clean.
6. Have an outdoor and indoor clothing fashion show. Talk about the value of dressing properly for all kinds of weather.
7. Discuss why tissues may be safer to use than a handkerchief.
8. Teach and play more advanced quiet games such as "Human Checkers," "Who Am I?" etc.[3] Discuss the relationship between rest and fatigue and health.
9. View and discuss films about all phases of this unit; see filmstrips about health heroes.[4]
10. Have a playground clean-up period, dividing the group in teams. Discuss the reason for keeping the playground free from trash.
11. Read aloud or listen to Basil Rathbone's recording of Poe's famous short story, "The Masque of the Red Death." Discuss the significance of this story. Make up and tell a similar one about any epidemic which might happen in your local community.
12. Appoint certain pupils each week to change the room thermostat or adjust room temperature and lighting. Discuss how the body adjusts to change.
13. Discuss the future professional plans of each student. Tell the group about the training needed to be a nurse, doctor, or dentist. Help the group see the relationship which exists between success as an elementary pupil and as a professional worker in the medical field in the future.
14. Go on a hike during school time, or as a class group on Saturday. Report on birds, animals, plants, and other things seen. Discuss how ani-

[3] For suggestions, see Maryhelen Vannier, *Methods and Materials in Recreation Leadership,* Philadelphia, Saunders, 1957.

[4] These are obtainable free of charge from the Education Department of the Metropolitan Life Insurance Company, New York.

mals and birds spread seeds, or destroy insects or pests. Talk about the creatures who spread diseases.

15. Divide into groups and discuss ways that sanitation in your school could be improved. Plan and conduct a campaign for doing so. Evaluate the results.
16. Assign each pupil to teach a game to a group of first graders or any younger children in the neighborhood. Have each give a brief oral report on this experience. Lead a class discussion on the value of older children setting a good example for younger ones by having good health, work, and play habits.

Demonstrations which can be useful and beneficial to pupils in this area are:

1. Demonstrate good sitting, walking, and moving posture. Use three blocks piled on top of each other to demonstrate body balance; have each child check a partner for good posture as well as look at his own in a large mirror during the day.
2. Demonstrate methods for sterilizing water, eating utensils, surgical instruments, etc.
3. Bring a dog to class and demonstrate the keenness of his hearing ability. Experiment with soundless whistles and other kinds of noises. Have the group observe birds and other creatures after school and report to the group how they hear. Stimulate interest by asking: if a tree crashed in the forest and no one saw it or was within ten miles of it, would there be a noise when it hit the ground? Why or why not?
4. Demonstrate ear, eye, and nose safety and the first aid which could be used to remove a foreign body from each.
5. Demonstrate how fast bacteria multiply in darkness, warmth, and moisture. Write a short summary of your findings.
6. Have pupils bring samples of improperly fitting shoes and socks to class. Demonstrate good foot care; the damage done to the feet by wearing shoes which are too small or large or have run-down heels, or wearing socks with many big holes or darns in them.
7. Conduct a Junior Red Cross First Aid course in class or as an after-school club activity. Demonstrate the latest methods of artificial respiration.
8. Have a handwashing demonstration; teach the necessity of keeping nails clean.
9. Demonstrate how milk is pasteurized; visit a dairy or ice cream plant. Have each child write a brief report on the value of drinking or eating pasteurized dairy products.
10. Demonstrate how the ear hears; play hearing guessing games by having the children close their eyes and identify certain objects dropped or sounds made in the room. Discuss how a hearing aid works. Show an actual hearing aid or pictures of people wearing one.

11. Measure and weigh the pupils periodically. Discuss ways to stimulate growth. Show each child his own growth chart.

Field trips can be especially valuable in helping pupils gain a better understanding of their community as well as their ownselves in relationship to it. Suggested places to visit include:[5]

1. A visit to an aquarium to observe how fish breathe. Use bellows to demonstrate how the lungs work. Discuss diseases of the lungs; value of fresh air.
2. A tour of the school cafeteria—learn how the dishes are washed, food stored, and waste disposed of.
3. A visit to a pet shop or an animal hospital. Discuss the value of protective rabies "shots," or those given for hepatitis or other diseases common to pets.
4. A visit to interview a local physician, public health official, or nurse. Summarize the important things learned from this experience.
5. A visit to a pharmacy to learn how prescriptions are filled, records are kept, etc.
6. A visit to a blood or bone bank to learn how these are stored and used in emergencies.
7. A trip to see the village dump or waste disposal plant. Discuss how diseases are spread.
8. A visit to a housing project and a slum district. Discuss how good housing affects health.

Storytelling can provide younger children with increased avenues for self-expression, as well as provide the teacher with added insight into their health habits, attitudes, and feelings. Almost any topic can be used for this purpose. The story can be told by the teacher, who should be well aware that children like stories best about real things they do and those characters which express feelings similar to their own. Some of the most revealing ones can be created and told by the children themselves about any of these suggested headings:

Birthdays
Why I like to play games
My house
My parents
Any fruit or vegetable
What I want to be
A farm
My favorite food
How puppies grow
A broken front tooth
Babies

[5] See also suggested field trips in the chapter on nutrition, dental care, and safety.

Role playing is likewise revealing, and is of high educational value. Although teachers should not try to be amateur psychiatrists, they can become skilled in understanding what the child is trying to communicate through this type of dramatic activity. This understanding is essential if adults are to have insight into what children say and do and why they are as they are. It is known that children in role playing assign to themselves parts which are an extension or expression of their own problems, and what they do is an indication of what they think and feel. Imitating adults, such as playing at being a nurse, doctor, mother, father, teacher, etc., creates not only better understanding of what these people do but also helps promote a feeling of identification with these adults. Sex differences in role playing are striking, for girls prefer roles to play which revolve around being the mother of the house, cooking, and feeding a family, while boys play variations on the one theme of riding or guiding vehicles, whether as a steamboat captain or an outer-space pilot, and rarely choose roles in which they identify with their own father. Although "cops and robbers" is played by most children, such roles are the favorites of children who are most aggressive. The anxious and withdrawn child rarely shows aggression in role choice or actions.[6]

The teacher can set up problem situations, and have the children act out their own selected roles in the following suggested ways:

1. Jane made a surprise present for her mother, who was in the hospital. The doctor said she was too sick to have visitors.
2. George's mother took him to the store to buy new shoes. The salesman helped him get a pair that were just right for a growing boy.
3. Tommy has a cold. He couldn't come to school but he had a happy, restful day in bed.
4. Mary wouldn't eat vegetables for dinner. Her daddy told her why she should do so and helped her learn to like them.
5. Jesse never took part in the games the other children played. His teacher found out why.
6. Our family has a new baby brother. I can help him be happy and grow. My parents told me how.

[6] Ruth Hartley, Lawrence Frank, and Robert Goldenson, *Understanding Children's Play,* New York, Teachers College, 1959, p. 9.

USE OF INSTRUCTIONAL MATERIALS

Free graphic materials are available in an abundance in the form of posters, charts, comic strips, and graphs, which can be powerful forces for shaping attitudes and motivating action among pupils so that they will learn to understand and have increased respect for their own bodies and know how to take better care of them. The types and suggested use of these materials include:

Models and specimens which show the entire systems of the body, or any specific part of it, such as a cutaway model of the eye, can enable pupils to gain a clearer understanding of where each body part is and its function in relationship to other parts, senses, or systems of a human being, such as the retina to the cornea and the sense of sight to that of smell. Many of these models can be obtained commercially and are relatively inexpensive. Pupils in some schools have made their own successfully from clay, carved soap or wood, papier-mâché, and other materials. Such models can be made of the entire body or almost any part of it including teeth, ears, bones, hands, feet, stomach, heart, etc. Such experiences help create increased pupil interest in and better understanding of materials covered.

Posters made by the children in this area might cover the following topics:

1. Any communicable disease, its symptoms, cause, and contagious period.
2. Outdoor play and exercise.
3. Cancer, diabetes, hepatitis, and other diseases.
4. The care and function of skin, muscles, teeth, etc.
5. How the body repairs itself.
6. Coworkers in health.
7. How to help yourself grow.
8. Kinds of germs, bacteria, and molds.
9. Harmful effects of tea, coffee, and alcohol.
10. How to protect your heart.

Cartoons and the daily comic strip are especially well suited for helping children realize the difference between positive and negative use of leisure time, how some people face problems concerning their health in a dentist's or doctor's office, hospital, at home, and else-

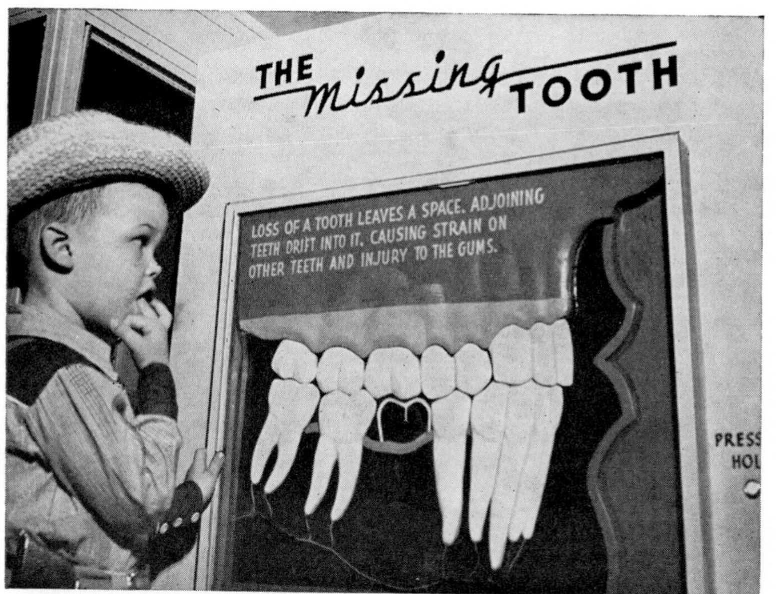

Models can help every child gain a clearer understanding of the values of good dental care. (Courtesy, Dallas Health and Science Museum.)

where. Younger children will enjoy bringing in their favorite comics to illustrate material studied in this area, such as "Dondi" or "Little Orphan Annie" facing a health problem. The comic strip "Peanuts" is especially well suited for this purpose and can supplement study about how to avoid accidents, staying in bed when you have a cold, and other topics.

Books and other supplementary reading materials can also be used to a good advantage in this area. Older pupils will profit from looking at illustrated materials on the human body found in many kinds of reference works in the school or local public library. They would especially be fascinated by looking closely at the wonderful drawings of the human body in the book, *Man in Structure and Function* by Fritz Kahn (Knopf). This beautiful, two-volume work was written and illustrated by a physician in Germany and should be found in every school library. Few other books can come close to it in helping the layman understand how each organ, part, and system of the human body looks and functions. Those who fear that these materials are too advanced for those in upper elementary school should remember that the unchallenged pupil will remain that way, and that our most gifted scholars, who are ready for and can digest a "banquet" of learning, are too often fed a steady diet of predigested pablum.

Suggested books, as well as films, that each class will enjoy and profit from reading or seeing in all grades of the elementary school are listed at the end of this chapter.

Films, television, and radio should also be used as supplementary teaching aids in this area. Popular programs which may be appropriate include "Medico," "Hennessey," "The Shirley Temple Show," "The Shari Lewis Show," and "Walt Disney Cartoons."

DESIRABLE OUTCOMES

A well-conducted instructional program on the human body, its structure, function, and care should produce the following desirable outcomes.

In the primary grades, the pupils will:

1. After vision and hearing tests, understand why they should move their chairs closer in order to see or hear better and then do so by themselves.
2. Engage in quiet activities in their own homes before bedtime; rest well at school and know the value of, as well as take part in, several kinds of relaxing activities.
3. Engage in vigorous play with their peers and be aware of the value of doing so, both at home, during leisure, and at school.
4. Be aware of the existing relationship between balanced diets, growth, and good health; eat nutritious meals; be concerned with growing up healthy and strong.
5. Protect others as well as themselves from accidents during spontaneous, unsupervised play.
6. Be well aware of the importance of the uniqueness of their own bodies and desire to take good care of them; realize increasingly that this is their own responsibility.
7. Know the value of and enjoy cleanliness and neatness; wear appropriate clothing.
8. Have good toilet habits; wash hands after play, after going to the bathroom, and before eating.

9. Know the relationship of lighting and seating to posture and good health, and act accordingly.
10. Remove heavy clothing such as snowsuits and boots by themselves and put them in their proper places at home, as well as at school.
11. Go to bed at the proper time according to their age; know the reason one needs lots of sleep; get up eagerly in the morning; use good health habits before retiring and coming to school every morning.
12. Know the value of having good posture and being physically clean and attractive and act accordingly; enjoy being clean and neat and be popular among their peers.
13. Know correct terms related to elimination, perspiration, and the names of some of the parts of their own body.
14. Make effective use of their own leisure; know how to relax and rest when tired.
15. Perform work duties and understand the need for being a worker in society.

In the upper elementary grades, the pupils will:

1. Understand the scientific reasons why they should have good health habits and keep themselves clean.
2. Keep good care of their own bodies, including teeth, nails, hair, and skin.
3. Be aware that many diseases can be spread through the unclean handling of food and eating utensils.
4. Use toilet and other facilities at home, school, and in public places correctly and be aware of good sanitary practices; avoid spitting on floors or sidewalks.
5. Adjust to any physical defect they may have and learn to compensate for it.
6. Be aware that good foot health contributes to good posture; practice good foot health habits.
7. Know the structure, function, and care of their own bodies.
8. Know the relationship which exists among all parts and systems of the body.
9. Be aware how blood circulates, food is digested, fresh air is used, skin and bones protect the body, and other such information which will help them desire to have and maintain good health.
10. Know how the human brain works; the role emotions play in health; what causes fatigue and how it can be eliminated.
11. Have good posture; know the relationship of body posture to body function.
12. Assume responsibility for their own sleep and rest and the room conditions under which they sleep.

A teacher demonstrates correct sitting posture. Note the use of the posture doll on the chalkboard. (Courtesy, Los Angeles Public Schools.)

13. Know the relationship of adequate sleep and rest to a happy state of mind, being safe, using good behavior, and having the ability to do good school work.
14. Know how to rest and relax frequently during the day.
15. Take part in vigorous physical education and leisure-time play activities.
16. Cooperate with parents and the teacher in planning and carrying out a healthful daily program of work, rest, and play.
17. Be aware of the relationship which exists between bacteria and viruses and health, and know how to protect themselves from such dangers.
18. Avoid handling or tasting unfamiliar medicines, cleaning agents, and insecticides.
19. Show individual evidence of growth, and adjust to body change.
20. Contribute to happy mealtimes at home and school; know the value to good digestion of eating in a pleasant environment.
21. Have periodic dental and physical examinations; know the value of such check-ups in the prevention and control of disease.
22. Increasingly become more self-disciplined and independent; know the value of setting a good example for younger children.
23. Engage in many wholesome boy-and-girl relationships.

SUGGESTED READINGS

Learning Aids

The following materials will assist pupils to learn valuable information which will help them protect and care for their own bodies:

FOR THE PRIMARY GRADES:

Pamphlets

Everybody Smile, American Dental Association.

Eyes That See—Ears That Hear, John Hancock Life Insurance Company.

Good Posture in the Little Child, Publication no. 219, Federal Security Agency.

How You Grow, Science Research Associates.

Little Red Sky, Bristol-Myers Company.

Wonder Stories of the Human Machine (nominal cost). *The Framework, The Running Gear, The Breather Pipes and Thermostatic Control, The Engine, The Electric System of the Human Machine, The Fuel System, The Exhaust,* American Medical Association.

A Trip with Baker Bill, Continental Baking Company.

Your Own Story (nominal cost) University of Minnesota Press.

Health Heroes; Measles; Common Childhood Diseases; Be on the Safe Side of Diphtheria; Respiratory Diseases, Metropolitan Life Insurance Company.

What You Should Know about Polio; A Message about Polio, The National Foundation.

Mad Dog, American Medical Association.

Posters and Charts

"A Modern Health Story" (chart of nine panels), Miller's National Federation.

"Guide for Good Grooming," Bristol-Myers Company.

"Posture Posters," American Seating Company, Samuel Higby Camp Institute.

"Teeth and How to Care for Them," Pepsodent Division, Lever Brothers.

"How to Catch a Cold," "How to Help Cure a Cold," International Cellucotton Products.

"I Promise Common Sense," Kimberly-Clark Corporation.

Radio Scripts

Keep Your Cold at Home; We Wash Our Hands before We Eat, Bureau of Research in Education by Radio, University of Texas.

Films and Filmstrips

Joan Catches a Cold (10 minutes); *I Never Catch a Cold* (10 minutes), Coronet Films.

Man against Microbes (10 minutes), Metropolitan Life Insurance Company.
This Is TB (10 minutes), National Tuberculosis Association.
Let's Look at Water (10 minutes), National Film Board of Canada.
Defending the City's Health (10 minutes), Encyclopaedia Britannica Films.
The Little Pink Bottle (color filmstrip), National Foundation for Infantile Paralysis.
Growing Girls (14 minutes); *Digestion of Food* (10 minutes); *Mechanics of Breathing* (11 minutes); *Posture* (15 minutes); Encyclopaedia Britannica Films, Inc.
Wonder Engine of the Body (11 minutes), American Medical Association.
Rest That Builds Good Health (15 minutes), Coronet Instructional Film.

Books and Stories for Children

Everybody Eats and Everybody Has a House, Mary Green Buerney, E. H. Hale Company.
In the Neighborhood, Paul Hanna and Genevieve Hoyt, Scott, Foresman.
Milkman Freddy, Elizabeth Helfman, Messner.
At Home, Cora Martin, Scribner.
Jimmy, The Groceryman, Jane Miller, Houghton Mifflin.
On Cherry Street, Odelle Ousley and David Russell, Ginn.
How We Grow, Patric O'Keefe and Jane Maxwell, Winston.
What's Inside of Me, Herbert Zinn, Morrow.
Story Pictures of Farm Foods, John Beaty, Beckley-Cardy Company.
Down Our Way, Guy Bond, Lyons and Carnahan.
Let's Go to a Dairy, J. M. Goodspead, Putnam.
I Want to Be a Baker; I Want to Be a Dairy Farmer; I Want to Be a Storekeeper, Carla Greene, Children's Press.

Health Readers

Health and Happy Days; Health in Work and Play; Health and Safety for You, Ginn, Health and Better Living Series.
Come On; Here We Go; Step Lively, Benefic Press, Health Action Series.
My First Health Book; My Second Health Book; Easy Steps to Health, Laidlaw, The Road to Health Series.

FOR THE UPPER ELEMENTARY GRADES:

Pamphlets

Sleep and Why Sleep; Posture from the Ground Up, Metropolitan Life Insurance Company.
Keeping Well, Row, Peterson.
Know Your Heart; Blood's Magic for All, Public Affairs Pamphlet no. 145.
Frank Visits the Dentist; Everybody Smile, American Dental Association.
Pain That Is Good for You; Healthy Eyes; Ears That Hear, John Hancock Insurance Company.

Publications about Your Health, including annotated materials on alcohol, tobacco, drugs and narcotics, oral and dental hygiene, feet, hair, skin, rest and relaxation, sex, and general health (posters and pamphlets), American Medical Association.

"Perspiration Is Helpful, but Exercise Is Vital" (poster), Bristol-Myers Company.

The Control of Communicable Diseases in Man, American Public Health Association.

Health Heroes Series; Health Through the Ages, Metropolitan Life Insurance Company.

What You Can Do about Colds and the Flu, Bristol-Myers Company.

The Doctor Is Your Friend, National Tuberculosis Association.

Posters

"We Had Polio Vaccine," The National Foundation.

"I Promise Common Sense," Kimberly-Clark Corporation.

Films and Filmstrips

Alcohol and the Human Body; Posture and Exercise (11 minutes), Indiana State Board of Health.

Keep Clean, Young American Films.

You're on Parade (11 minutes); *Tale of a Toothache* (12 minutes), Society for Visual Education.

Posture (15 minutes); *Care of the Hair and Nails* (20 minutes); *Care of the Skin* (20 minutes); *Eyes and Their Care* (15 minutes), Encyclopaedia Britannica Films.

Good Reading Habits (20 minutes); *Your Health at School* (12 minutes), Coronet Instructional Films.

The Nose, Throat and Ears, McGraw-Hill.

There Is No Substitute (20 minutes), American Red Cross.

Walter Reed and the Conquest of Yellow Fever; Health Heroes Series, Metropolitan Life Insurance Company.

Maintaining Community Health, Young American Films.

Sewage Disposal, McGraw-Hill.

Immunization (11 minutes); *Tuberculosis* (11 minutes); *The Body Fights Bacteria* (15 minutes), McGraw-Hill.

Defending the City's Health (12 minutes), Encyclopedia Britannica Films.

Story of Dr. Jenner (10 minutes), Teaching Film Custodians, Inc.

Books and Stories for Children

Around the Corner; The Little White House, Odelle Ousley and David Russell, Ginn.

The Yellow House Mystery, Gertrude Warner, Scott, Foresman.

People to Remember, Jack Brown and Georgia Moderow, Scott, Foresman.

Hidden Silver, Georgene Jenson, Scott, Foresman.

Susan, Be Smooth, Nell Giles, Charles Branford.

On Land and Water; In the Swim, Horace Buckley, American Book.
The Door in the Wall, Marguerite De Angeli, Doubleday.
75 Ways for Boys to Make Money, A. A. Parodis, Gruenberg Publishing.
Call It Courage, Armstrong Sperry, Macmillan.
The Blind Colt, Glen Rounds, Holiday House.
The New Boy, Mary Urmston, Doubleday.
The Blue Willow, Doris Gates, Viking.
Your Manners Are Showing, Betty Betz, Grosset and Dunlap.
Mozart, the Wonder Boy, Opal Wheeler, and Sybil Deucher, Dutton.
Clean and Strong, Clifford Brownell and Jesse F. Williams, American Book.
The True Book of Health, Olive Haynes, Children's Press.
Jill's Check Up, Ruth Jubelier, Melmont Publishers.

Health Readers
Among Friends; Broad Streets; Cross Roads, American Book Company Health Series.
Health Trails; Your Health and You; Keeping Healthy, Laidlaw Road to Health Series.
You; You and Others; You're Growing Up; In the Teens, Scott, Foresman Health and Personal Development Series.
Books IV, V, and *VI,* Macmillan Science, Health and Safety Series.
Bigger and Better; Getting Acquainted; Knowing Yourself, Winston Health Series.

Teaching Aids

FOR THE PRIMARY GRADES:

Experiments in Science, Nelson Beeler and Franklyn Branley, New York, Crowell, 1961.
What We Can Do about the Drug Menace, Deutsch, Albert, Public Affairs Pamphlet, New York, 1952.
Instructor's Guide to Facts about Narcotics, Victor Vogel and Virginia Vogel, Science Research Associates, Chicago, 1958.
Body Dynamics, Eleanor Metheny, New York, McGraw-Hill, 1952.
Teaching Posture and Body Mechanics, Ellen Kelly, New York, Barnes, 1949.
American Red Cross First Aid Textbook, New York, Blakiston, 1958.
How Children Grow and Develop, Willard Olson and John Lewellan, Chicago, Science Research Associates, 1953.
Healthier Living, 2nd ed., Justus Shifferes, New York, Wiley, 1960.

FOR THE UPPER ELEMENTARY GRADES:

Teacher Observation of School Children (pamphlet and sound filmstrip in color), Metropolitan Life Insurance Company.

Henderson, John, *A Parent's Guide to Children's Illnesses,* New York, Duell, Sloan and Pearce, 1957.

Karelitz, Samuel, *When Your Child Is Ill,* New York, Simon and Schuster, 1957.

Bennett, Margaret, "Health Committee Projects," *Health Education Journal,* vol. 20, no. 2 (November, 1956), 12–14.

Guarding the Health of Pupils, Los Angeles City Schools, no. 367, 1957.

Jordan, Edwin, *You and Your Health,* New York, Putnam, 1954.

Wheatley, George, and Grace Hallock, *Health Observation of School Children,* New York, McGraw-Hill, 1951.

Issues of the *Journal of American Association for Health, Physical Education and Recreation; The Health Education Journal; Today's Health.*

Wilson, Charles, "Where Are We Going in School Health?" *Health Education Journal,* vol. 22, no. 3 (January, 1959), 17–18.

AAHPER, *Fit to Teach,* Washington, D.C., 1954.

Chenoweth, Lawrence, and Theodore Selkirk, *School Health Problems,* 4th ed., New York, Appleton-Century-Crofts, 1953.

Harnett, Arthur, and John Shaw, *Effective School Health Education,* New York, Appleton-Century-Crofts, 1959.

Jenkins, Gladys, Helen Shacter, and W. W. Bauer, *These Are Your Children,* Chicago, Scott, Foresman, 1953.

National Committee on School Health Policies, *Suggested School Health Policies,* Washington, D.C., National Education Association, 1956.

What Teachers See; Absent from School Today (pamphlets), Metropolitan Life Insurance Company.

12 MENTAL HEALTH

The mentally healthy person is one who enjoys life, is on good terms with himself and other people in his environment, and can work and play well with others. Children who receive love and acceptance, feel secure, can control their emotions, show consistency in behavior patterns, can be intellectually stimulated, adjust to failure, accept success as something earned rather than automatically received, are reasonably independent for their age, and have a sense of values and a faith in a Creator are not only mentally healthy but possess a strong foundation upon which a happy, productive adulthood can later be built. All children need to receive as well as give love. Every child has the right to receive from his teachers at least three "A's" throughout his entire educational experiences in schools—affection, acceptance, and achievement. Some, unfortunately, are neither wanted nor accepted by their own parents. These children especially need to be in the class of a friendly teacher who cares about them and their well-being. Recognition and praise both are tremendous motivators among youth, but if used too much will lose effectiveness and even cause children to gain an inflated concept of themselves. All children need to feel that they belong to a closely knit class group, even though some few seemingly never have that feeling.[1] Since youngsters are brutally frank and often cruel to each other, they early discover weaker classmates who can easily be run over and become their victims. It is the teacher's duty to observe

[1] Harold Bernard, *Mental Hygiene for Classroom Teachers,* 2nd ed., New York, McGraw-Hill, 1961, p. 12.

class behavior closely for signs of such treatment and put a stop to such practices at once. Such minor negative actions, if ignored, can snowball quickly and soon get out of hand; they may even cause permanent damage to the poor victim. Every child also needs to be controlled and guided by a firm, strict, consistent, but friendly teacher who sets behavior boundaries and sees to it that they are not crossed; inconsistency and too much freedom cause children to become fearful and feel insecure, and can retard progress in school.

The teacher who is aware of the facts concerning mental health can do much to recognize symptoms and eradicate causes of emotional maladjustment. The following behavior *when occurring very frequently,* may be symptoms of an emotional or physical health problem. Before conferring with the principal, the teacher would find it helpful to have a record of specific incidents, settings, and steps taken to correct the problem.

BEHAVIOR	***WAYS TO HELP***
Provocative Behavior	
The pupil Tattles Talks back Is snobbish Is untidy Shows destructive leadership Complains frequently of being "picked on" Resists authority	The teacher should Be alert to clues of causes Remember . . . Don't take it personally. The pupil is talking back to trouble, not to the teacher. Events, little and big, piling up in the pupil's past make it difficult for him to grow with stability and order.
Insecure Behavior	
The pupil Clings to teacher Is timid Is seclusive Is overly fearful Cheats Does not play fair Is unwilling to participate in activities in which he may lose Boasts Has easily hurt feelings Shows extreme desire to please	The teacher should Notice the pupil and show this recognition by a smile or remark. Praise the pupil or his work. Choose the pupil for special tasks. Catch the pupil's eye. Work with the pupil. Call upon the pupil for specific work.

BEHAVIOR	WAYS TO HELP
Motor Disturbances	
The pupil Has tics Bites fingernails Sucks lips Grimaces Stutters Shows undue restlessness	The teacher should Watch for times of strain or stress and try to reduce them. "Stand by" the pupil until feels more sure of himself. Correct the pupil less and pr: him more. Guide the pupil into more quiet activities until he builds up reserves within himself.
Withdrawn Behavior	
The pupil Daydreams Is inattentive Uses illness as an escape Plays hooky Is apathetic Lacks interest Doodles Is nonparticipating	The teacher should Help the pupil feel at ease. Encourage the pupil. Give recognition to the pupil or to his work in the presence of other children. Interest the pupil in new avenues of expression. Teach the pupil a skill in which he may excel. Help the pupil feel better about himself, such as suggestions about improvements in his appearance and grooming. Recommend a health examination. Plan committee work and include the pupil in the group. Encourage friendship with another pupil.
Aggressive Behavior	
The pupil Is overactive Is mischievous Has temper outbursts Fights Steals Is rivalrous and quarrelsome	The teacher should Show the pupil safe and acceptable ways to exert his energy.

BEHAVIOR	WAYS TO HELP
Attention-getting Behavior	
The pupil Is competitive in school work Shows off Clowns Interrupts	The teacher should Give the pupil a "place in the sun." Discover the pupil's interests. Speak about the pupil's possessions. Help the pupil attain a specific skill. Compliment the pupil for any improvement.[2]

Every experience a child has affects him to some degree, and serves to make him inwardly stronger or weaker, confident in his ability to solve his own problems or a "scaredy cat" who withdraws from social contacts. His experiences, like blocks piled on top of each other, can make him upright, wobbly, or can finally push him over. Seldom, it is claimed by psychiatrists, can one incident have a lasting damaging effect upon the emotions of a child, unless it be a traumatic one, such as the death of his parents. Yet constant tension, pressure, fear, anger, and hatred have a strong lasting influence not only upon a child's present behavior but also upon his future well-being. Some experiences which may prevent normal growth and might contribute to mental illness are:

Lack of parental affection.
Overprotection of parents.
Failure of adults to accept normal childish behavior.
The frustration of being constantly faced with expectations, standards, or ideals which cannot be achieved.
Few opportunities in childhood to associate freely with other children.
Unrealistic viewpoint of many adults toward normal sexuality in life.
Frequent experiences of hostility from adults, particularly parents.
Insecurity, because of economic factors and attitudes of others to economic background.
Attitudes of others toward uniqueness in appearance, intelligence, dress, etc.
Poor nutritional status.
Glandular disorders.

[2] Reproduced by permission from *Health in the Elementary Schools—An Instructional Guide,* Los Angeles Public Schools, 1961, pp. 288–289.

Prolonged or frequent illness of the child or his parents.
Separations, including divorce.
Death of a parent.
Membership in a minority group.
Placement away from home.
Membership in a migratory family.[3]

Although a child's basic behavior patterns have been largely set by the time that he enters the first grade, this does not mean that his personality cannot change. Certainly, the school can and should guide, direct, and mold youth into developing socially accepted actions and values, as well as providing boys and girls with many opportunities to rid themselves of their feelings of guilt, hostility, fear, and aggression in legitimate ways. Although behavior cannot be changed overnight, the daily contributions made by a teacher who really cares about any particular pupil, can in the long run be of major importance and serve to steady an emotionally wobbly child.

Psychologists say that learning to live with other people is a major life task. Those who best fit into and contribute to worthwhile group endeavor are those who are independent, sure of themselves, dependable, and capable of producing something of value for the benefit of all. Such people are mature and have a clear, realistic view of themselves. They are the balanced ones who have their basic psychological needs satisfied as growing children to the degree that their physical-emotional growth becomes consistent and normal. All school experiences, whether they occur in the classroom, in the hall, or on the playground, can promote or retard growth toward maturity.[4] Actually, positive experiences which take place at school can do much more to develop emotional well-being and mental health than any instructional unit can do. Likewise, the relationship, rapport, and interplay between the teacher and the pupil is vastly more important than many lessons which stress the importance of freedom from worry or other similar topics. Every instructor should

[3] *Health Education,* North Carolina Public Schools, Raleigh, State Superintendent of Instruction, 1953, pp. 86–87.

[4] Marie Rasey, *Toward Maturity, How Children Think and Grow,* New York, Barnes & Noble, 1950, p. 18.

realize that her "actions, indeed, speak louder than words" and, in order to foster good mental health among her pupils, she must "practice what she preaches" about the worth of *every* human being. Likewise, each teacher must accept each child as he is, not as she would like him to be. She must also realize that (1) all behavior is *caused* and is *understandable* to any child-sensitized educator, and (2) that her attitudes and actions toward children and other adults must serve as a model.

Children do grow, in spite of our fearful concern that they never will get over what some oldsters refer to as "a child's fool's hill." Because of admired adults who love and believe in them, young people can be helped to become not just children who have grown older, taller, and heavier but wisely educated, happy, and mature people. Educators must remember that children are not miniature adults but children who must grow into adulthood.

Direct instruction in mental health should be coupled with numerous opportunities for children to explore, develop, and practice social skills. Freedom of movement, approval for expressing oneself, opportunities to be boisterous and let off steam, frequent changes of activities, and a wide variety of problem-solving experiences, can all help children in their search for and struggles toward maturity. The difference between childhood and adulthood is that between becoming and being. To grow up or become a mature person is for many children a long, arduous, and often painful task, in which the right teacher at the right place in their development who does the right things can play a major role.

SUGGESTED GRADED TOPICS

Suggested graded topics for instruction in mental hygiene are:

GRADE 1

1. How to be a friend.
2. Our classmates as friends.
3. Helping each other and our parents.
4. Talking things over with adults.
5. Our feelings.

6. Rules and why we should obey them.
7. Good health practices.

Grade 2

1. Our emotions and how to control them.
2. Working and playing together.
3. Learning to be a good sport.
4. How to accept sadness and disappointment.
5. How to have others like you.
6. How our bodies show how we feel.
7. What to do about angry feelings.
8. Good health practices.

Grade 3

1. Our actions and how to control them.
2. How to cooperate with others.
3. How our emotions can help or hinder us.
4. Developing good physical and emotional health habits.
5. Using time wisely for our own good.
6. How our body works and rests.
7. How to be a good leader and follower.

Grade 4

1. Self-discipline.
2. How to express and control our feelings.
3. The correct name and function of bodily organs.
4. The role of parents and children in the family.
5. Ways to acquire new friends.
6. How to be considerate of those who wear correctional aids such as glasses, braces, or crutches.
7. The effect of stress and tension on the body.
8. Mental health and how to achieve it.

Grade 5

1. Basic needs of all people.
2. Importance of self-acceptance.
3. Respecting the beliefs and rights of others.
4. How to solve personal problems.
5. Importance of attending church.
6. The nervous system.
7. How our brain and emotions function.
8. Why we act as we do.
9. Self-reliance and courage.

GRADE 6

1. How to be attractive and popular.
2. Importance of good health practices and grooming.
3. How to grow up successfully.
4. Solving individual and group behavior problems.
5. How to recognize the strengths, weaknesses, and capabilities of ourself and others.
6. Social habits, courtesy, and good manners.
7. Boy and girl relationships.
8. How we learn and think.
9. Emotions and their regulators.
10. Individual differences.
11. Behavior disorders.
12. The effect of alcohol, tranquilizers, tobacco, and narcotics upon the body and behavior.
13. Mental health habits.

CURRICULUM PLACEMENT

Regardless of where instruction in mental health occurs in the school curriculum, and whether it is a part of a core, broad-fields, or any other curricular plan, materials covered in this area and learning experiences conducted around them are of little value if the day-to-day relationships between teacher and child, pupil and classmates, are strained and full of tension and frustrating fear. The child is the total product of the home, school, and playground. Each boy and girl needs help in learning how to solve his own unique personal problems as well as assistance in developing steady qualities which will ensure his successful adoption to his own ever-changing self and environment.

Studies show that teachers who possess the best mental health themselves have the most stable pupils. Research also discloses that the actions, attitudes, and behavior of the teacher have a marked effect on the pupils' sense of security, freedom from tension, courtesy, resourcefulness, and methods used for obtaining social recognition.[5] It is imperative, then, that the teacher set the example in her relationship with others and that her own conduct be worthy of

[5] Delbert Oberteuffer, *School Health Education,* New York, Harper, 1960, p. 363.

emulation. Since the classroom is where the child spends most of his time when away from home, this must be a place wherein he is accepted and assisted as an individual and as a group member.

There are many ways in which mental health education can be integrated and correlated with other subjects in the school curriculum. These include the following:

Social science is a field of study especially well suited for integrating mental health with history, civics, geography, and in other included areas. Actually, almost every daily classroom experience provides pupils with opportunities for personality interaction, whether these be when pupils are discussing problems, engaged in group planning, or working on committees. Every teacher with insight and concern for the rights and well-being of each individual child, will utilize every moment which arises for promoting good mental health as the pupils work and play together.

The following topics can be used for correlating and integrating mental health with social science:

1. Living in an urban versus a rural community.
2. Housing problems.
3. Cause and prevention of juvenile delinquency and crime.
4. Unemployment and its effect upon morale.
5. The reactions of people in wartime and peacetime.
6. The prevention and treatment of mental illness.
7. The effect of economic conditions upon health.
8. The functions and programs of voluntary health agencies.
9. Relation of labor laws to health.
10. The recreational, educational, and work patterns of early Americans or other civilizations in contrast to those of today.
11. Changing patterns of the role of men, women, and children in society.
12. Proper use of recreational facilities.
13. Citizenship and civic responsibilities.
14. The influence of the space age upon health.
15. The conservation of human resources.
16. Local and state resources for mental health.
17. Understanding the problems of the aged.
18. Minority groups and their problems.
19. Youth in other lands.

The communicative arts of reading, writing, and speaking should provide children with numerous opportunities to learn more about themselves and other people, places, and things. Each classroom activity, whether it be reading a book about a famous health hero, writing a short paper on such a topic as "My Happiest Experience," or taking part on a panel and speaking on the subject, "Health Careers and Health Workers in Our Community," should have the purpose of helping each pupil develop as an emotionally healthy individual and group member. Likewise, each activity selected by the pupil or assigned to him by the teacher, who wishes to correlate instruction in mental health with that in the communicative arts, should aid in the emotional development of that child from:

Dependence toward independence.
Being a receiver toward becoming a giver.
Self-centeredness toward socialization.
Ignorance and fantasy toward recognition and acceptance of reality.
Aggressive hostile actions toward self-satisfying activities.
Feelings of inadequacy, fear, and timidity toward realistic self-confidence.

The following suggested activities can help youngsters grow closer to maturity:

1. Provide children with a wide variety of opportunities to share experiences and stories in daily "show-and-tell" sessions. Encourage all to speak freely and bring things to share with others. Talk less and listen more as a teacher, remembering that actions can speak louder than words and people "tell on themselves" by what they do, just as much as by what they say.

2. Encourage individuality and creativity, as well as needed group conformity for the benefit of all by providing a variety of individual, small group, as well as class projects.

3. Use teacher-pupil planning as much as possible in all learning activities.

4. Give children opportunities to show their work to teachers, parents, and other schoolmates through displays, demonstrations, shows, or other means. Be sure that every child takes part, not only the best ones.

5. Provide many opportunities for children to be leaders and helpers. Help them learn to recognize the characteristics and techniques of democratic leadership; teach them how to elect their own leaders wisely.

6. Use praise for work done well. Talk individually with those who seemingly are kinder and more sensitive than others, letting them know how valuable such qualities are and how glad you are that each has these qualities. Such praise helps children by bolstering their desire to continue being the type of person a respected teacher admires.

7. Have a "high degree of expectancy" in each child and help him select tasks which will bring success, challenge, and individual growth. Help children realize that mistakes are a vital part of learning.

8. Discuss the necessity of having rules or laws. Help the class select a class motto, such as "One for all, and all for one," etc. Keep this in plain view of the group. Refer to it often, so that the motto becomes part of a foundation on which other life values can be built. Draw out the group through discussion as to individual and class progress toward reaching this ideal.

Other ways in which mental hygiene can be integrated and correlated with materials covered in the communicative arts are:

1. Let children read widely stories of their own choosing which stress courage as found in the actions of heroes, heroines, or animals. Have each tell his favorite story to the class and make a tape recording of this class experience.

2. Write letters or visit ill classmates or friendless, hospitalized adults.

3. Provide numerous opportunities for small group projects; rotate group membership frequently and assist each pupil to widen his circle of friends.

4. Give an oral book report on any courageous person you have read about.

5. Give an oral or written book report on any hero or heroine story read or told by a family member. Give reasons why the main character is to be admired.

6. Give a situation test to evaluate each pupil's ability to face reality by telling the class a story about a boy or girl who worked hard and wanted to be chosen for the main part in a school play, but who was not. Have them write down the suggestions they would give to this person.

7. Write a poem about why we should be considerate of those who are in wheelchairs, wear a brace, walk with a crutch, etc.

8. Draw up a class-devised good grooming check list. Have each child write a short paragraph periodically about his progress made in developing good grooming habits.

9. Have the class make a typical individual day schedule. Counsel with each pupil, discussing the need to be alone sometimes, time spent in self-care, etc.

10. Prepare questions for a question box on any aspect of health, going on to junior high school, or any life experience the children have or might have.

11. Choose any trait of character any adult has. Write a story or play about it. Have the class draw their conclusions and list desirable character traits to have.

12. Write a short story about the meaning of the phrase "a sense of values."

13. Have the pupils write a paper on how they would spend a thousand dollars won in a contest. Arrange a sample of budget items, saying that so much should go for gifts, a trip, college, or other future plans, etc. Read this report carefully in order to detect if the class is developing a good sense of values.

Mathematics can also be closely integrated and correlated with mental health. Suggested activities for doing so are:

1. Making graphs to show the rising cost and incident of crime and delinquency.
2. Determining the cost of mental illness to the family, community, state, and nation.
3. Showing by graphs the reported income from the sale of alcohol, narcotics, and tranquilizers in contrast to that spent on public education.
4. Discovering the amount of money spent in America on passive types of recreation such as movie-going, watching television, or attending football games.
5. Making pie graphs to show how much of the community's budget is spent on health and medical care; how much on safety protection for its citizens.
6. Determining the amount of money spent yearly by the nation on cosmetics or medication.
7. Comparing advertising costs on sleeping pills or other such articles to net profits and benefits to the individual.

Physical education, like music and art activities, can also be well correlated and integrated with mental health by providing pupils with opportunities to (1) learn recreative skills with high carry-over value into adult life, (2) belong to a group and obtain status, and (3) participate in free, joyous activities which help them express their inner feelings. The greatest values found in physical education are in developing physical fitness, increasing movement skills, socializing the pupil, creating improved mental and physical health, and increasing knowledge of and appreciation for one's own body, its care, protection, and development. Like the two sides of a coin, a sound mind and a sound body are inseparable, and the health of one, or lack of it, affects the health of the other. Total fitness, physical, mental, and emotional, cannot be stored away for future use, like money or food, but must be maintained when once acquired, and replaced when used.

One of the greatest values of sports and games is in socializing the individual, who as a group member engaged in team effort contributes and cooperates by substituting the finer "we" drives for selfish "I" drives. Through winning and losing one learns the give and take of life, the necessity of obeying and behaving according to rules, and being a good sport. It is when playing on a team that many of the techniques for successful group life, both for now and the future, are best learned. It is here that good followers and leaders can be made. Likewise, it is then when our American way of life, our cultural values of "all for one and one for all," "where there is unity there is strength," or "unite or perish," gain fuller understanding.

Games and modified sports for children also give them chances to work out feelings of hostility and aggression in legitimate ways, such as hitting a ball with a bat, or "destroying" an opponent by tagging him out. Such activities as learning to take turns and playing games without a referee help a child gain friends, self-respect, and develop habits of independence and truthfulness. Just as a good teacher, like a wise parent, becomes progressively unnecessary, children will not automatically become self-controlled or mature in their behavior unless they have chances to experiment and learn how to become so.

How a child learns to spend his leisure time is vastly important to himself as well as to his civilization, for leisure time offers rich opportunities which, when rightly used, can benefit us all. Leisure can be spent in positive or negative ways. The former are made up of those activities which benefit each person and society, the latter are detrimental to the individual and the group. Playing on a kickball team can be as highly beneficial as robbing a store is detrimental. Both activities contain the same basic elements of trying to get away without getting caught. Since children seek adventure, they will find it. Because of teachers, their parents, and some few other adults, what they seek and discover can be of the highest value according to society's preconceived social standards of what is "good" or "bad."

Science with its many facts can assist children in learning much about the many mysteries and wonders of their own bodies, as well as help them gain insight into their own behavior and that of others. The pupils should learn about the basic life processes of circulation, respiration, digestion, excretion, metabolism, movement control, and human reproduction, so that they can increasingly make more intelligent choices regarding their own health. Likewise, they should become aware of the psychosocial basic needs of all people to belong, be loved, have self-respect, and obtain recognition.

The older pupils will be ready for more scientific information and will welcome the challenge of learning more advanced materials. In a sixth grade science and health class in Dallas last year a teacher motivated her pupils to want to find out more about their own minds, and how feelings and emotions influence, help, or hinder human behavior. The class listed the things they wanted to learn about their "thinking selves." They sought the answers to such questions as:

1. How big is the human brain?
2. How do nerve impulses make the brain react so fast?
3. What causes us to remember some things and forget others so quickly?
4. What happens to the brain when we go to sleep?
5. What causes us to have dreams and nightmares?
6. Why don't we dream in color more often?
7. How can a person be hypnotized?
8. What is brainwashing?
9. Do animals think?
10. What are mental images?
11. Where is our conscious mind?
12. What are daydreams?
13. Why do some people learn more quickly than others?
14. What causes "mental" illness?
15. What is shock treatment and how does it make a person react?
16. What can we do to have good self-control; how does our brain help us have it?

Although the teacher herself did not know all the answers to these questions, she and the class working and sharing together had an unforgettable learning adventure. The group leader, who had already decided to become a physician and follow his father's chosen profession, brought medical books into the classroom. Even though these materials were far beyond the comprehension of most of the children, certain individuals did glean some needed information from them. The class divided up into committees, with each working on certain of their group questions, other voluntarily accepted library assignments and consulted reference materials, and still others made visual aids in the form of a papier-mâché brain, posters, and charts. The teacher's fiancé, who was in his third year at medical school, was invited to speak to the class and share needed information with them that they were unable to find. All in all, this exciting learning adventure was, for many, one of the most challenging educational experiences they had had in school that year. From it they learned far more than mere facts about the human mind, for they also learned to work cooperatively and that each individual in the class could make his own unique contribution to their group endeavor. These children were fortunate to have a teacher with enough insight to draw from them things they wanted to know about, and with enough skill to organize their efforts according to the learning goals she helped them bring clearly into focus.

USE OF TEACHING METHODS

Among the many kinds of teaching methods which can be used successfully in mental health education are:

Class discussions. Elementary pupils often express themselves more frankly and honestly than older students, thus making it easier for their teachers to gain insight into their behavior, feelings, and emotional needs. Care must be taken not to "pry" into the personal lives of each family member, for these younger pupils often unknowingly reveal family secrets without realizing that they have done so.

Suggested topics for class discussions might well include the following:

1. Homesickness.
2. Fear of competitive games.
3. Wanting to play and being alone.
4. Dislike of the opposite sex.
5. Stealing, cheating, and lying.
6. Temper flare-ups.
7. Poor sportsmanship.
8. Cruelty to others and to animals.
9. Inability to make decisions.

10. Dependence upon others for praise and attention.
11. Daydreaming and absent-mindedness.
12. Fear.
13. Feelings of inferiority and inhibition.[6]

Problem solving. This teaching method is especially well adapted to the field of mental health. Although primary children have seemingly small individual and group problems, these can become larger learning and developmental stumbling blocks if ignored or neglected. Numerous moments for instruction arise in every class situation, whether it be one of masturbation or of stealing. As children learn to share limited materials, organize a club, or work together making a survey, they are learning to solve their own basic problems of how to get along well with others, and the give and take of life.

Upper elementary pupils will profit from studying larger group problems and areas such as learning why human beings become mentally ill, are prejudiced, or fail in life. Often current events, such as reading about the Freedom Riders or a summit meeting, can help motivate student interest in determining which of these many larger problems of life they should learn more about. Regardless of what problem areas are selected, however, the teacher should help each pupil, through these learning experiences, to gain more insight and a better understanding of himself.

Frequently, problems arise in the extracurricular school program which can be brought into the classroom for study, such as boys clustering together like scared rabbits at a school party and refusing to dance with girls. Even those events which occur outside of school but which cause children to be unhappy at school and frustrated in their learning attempts can become problems for a class to study and solve. The following incident was reported by an elementary education major preparing to become a teacher. When asked to record her most memorable learning experience in grade school, she wrote:

When I was in the fifth grade, I unknowingly almost caused a riot in our school. I shared with a sixth grader a "secret" told to me by one of my classmates. A distorted version of it spread throughout the entire school.

[6] Oberteuffer, *op. cit.*, p. 165.

My friends deserted me. The kids took sides, and called certain people, including me, "a dirty liar." The boys and girls took sides, and even several serious fights occurred. Finally, the principal called us all down to the auditorium. He talked to us for a long time, trying to find out what was behind all of this trouble. He made me understand that I was wrong to have told a secret, and that the class had made a serious mistake by magnifying and distorting it. He then asked us to go back to our classroom and work out an answer to our big problem of how to get along and work together better and in harmony as a class. We all were frightened but determined not to fight among ourselves any more. Our teacher helped us work out the answer to our problem, but it took a long time. I was miserable all during that year at school; my grades were terrible, and the poorest I have ever made in school before or since then![7]

Guidance and counseling. Every teacher has a responsibility not only to help children become healthy, happy, and successful learners, but also to provide them with wholesome and meaningful educational experiences. Emphasis should be placed upon helping children develop proper attitudes, values, conduct, and appreciation. The teacher should not only set the example children will want to copy, but she should help them develop a respect for the rights and opinions of others, develop skills in learning to control their own behavior, become good leaders and followers, and learn to use their leisure time constructively. Children do not change in behavior overnight, and no teacher, regardless of her skill and understanding, can make any pupil over in a few months, for each has been developing behavior patterns for several years which cannot easily be changed or eradicated. Since misbehavior is usually a question of degree, and is not serious unless it interferes with a child's social, emotional, and physical growth, the role of the teacher working within the area of guidance and counseling should be to help the child determine reasons for his misbehavior. Regardless of whether the problem may be one of showing off, bullying, stealing, disobedience, or using dirty words, the following principles should help those dealing with misbehavior:

1. All behavior is caused; atypical actions occur when basic human needs or drives clash.

[7] Reported in the class, "Teaching Health and Physical Education in Elementary Schools," Southern Methodist University, June, 1961.

2. Each human being is unique; therefore a method that works with one child may not necessarily be successful with another.
3. When children are engaged in activities they have selected to do and when they have a feeling of taking part in that activity, they are less likely to develop problems.
4. Behavior changes can only occur slowly; each child must be patiently aided to learn to help himself and to solve his own problems.

When teaching children in learning, working, and playing, the best results will be obtained if the following suggestions are kept in mind:

1. Always be fair, considerate, and show a genuine liking for all children.
2. Avoid showing favoritism.
3. Be sympathetic and understanding of children's problems, even though the difficulty may seem absurd, unimportant, and small from the adult viewpoint.
4. Avoid being shocked at a child's actions; seek the reason behind them.
5. Give each child a genuine feeling of belonging, security, and achievement.
6. Give each child increased opportunities to assume responsibilities of real worth.
7. Remember that every human being reacts favorably to praise.
8. Become more sensitized to children—their hopes, fears, and ambitions.

Ullman has identified children with these serious problems which need the attention of a psychologist, personal counselor, physician, or all three.

1. Frequent absences, tardiness, and inattention in school.
2. Nervousness, irritability.
3. Lying, cheating, evasiveness, shiftiness.
4. Fearsome, withdrawing, overly shy behavior, no confidence.
5. Bullying, selfishness, overaggressiveness, quarreling.
6. Dawdling, time wasting, lack of purpose.
7. Unacceptable sexual conduct, "mashing," overinterest in the opposite sex.
8. Noncooperation and negativeness.[8]

Although most teachers are not prepared to deal with such problems or such children, help should be found for these individuals. Many large school systems now have the services of a school

[8] Charles Ullman, "Identification of Maladjusted School Children," *Public Health Monograph* no. 7, Public Health Services Publication no. 211, Washington, D.C., Government Printing Office, 1952, p. 72.

psychologist or psychiatrist, and most large cities have child guidance clinics. The teachers of pupils who are referred to such specialists should work closely with them. Every attempt should be made to keep the child in school, even though this may require the adjustment of his schedule, closer supervision, and additional, more personalized, and patient understanding. Many of the problem children who are "kicked out of school" are harmed greatly by this action, for many of them are already burdened by their inability to belong and be accepted by the group, and this final act of rejection only helps them to become more maladjusted, and often even more delinquent in their actions. The "kicked out" youngster too often, then, becomes "kicked into" more serious trouble.

Demonstrations. The use of this teaching method can assist children to see, hear, and take part in many kinds of splendid educational experiences in the area of mental health. Suggested activities suitable for demonstration purposes are:

1. Demonstrate ways in which feelings of anger, hostility, etc., can quickly get out of hand; how to keep emotions well under control.
2. Demonstrate a wide variety of movements for relaxation, such as how to be as limp as a rag doll, float with your eyes closed while stretched out on the floor, stand on your toes and pick fireflies from the ceiling, etc.
3. Demonstrate the techniques of good grooming.
4. Demonstrate role playing in couples: ordering a meal in a restaurant; walking together to school; dancing together at a party; going to a movie.
5. Demonstrate childish and mature behavior in the classroom and in the playground. Discuss how pupils can act in mature ways.
6. Demonstrate by using a cutaway model how each part of the human brain functions.

Dramatic Activities. Role playing, puppet shows, one-act plays, charades, story telling, and shadow plays can be used in the following ways to help pupils learn much in the area of mental health:

1. Make a class sociogram, keep a running leadership list, and see that each child becomes a leader or helper periodically. Stress the importance of dependability and being a good follower. Act out the difference between being a good and "bossy" leader.

A classroom demonstration on cleanliness. (Courtesy, Los Angeles Public Schools.)

2. Give a talent show, using all pupils, to some outside group. Evaluate the results with the class, using the approach of "how could we have done this better."
3. Have each pupil give in charade form or verbally describe ways in which he is learning how to make wiser decisions and choices.
4. Dramatize a happy family sharing several experiences in and away from their home.
5. Act out your most embarrassing moment, and describe how you got out of it.
6. Give puppet shows showing the difference between good humor or clean fun and harmful practical jokes.
7. Divide into subgroups and create a clown act or animated cartoon. Discuss the value of laughter and fun in life.
8. Use role playing of problems commonly found in everyday human relationships at home or school.
9. Have subgroups give puppet shows, playlets, or act out in pantomime how fear can be both a means of protection and bring damage to a person; the harm that prejudice can do, etc.

Children learn much from playing at being a doctor, nurse, or patient. (Courtesy, Los Angeles Public Schools.)

10. Have children tell about their favorite adult neighborhood friends, and describe why they chose to tell about these adults. Make a list and discuss the qualities these respected adults possess.

Field trips. There are many places the children can go on field trips within their community to learn from first-hand experiences more about mental health. Visits taken to such places as a kindergarten, day-care center, sheltered workshop for the handicapped and disabled, home for the aged, health museum, zoo, public library, traffic court, and baby clinic will broaden their understanding of other people, places, and problems in their own community. The maturity level, interest, and intellectual background of the class should be the determining factor in selecting which of these places can be profitably visited.

THE USE OF INSTRUCTIONAL MATERIALS

Throughout the school year, the teacher should observe the changes in behavior made by each pupil in his attitude toward himself, other pupils and adults, life in general, and his school work in particular. There are many ways in which the teacher can assist the children to be even-keeled, including listening carefully to what they say and watching closely what they do. It is wise occasionally to give pupils an assigned task, then leave the room briefly. If nothing has been accomplished, or the group has become rowdy during her absence, this is a warning sign that the relationship between the teacher and the class is not what it should be, nor is that among the children themselves.

There are many instructional materials which can be used to help teach the pupils needed material in the area of mental health. These include:

The chalkboard. The pupils will learn new words for their ever-growing vocabulary more quickly when they see them written on the board, hear each pronounced and used correctly by the teacher, and then copy, pronounce, and use each correctly at frequent intervals throughout the class and week. Other suggested ways in which a chalkboard and bulletin board can be used for instructional purposes are:

1. Several times each semester, have the pupils write a paper and read it to the group on any new hobby developed. Keep a running chalkboard list or record in each child's folder of these new interests. Check this periodically for progress.
2. Have each child make a list of his New Year's resolutions or a list of bad habits he wishes to change. Post each list on the bulletin board. Check progress in this direction periodically.
3. Discuss ways of listening to and accepting criticism; have one pupil summarize the suggestions agreed upon by the class, and post these on the bulletin board.
4. Have a committee plan, make, and display a bulletin board expressing any one idea stressed throughout this unit such as "Making Friends," or "Happy People Are Healthy People."
5. List on the chalkboard the ways pupils can protect themselves when playing active sports and games. Discuss permanent brain injuries, how they affect the body, and how they can be avoided.

6. Work in committees and draw up a list of reasons why laws should be obeyed. Have a person from each group write its list on the board. Have the class select the best one.
7. Make a list of those adults who might help children solve their problems. Write this on the board.

Cartoons and Comics. Every daily newspaper and many periodicals contain cartoons and comic strips which can be used to help children see humor in life, as well as problems faced by other people and how they solve them. The comic "Peanuts" is especially suitable for such classroom use. Many children who are afraid may not, like the character Linus in this comic strip, have to carry a blanket around with them to help bolster their courage, yet the teacher can use pictures of this little boy with his protective blanket clutched to his breast to stimulate a class discussion on fears. Another daily comic strip which could be used successfully is "Nancy," a most ingenious little girl who gets into and out of many of the problem situations faced by most children. For the older pupils, "Little Orphan Annie," "Mutt and Jeff," "Blondie," "Archie," and "Rex Morgan, M.D." are recommended. Some pupils will profit from and be interested in drawing their own cartoons, or making their own animated mental health films which they can show through improvised cardboard movie projectors.

Books and Supplementary Reading Materials. Children delight in being read to by their teacher. Those working on the primary level are well aware that most youngsters of this age are eager to come to school. Each soon finds out, however, that many other children are there competing with him for the teacher's attention and that many of them can do many things better than he can. These pupils need many opporunities to talk over the feelings they have, whether of fear, anger, shyness, or happiness. Knowing that everyone has these reactions, and that they are normal and can be handled, will often help these children gain increased self-understanding and control. Often a simple story read aloud by the teacher and discussed by the class can help each pupil gain needed insight into himself, increase his confidence in his own abilities and attitudes, learn how to face up to and solve his own problems, and give him courage to face challenging new situations, and an understanding of the correct place of emotion in life. Suggested materials to be used for this purpose

Observing children's drawings carefully is one way to measure what they have learned about health in school. (Courtesy, AAHPER.)

are Joan Anglund's charming little books, *Look Out the Window* and *A Friend Is Someone Who Likes You* (Harcourt, Brace), or *The Little Frightened Tiger* by Golden MacDonald and Leonard Weisgard (Doubleday).

Upper elementary pupils can profit greatly from reading books of their own choosing, as guided by the teacher and librarian. Boys will find the splendid book *Fear Strikes Out* by Jim Piersall (Little, Brown) especially interesting. Most girls will prefer books such as *The Diary of Anne Frank* (Houghton Mifflin), *Desirée* by Annemarie Selenko (Morrow) or *The Yearling* by Marjorie K. Rawlings (Scribner). Reports given by each pupil on the book of his own choice will provide each with the opportunity to share with classmates and to express himself.

The Radio and Television. Increasingly, large school systems are sponsoring their own television and radio educational programs. Teachers will profit from checking the weekly broadcast schedules found in most Sunday papers and requiring pupils to see certain well-selected programs. Class discussions should be planned so that the full educational values inherent in the programs are brought into proper focus. Serialized daily radio programs can also be used as a means of helping children learn how other people go about solving their problems. Another suggested activity is to have the class pick out the happiest-looking faces they see on television programs, and tell what they think makes people happy.

The Phonograph. Most schools have a record player for classroom use. Children can gain a lifelong appreciation for good music from records played for them and explained to them by their teacher. They can be taught to pick out noisy, quiet, and happy sounds for a discussion of moods of people. Almost any type of light classical music can be used for this purpose, ranging all the way from Grofé's *Grand Canyon Suite* to Beethoven's *Pastoral Symphony*. Musical comedy tunes such as those from *Oklahoma!* or *My Fair Lady* can be played frequently to brighten a gloomy day at school or stimulate lagging interest in classroom work.

Since tension is one of the problems most Americans face, it is also recommended that children learn to relax through music, whether this be by doing mild exercises to records such as "Sentimental Journey" or "Sunrise Serenade," or pretending they are floating logs moving slowly down a lazy stream as they listen to a soothing melody. Children should learn why and how tensions build up as well as how pressures can be reduced by mild exercise, relaxing activities, and practicing good health habits.

Creative dance can be done in a classroom, gymnasium, or on the playground and children can be given opportunities through this activity to express in body movements such feelings and emotions as joy, fear, hatred, anger, love, shyness, or bolstered courage. A child can lose his self-consciousness quickly in interpreting such things as a clock, bicycle, pony, or elephant. They can also express inner feelings by dancing out such colors as red, yellow, black, or green.[9] Imagination is innate in all children. It flowers richly in

[9] Maryhelen Vannier, and Mildred Foster, *Teaching Physical Education in Elementary Schools,* 3rd ed., Philadelphia, Saunders, 1963, p. 161.

some but must be extracted with consummate skill from others. Whenever an exercise involves abstract feeling or a story or a theme, a picture should be painted by the teacher to fire the imagination.

DESIRABLE OUTCOMES

As a result of materials learned in mental hygiene, the following outcomes should accrue in terms of knowledge, attitudes, and practices:

In the primary grades, the pupils will:

1. Be able to get along well with others in their class, teachers, members of their family, and other adults.
2. Understand and accept themselves.
3. Recognize that emotions of fear, anger, hate, jealousy, and love are universal, and be able to control these emotions well according to their present stage of development.
4. Feel accepted by a group and contribute to group welfare and projects.
5. Know their own weaknesses and abilities.
6. Understand that every group has rules which must be obeyed, and that such rules are for the happiness, protection, and well-being of all.
7. Welcome and enjoy new experiences.
8. Accept disappointment and adjust to things which do not always go according to previously set plans.
9. Be able to cooperate with other children and adults, realizing that their contribution will help make any group endeavor become successful.
10. Make friends easily.
11. Increasingly be able to evaluate their own actions and can realistically analyze their contribution to group welfare or a group project.
12. Increasingly assume greater responsibility for their own actions, take the consequences for failure, and act according to rules.
13. Participate skillfully in solving individual and group problems.
14. Gain satisfaction from being alone sometimes and not always needing to be "doing something" or be entertained.
15. Accept those who have physical, social, or economic handicaps and be kind to more unfortunate people of all ages.
16. Receive pleasure from "doing the right thing" and taking turns.
17. Have a best friend and several close friends.
18. Take care of their own possessions and respect the rights and property of others.

19. Gain satisfaction from possessing acceptable work habits, and see an assumed task through to the end.
20. Be aware that to be a good leader one must use democratic methods, and practice this concept; good followers as well as leaders use increased understanding of the democratic method.
21. Know the difference between humor and harmful practical jokes which may hurt or embarrass others.
22. Gain real satisfaction from creative experiences, caring for a pet, and hobbies.
23. Play with others cooperatively and enjoy vigorous activities, be courageous, and sure of themselves.

In the upper elementary grades, the pupils will:

1. Possess deeper self-understanding and esteem for the rights of others.
2. Know how to express feelings of anger, hostility, aggression, love, joy, and fear in legitimate ways and can control these feelings.
3. Recognize their bodies are changing and ask frank, reasonable questions and know where to find information regarding their changing selves.
4. Understand their need for other people and yet know the value of independence.
5. Belong to a closely knit group of friends.
6. Recognize that home, church, and community approval for actions is a necessity.
7. Develop a higher sense of values; desire to have a good character.
8. Recognize and accept individual differences.
9. Develop greater appreciation for their families, home environment, and teachers.
10. Make increasingly wiser decisions and better choices.
11. Find that accepting and carrying out responsibility brings more satisfaction than negative behavior.
12. Be self-confident, loyal, trustworthy, dependable, honest, and sensitive to others.
13. Realize the importance of personal appearance, being popular, and respected among peers.
14. Participate, cooperate, and share in group activities.
15. Know practical ways to face failure.
16. Disagree with others without becoming angry or arousing anger.
17. Compete fairly and successfully against others; not always have to win in order to gain satisfaction from competition or cooperation.
18. Be a working member of any church or youth group.
19. Have a variety of skills for relaxation through creative experiences, clubs, and hobbies.

20. Appreciate the qualities of good leadership and select their own leaders wisely.
21. Accept the use of glasses, braces, or other correctional aids.
22. Have effective, independent study and work habits.
23. Become increasingly more skilled in solving their individual problems.
24. Recognize the value of strong emotional drive and possess favorable attitudes toward themselves, their school, and home.
25. Realize the importance of good manners and use them.
26. Use their individual talents for school and community services.
27. Increasingly practice self-discipline and feel responsible for their behavior when alone or away from adults.
28. Be well adjusted, happy, and eager for approaching junior high school experiences.
29. Have a high regard for the opposite sex and have both boy and girl friends.
30. Be courageous, independent, possess strong, skillful bodies, and take part in both vigorous physical activities and quiet recreational games.

SUGGESTED READINGS

Learning Aids

The following materials are recommended for pupil use in the area of mental health and self-understanding:

IN THE PRIMARY GRADES:

Pamphlets and Posters

Six to Twelve, John Hancock Mutual Life Insurance Company.

How Old Are You?; About Us and Our Friends, Metropolitan Life Insurance Company.

Change of Pace, Equitable Life Assurance Society.

Betty Jean Is Ready for School; Betty Jean Grows Up, State Board of Health, Raleigh, N.C.

Shyness; Stuttering, Department of National Health and Welfare, New York, The Mental Health Materials Center.

Films and Filmstrips

Don't Be Afraid (12 minutes); *Don't Get Angry* (12 minutes); *Developing Responsibility* (10 minutes); Encyclopaedia Britannica Films.

Am I Trustworthy (11 minutes); *Shy Guy* (13 minutes); *Fun That Builds Good Health* (11 minutes); *How Friendly Are You?* (15 minutes), Coronet Instructional Films.

When All the People Play (27 minutes); *Family Circles* (31 minutes); National Film Board of Canada.

Books and Stories for Children

David's Bad Day, Ellen McKean, Vanguard.

Here's a Penny, Carolyn Haywood, Harcourt, Brace.

Play Fair, Munro Leaf, Lippincott.

Jerry at School, Kathryn Jackson, Simon and Schuster.

Growing Up Big and Strong, Andress, Goldberger, Dolchand, and Hallock; Ginn.

A Friend Is Someone Who Likes You, Joan Anglund, Harcourt, Brace.

The Diary of Anne Frank, Anne Frank, Houghton Mifflin.

Call Me Charley, Jesse Jackson, Harper.

Follow the Leader, Bernice Bryant, Houghton Mifflin.

Readers

Bobbs-Merrill Health for Young America Series, *Health at School; Health Day by Day; Health and Fun.*

Macmillan, Science, Health and Safety Series, *Books I, II,* and *III.*

Scott, Foresman Health and Personal Development Series, *Happy Days with Our Friends; Good Times with Our Friends; Three Friends.*

Scott, Foresman Basic Health and Safety Program, *Just like Me; Being Six; From Eight to Nine.*

Wilcox Health Action Series, *Come On; Here We Go; Step Lively.*

IN THE UPPER ELEMENTARY GRADES:

Pamphlets

The Story of Life—Sex Education for the Ten Year Old, American Medical Association.

Very Personally Yours; Teaching Guide—Mental Hygiene, Kimberly-Clark Corp.

Mental Health Is a Family Affair; Teamwork for Emotional Maturity, National Association for Mental Health.

From Boy to Man, Social Hygiene Association.

How to Live with Parents, Science Research Associates, Inc.

Leisure Time, Equitable Life Assurance Society.

Mind, The John Hancock Insurance Company.

Films

Children Learning from Experience (30 minutes); *Children Growing Up with Others* (30 minutes), National Film Board of Canada.

Act Your Age (13 minutes); *Control Your Emotions* (13 minutes); *How We Cooperate* (10 minutes); *Let's Play Fair* (10 minutes); Coronet Films.

Don't Be Afraid (12 minutes); *Don't Get Angry* (10 minutes), Encyclopaedia Britannica Films, Inc.

Over-dependency (32 minutes), McGraw-Hill.

The Baby Sitter (15 minutes), Young American Films.

Books and Stories for Children

The Education of Pretty Boy, Harold Babcock, Holt.

Granite Harbor, Donald Bud, Macmillan.

Judy's Journey, Lois Lenski, Lippincott.

North Fork, Doris Hates, Viking.

The Wonderful Year, Nancy Barnes, Messner.

What Is She Like?, Mary Brockman, Scribner.

Young Collector's Handbook, A. H. Verill, McBride.

Your Own Book of Campcraft, Catherine Hammett, Pocket Books.

Readers

American Book Company Health Series—*Among Friends; Keeping Well; Healthy Living.*

Bobbs-Merrill American Health Series—*Health at Home and School; Health at Work and Play; Growing Healthful.*

Bobbs-Merrill Health for Young America Series—*Health and Happiness Science and Health; Health, Fitness and Safety.*

Macmillan Science, Health and Safety Series—*Books IV, V, VI.*

Scott, Foresman Basic Health and Safety Program—*Going on Ten; About Yourself; You.*

Teaching Aids

The following teaching aids are recommended for use in the area of mental health:

IN THE PRIMARY GRADES:

Pamphlets

Children Are Our Teachers, Federal Security Agency.

Emotions and Your Physical Health, Metropolitan Life Insurance Company.

Forgotten Children, National Association for Mental Health.

Mental Health, Everybody's Business, Public Affairs Committee.

Your Child Grows Up, John Hancock Life Insurance Company.

The Teacher's Role in Mental Hygiene, American Medical Association.

Emotional Problems of Growing Up; How to Live with Children; When Children Face Crisis; Why Children Misbehave; Fears of Children, Science Research Associates, Chicago.

Personality Adjustment of Individual Children, Department of Classroom Teachers, National Education Association.

Films

Fun of Making Friends; Fun That Builds Good Health, Visual Aids Department, University of Indiana or Indiana State Board of Health.

Feelings of Rejection (40 minutes); *Feelings of Hostility* (40 minutes), National Film Board of Canada.

Recognition of Emotional Needs; Do's and Don'ts for Teachers, Modern Education Service, Box 26, Bronxville, N.Y.

Books

Baruch, Dorothy, *New Ways in Discipline,* New York, Whittlesey, 1959.

Teacher Listen, The Children Speak, New York, National Association for Mental Hygiene, 1950.

Johns, Edward, Wilfred Sutton, and Lloyd Webster, *Health for Effective Living,* New York, McGraw-Hill, 1954.

Fostering Mental Health in Our Schools (1950); *Growing Up in an Anxious Age* (1952), Washington, D.C., Association for Supervision and Curriculum Development.

Redl, Fritz, and G. Wattenberg, *Mental Hygiene in Teaching,* New York, Harcourt, Brace, 1951.

Cunningham, A. R., and associates, *Understanding Group Behavior of Boys and Girls,* New York, Teachers College, 1954.

National Society for the Study of Education, "Mental Health in Modern Education," *54th Yearbook,* Part II, Chicago, University of Chicago Press, 1955.

IN THE UPPER ELEMENTARY GRADES:

Pamphlets

Baruch, Dorothy, *How to Discipline Your Children,* Public Affairs Pamphlet, 1960.

Bullis, Ann, "How the Human Relations Class Works," in *Understanding the Child,* vol. 10 (1941).

Hymes, James L., Jr., *A Pound of Prevention; How Teachers Can Meet Emotional Needs of Young Children,* New York, Teachers Service Committee, 1960.

Hymes, James L., Jr., *Teachers Listen—The Children Speak,* National Association for Mental Hygiene, 1958.

Menninger, William, *Growing Up Emotionally,* Chicago, Science Research Associates, Inc.

Mental Hygiene in the Classroom; How Would You Help a Child like This? American Medical Association.

Mental Hygiene in the Classroom, National Association for Mental Health.

Ojemann, Bertrand, *Teacher's Manual for Behavior Materials in the Primary Grades,* University of Iowa.

Ojemann, Bertrand, and John Byrnes, *The Teacher's Reaction to Child Behavior,* University of Iowa.

Lying and Stealing, Department of National Health and Welfare, The Mental Health Materials Center.

Do Cows Have Neurosis? New York, National Association for Mental Health.

Strang, Ruth, *Helping Children Solve Problems,* Science Research Associates, Inc.

What Every Child Needs for Good Mental Health, National Association for Mental Health.

Your Child from Six to Twelve, Washington, D.C., Children's Bureau, Federal Security Agency.

Books

Breckenridge, Marian, and Lee Vincent, *Child Development, Physical and Psychologic Growth Through the School Years,* Philadelphia, Saunders, 1959.

Hymes, James, *Effective Home-School Relations,* Englewood Cliffs, N.J., Prentice-Hall, 1954.

Loomis, Mary Jane, *The Pre-Adolescent,* New York, Appleton-Century-Crofts, 1959.

Lowman, Emma McCoy, *Mental Health Through Physical Education and Recreation,* Minneapolis, Burgess, 1955.

Redl, Fritz, and David Wineman, *Controls from Within,* Glencoe, Ill., Free Press, 1952.

Ridenour, Nina, *The Children We Teach,* New York, Mental Health Materials Center, 1960.

Strang, Ruth, *An Introduction to Child Study,* 4th ed., New York, Macmillan, 1959.

Selye, Hans, *The Stress of Life,* New York, McGraw-Hill, 1956.

The Teacher and Mental Health, National Institute of Mental Health, Washington, D.C., U.S. Department of Health, Education, and Welfare.

Wheat, H. G., *Foundations of School Learning,* New York, Knopf, 1955.

Willey, Roy, *Guidance in the Elementary School,* rev. ed., New York, Harper, 1960.

13 SAFETY

The chief cause of death among children is accidents. According to the National Safety Council, there were 6,500 accidental deaths of school-age children in 1959.[1] Most of these tragedies were preventable. Forty-three percent of accidental deaths among school-age children are connected with school. Of these accidents, 20 percent occur in school buildings, 17 percent on school grounds, 6 percent on the way to and from school in pedestrian-motor vehicle and bicycle-motor vehicle accidents.[2] In the school plant, two out of every five accidents occur in organized athletics, principally football and basketball. Accidents which occur in auditoriums and classrooms are second most common, and those which happen while playing on school ground apparatus rank third. Many pupils are seriously injured going to and from school and are involved in accidents caused by their own carelessness or that of drivers of motor vehicles. In addition, many children are injured, and some are killed, while riding in school buses. Although in 1959 29 children were killed in school-bus accidents, these vehicles were involved in some way in 7,186 accidents, and 1,580 children were injured while riding in them while on their way to or from school. Although safety education should begin at home and largely be its responsibility, every school throughout the nation must also assume increased responsibility for conducting a well-planned and well-conducted

[1] *Accident Facts,* National Safety Council, Chicago, 1959.

[2] C. L. Anderson, *School Health Practice,* St. Louis, Mosby, 1960, p. 193.

safety education program. Likewise, pupils must be taught in a safer school environment by more well-rounded teachers who are alert to their needs for safety education and are able to help them gain emotional maturity and safety competence. Furthermore, the program of safety instruction must become a closer and more vital part of the school curriculum and strive harder to develop understanding, shape the attitudes, values, appreciations, habits, and skills which will enable children to assume responsibility for their own safety in their danger-filled world of today. Safety education experts believe that a vitalized safety education program can and should provide rich experiences through which many of the desirable traits of personality and character, which reflect the democratic ideal of concern for others, can be developed by the school.

The National Safety Council, which has an abundance of outstanding materials for teaching safety effectively, has made the following recommendations for those planning a program in school safety education.[3]

1. Safety education should be concerned with worthwhile activities rather than negative prescriptions and should thereby contribute to the enrichment rather than the impoverishment of living.
2. Since the field of safety education is as broad as life itself, it should be approached from every angle.
3. The curriculum should be closely related to community needs—community being defined as the area in which the pupil lives—but ability to meet the problems of a new environment should also be developed.
4. The curriculum should emphasize pupil growth in safety responsibility.
5. Although there are marked limitations in the use of personal first-hand experiences in safety education, this method should be used insofar as practical and possible.
6. The curriculum should be developed in the light of best practices of mental hygiene which place emphasis on the development of personal security.
7. The curriculum should be evaluated in light of each of its objectives, including the intangibles as well as the tangibles. The Standard Student Accident Reporting System[4] should be an essential part in the evaluation of the tangibles.

[3] "Curriculum Planning for Safety," National Safety Council, *Safety Education,* (December, 1961), 18–19.

[4] Available from the National Safety Council upon request.

8. Safety instruction, to be effective, must be an integral part of the curriculum. Certain areas of the program, however, may best be provided for by special "courses" or "units."
9. Safety can well be used as a spearhead in the development of current curricular trends.
10. Safety education activities in the school should be properly integrated and correlated with worthwhile programs of safety education of all other appropriate agencies.

As Patty points out, the three major factors which should govern the allocation of subject matter in safety education to each grade are (1) the immediate needs of the child for this education, (2) the child's ability to comprehend materials, and (3) the interests of the child.[5]

Every city school should have a safety patrol. Since the youngest children, aged 5 to 9, have three times more pedestrian injuries than the 10-to-14-year-olds, school safety patrols, police, and teachers need to work together with parents in sharing responsibility for pedestrian safety education.[6] Careful supervision and planning are necessary if the safety patrol system is to be an effective educational, protective program. Most states have adopted standards and governing rules for such patrols, which can be obtained from state departments of education upon request. The National Safety Council also has such materials available and will gladly work closely with schools or other organizations on all matters pertaining to protection or safety education. The functions of the school safety patrol should be to (1) instruct, direct, and control traffic of the pupils in crossing the streets and highways at and near schools, and (2) assist teachers and other adults in teaching children safe practices in the use of streets and highways at all times and in all places. In addition to the traffic safety patrol, schools should have a fire patrol, building safety patrol, and playground safety patrol. Each of these groups should have clearly defined duties to perform, and it should be considered a school honor to be selected to serve on any of these patrols.

The safety education program should also be bolstered by an all-school safety council, as well as a class or homeroom safety com-

[5] Willard Patty, *Teaching Health and Safety in Elementary Grades,* Englewood Cliffs, N.J., Prentice-Hall, 1951, p. 249.

[6] William Ridgeway, "Protection without Education, A False Sense of Security," *Safety Education* (February, 1960), 10–12.

mittee. The former might well consist of selected teachers, including those from shop, laboratory, and physical education classes, the nurse, school physician, selected pupils, and the principal who would serve as an *ex-officio* member. The homeroom safety group should be made up of several pupils and their teacher. The purpose of such a committee should be to prevent accidents in the classroom or any place else at school. Membership changed periodically will help increase the effectiveness of the group as well as help sustain pupil interest in such a committee.

Children do not want to be hurt or killed, and yet many of them are involved in serious accidents at school, while traveling, or in their own homes every day. They must be made aware of existing dangers in their environment and know how to cope with them successfully. Rules, warnings, and threats mean little to most children. Consequently, teachers must somehow help youth develop safety habits, values, and the "know how" which will enable them to survive and enjoy a long lifetime of happy living. In the primary grades, safety should be stressed informally daily. First aid should be taught in the intermediate grades so that pupils will learn how to take care of their own simple injuries, as well as know what to do in an emergency. Bicycle care and safety should also be included in the safety education programs at this level, for every 19 minutes some young cyclist is seriously injured, and every 21 hours a bicycle rider is killed by an automobile.[7] The majority of those maimed or killed in such accidents are children between the ages of 6 and 16. Every school should also have a training program in bicycle safety, and each community should enforce a program for the periodic inspection and licensing of all bicycles.

SUGGESTED GRADED TOPICS

Suggested graded topics in this area include the following:

Grade 1

1. Safety in going and coming to school.
2. Safety in the classroom.
3. Safety in the entire school building.

[7] *Accident Facts,* National Safety Council, Chicago, 1960, p. 15.

4. Safety using scissors, sharp pointed articles, and other equipment.
5. Playground safety.
6. Safe places to play.
7. What causes accidents; how can they be prevented.

GRADE 2

1. Review of all the above-mentioned topics.
2. Safety at home.
3. Safety around pets and other animals.
4. Fire safety.
5. Extent and cause of accidents.
6. School bus safety.
7. Safety riding in automobiles and other vehicles.
8. Safety on hikes and cookouts.
9. Safety rules for summers and in boats.

GRADE 3

1. Bicycle safety.
2. Fire prevention and protection.
3. Safety using tools and equipment such as a knife, saw, plane, scissors, ice pick, nail file, etc.
4. Community protection of the health and safety of children.
5. Safety laws.
6. Safety at home.
7. Why we should report accidents.

GRADE 4

1. Safety problems of school-age pupils.
2. Hazards in the school, home, and the community.
3. Safety in physical education and recreation.
4. Weather hazards.
5. Community and governmental agencies of protection.
6. Safety for special events and happenings, including Hallowe'en and Christmas, floods, and air attacks.
7. Gas and poisons.
8. Rabies and tetanus prevention.

GRADE 5

1. Junior first aid.
2. Home care and nursing.
3. Use of flammables.
4. Accidents in the home, including falls and burns.
5. Water safety.

6. Accident facts, cause and prevention.
7. Electricity and electric appliances.
8. Industrial safety.
9. Safety on the farm.

Grade 6

1. First aid.
2. Safety problems in the community.
3. Predriver training.
4. The home medicine cabinet.
5. Self-medication; poisons.
6. Forest conservation and fire prevention.
7. Safe use of laboratory equipment.
8. Safety in sports.
9. Safety in aviation.
10. Travel safety.

CURRICULUM PLACEMENT

Many schools allocate safety education to the various areas already established in the curriculum. There are certain elements of safety education in every program area, for if pupils are learning to use laboratory equipment they should be taught to use it safely, or if they are learning to use a hammer or cut paper dolls with scissors in the first grade, they should learn to use this kind of equipment without danger to themselves. In some schools, the physical and safety education programs are combined, while in still others the physical education director or a teacher specialized in this field coordinates the entire safety program. In still others, it is taught as a separate subject. Ideally, safety education should be a major part of the course of study in health and safety and should be correlated and integrated with other subjects at every grade level. Throughout the elementary grades, safety education should be the classroom teacher's responsibility, and the educational program should consist largely of helping children develop desirable habits and attitudes toward healthful, safe living. The alert teacher will relate her instruction to such life experiences as the proper use of toilet, handwashing, and other facilities, medical and dental examinations and tests, weighing and measuring, visits of the school health specialists, playground activities, and the lunch program. Thus, the amount of time needed for health and safety instruction cannot become set or predetermined. Fortunately, capable administrators and skilled teachers will always provide whatever time is needed to help boys and girls live healthfully and safely at school and elsewhere. Since health, its development and protection, is one of the primary objectives of education, the amount of time devoted to this area should be at least equal, if not more than, that devoted to any other major area included in the school curriculum.

Suggested subject areas and ways in which safety education can skillfully be correlated and integrated include the following.

Social sciences can be used successfully for this purpose. As pupils study materials in history, civics, government, geography, economics, and sociology they can also learn about safety problems and their solutions in each of these subjects. Suggested topics which could be used for doing so at the elementary level are:

1. The westward movement and pioneer days.
2. The periods of colonization and settlement of early America.
3. Safety developments in transportation.
4. The development of the machine and resulting problems.
5. Types and causes of major accidents in America.
6. Accident prevention in the home, school, community, and nation.
7. The cost of accidents in comparison to safety education and safe practices.
8. The work of the state and federal government in local safety education and protection.
9. Fire prevention and control in the community, state, and nation.
10. City planning.
11. The rights, duties, and obligations of citizenship.
12. Protective safety laws and their enforcement.
13. Standards of living and the effects of poor housing and inadequate education upon accidents.
14. The growth and kinds of industrial safety programs.
15. Public utilities and community safety.
16. Community safeguards in time of flood or other catastrophes.

Science can become a splendid avenue for integrating and correlating certain materials in safety education. Suggested ways for doing so are through the use of the following broad topics:

1. Fire control and prevention.
2. Use and dangers of electricity.
3. Air, weather, and ventilation and their effects upon the health and welfare of people.
4. Sewage and waste disposal.
5. Food and drug laws.
6. Patent medicines.
7. Land, water, and air transportation safety devices.
8. Conservation of human and natural resources.
9. Hazards of smog and poisonous gas.
10. Germ warfare.
11. Cause and prevention of epidemics.
12. The relation of plants and animals to human life and welfare.
13. Survival procedures when lost in the woods, shipwrecked, or in a plane crash.
14. Effect of drugs and drinking and their relationship to rising accident and crime rates.
15. Handling of hot substances.
16. Proper use of radio and television aerials and grounds, dangers of power and electric lawn mowers, size of fuses, insulators, and electrical circuits.
17. Emotional causes of accidents and accident proneness.
18. First aid.
19. Safety engineering as a profession; the duties of a safety engineer.
20. Safety devices and programs used in industry.

Physical education includes many vigorous activities wherein children can have adventurous, joyful experiences. Many activities are danger-filled, which is the reason they are so appealing and challenging to youth. However, under skilled leadership and proper instruction physical education classes need not be any more dangerous than those in other subjects. One way to safeguard against accidents is to be sure that pupils engage in activities for which they have been prepared in age, strength, and skill. Adults should help children see that if they are safety conscious they can have fun over a longer period of time.

All teachers, whether or not they are trained physical education specialists, who are assigned gymnasium or playground instructional or supervisory duties can safeguard against accidents by:

1. Checking all apparatus and equipment periodically and keeping both in good repair at all times.

2. Finding and marking all hazards with the pupils.
3. Directing all pupils in safety measures.
4. Using activities in a graded program which are best suited for the children at each grade level, and for those who are awkward and poorly skilled.
5. Insisting that all pupils wear protective and suitable apparel for all activities.
6. Teaching children to swim, if possible, at school. Encourage parents to see to it that their child has lessons and learns during the summer or at other times, if the school does not have a pool. Teach basic water, boating, and fishing safety.
7. Supervising children during recess or other play periods. Know whether they are playing according to rules, and if not, insist that they do so. Discuss with the class the necessity of playing according to game rules, taking turns, and why one should be aware of his own safety and that of others, especially during play.

There are numerous ways in which the physical education teacher or classroom instructor teaching physical activities can integrate and correlate materials in this field with those in safety education. These include discussing with the pupils at teachable moments such topics as:

1. Cause and prevention of accidents in the playground, in the gymnasium, and elsewhere.
2. The effects of alcohol, drugs, and tobacco on health, safety, and efficiency.
3. The danger and proper use of all equipment, such as bat, archery bow, trampoline, swing, etc.
4. Prevention of water accidents.
5. Prevention of accidents and diseases such as athlete's foot, ringworm, itch, etc., through proper use of pool and locker room facilities.
6. First-aid treatment for minor injuries.
7. Protective sports equipment and its proper use.
8. The causes of injuries in sports and games such as fatigue, lack of skill, and other factors.
9. Why and how game rules protect the safety of the players.
10. Kinds and use of accident reports and insurance plans for players.
11. Allocation of different sections of the playground for each grade for the safety and protection of the children, assigning to those in the primary grades a spot close to the building, those from the oldest group being farthest removed.
12. The proper location of all apparatus, equipment, and game space for

courts, horseshoe pitching, and other activities along one side or at the end of the play area.

13. Common types of athletic injuries and how to avoid them.
14. Why all pupils should have a physical examination before participating in strenuous activities.
15. Why pupils are classified for competition.
16. Adequate supervision of all participants; safety procedures to follow when playing alone.
17. How and why the body should be warmed up before strenuous activity.
18. Why proper skill progression in sports and games is taught and how this is done.
19. How accidents are recorded and why.
20. Diets for competitors as a means of avoiding illness and accidents.
21. The results of a survey made *with* each class of the hazards in the gymnasium, playground, pool, locker room, and shower room.

Mathematics can also be correlated and integrated with safety education. Here again, however, the purpose for doing so should not primarily be to give pupils added experience in learning to apply mathematical concepts, but to teach them significant facts about safety, and the causes and preventions of accidents in order that they may better protect and prolong their own lives, as well as those of others.

Suggested areas of study and activities include those which will enable the pupils to:

1. Study the accident statistics of their own school, community, county, and state. Classify these by types and within age groups.
2. Make graphs showing the accident problems of primary, intermediate, junior, and senior high school groups.
3. Make graphs showing accident trends among elementary and secondary school age groups from 1930 to the present.
4. Study the accident reports of a school system for one year. Classify reported accidents. Draw up an accident prevention plan for your own school from these data.
5. Evaluate the school's accident-prevention plan by tabulating accident causes for a 6-month period.
6. Make a study of the extent, types, and costs of accidents in your own family for one year. Combine your findings with those made by all other pupils. Draw up a preventive plan from this study which could be adopted in every home.
7. Interview the high school coach to find out which athletic benefit in-

surance plan is used. Learn the costs, benefits derived, and value of such a plan. Report your findings to the class.

8. Discover the total cost of school bus transportation in your county and state.
9. Inspect your own home and a farm. Make a comparative study of hazards found in each place.
10. Find out the number of school buildings in your state or the nation which were destroyed by fire last year. Determine the total cost of these fires.
11. Make a study of the costs of motor vehicle deaths in your community, state, and nation for one year. Determine in percentage the causes of those accidents reported.
12. Make a bar graph of the principal types of accidents which occur in your school.
13. Make a pie graph showing the location in which accidents of school-age children most frequently occur.
14. Make a line graph showing the increase of accidents as reported by the National Safety Council from 1900 to 1960.

As McGill has pointed out,

> Relating classroom lessons in safety to safe living at home is the most effective teaching technique. Teaching activities which help children to identify the hazards to safe living in the home and school and to examine their activities for the potentially injurious consequences which may be present are basic to safety education. The safety rules which parents stress should be further emphasized through classroom study.[8]

If children are to learn to live safely, all teaching in this area must be conducted in a functional way. This means that besides direct safety instruction, all elementary teachers must do much more effective correlating safety learning with all other subjects included in the curriculum. Likewise, they must increasingly relate safety lessons to all activities which enter into each pupil's daily life at home, at school, and in the community.

THE USE OF TEACHING METHODS

Almost every kind of teaching method can be used in safety education, providing they produce desired results. The following methods are especially adaptable for effective instruction in safety.

[8] John McGill, "How to Teach Children to Do Things the Safe Way," *Journal of Health, Physical Education and Recreation,* vol. 310 (March, 1961), 29.

Problem Solving. There are many problems which can be studied in safety education through the use of this method. Safety education itself is a gigantic problem which remains unsolved, for we still have to discover ways to prevent the tragic loss of human lives from accidents. Indeed, the problem is becoming increasingly greater, in spite of the fact that more Americans are now going to school and staying there for a longer time. Seemingly, then, education which consists of doing the same old thing in the same old way is *not* the answer.

Suggested problem areas which pupils would profit from exploring should be those which are meaningful to them at their own particular stage of development in each school grade. Primary youngsters should study safety problems which have a direct effect upon their behavior, whether this be when coming and going to school or while they are at school, home, or at play. Upper elementary pupils, who are increasingly becoming more civic-minded, might well study larger safety problems, such as traffic accidents in their own city and state. Regardless of the problem selected for study by each class through teacher-guided class discussion and planning, these problem areas must become real and vitally important ones to each learner.

Every school and each class in it has a safety problem of some kind which can be solved (either partially or completely) by pupils, as guided by their teacher. Some of these problems are:

1. Pupil traffic in corridors, lunchroom, etc., which may be solved by rerouting or channelization.
2. Horseplay in locker rooms, in the playground, toilets, and around drinking fountains.
3. Problems involving the transportation of pupils to the school whether this be in a school bus, private car, or public bus.
4. School ground and play area hazards.
5. Safety problems which center around the arrival and dismissal of school every day, and before holiday periods.
6. Parking of vehicles, including bicycles.

Also, every school has its own unique safety problems due mostly to its location, whether this be because the school has been built near a railroad crossing or a jet airport. Still others have increased in-school traffic problems, due largely to the vast influx of children. Regardless of the cause and type of safety problem, it cannot be solved by the adults alone. Merely setting up conduct rules certainly will not do it, nor punishing children for disobeying rules. The pupils themselves can help solve it, but not by themselves, for the solution of all school safety problems lies only in the working together of both the children and adults involved. Safety work *must* be carried on by pupils if education in this subject is to be effective.[9]

Class discussions in safety education can evolve around many kinds of topics. Here again, the role of the teacher is to draw the pupils out and to enter into the discussion at the best moment. Suggested topics for discussion and activities are:

1. Have each child report on exit signs they have seen in theaters, restaurants, stores, etc. Encourage each to tell how he would escape if his own house caught fire. Discuss protection from fires.
2. Show and discuss safety films or filmstrips.
3. Have each child report on an accident he saw and tell what caused it. Discuss what causes accidents.
4. As a class group, draw up safe passing rules to be observed when changing rooms at school or going from one place in the building to another. Talk about why people break rules and what should be done about this.
5. Bring newspaper clippings for the class bulletin board of accidents which happen in the local community. Discuss these as a class group.
6. Invite a local safety specialist to talk to the class and describe the work he does. Have the class discuss what they learned from this experience.
7. Divide into groups of four to make an on-the-spot survey of pedestrian and motor traffic at several of the busiest city street intersections. Compare results, draw conclusions, and make recommendations from the information gathered from this experience.
8. Show pictures of accidents taken from magazines or newspapers. Select various students to discuss how such an accident might have been caused, how it could have been prevented, etc. Listen carefully to answers given in order to determine if pupils have gained workable knowledge concerning safety.
9. Discuss as a class or in panel groups why one should obey traffic rules and school safety rules.
10. Compare American life today with that of a century ago.

[9] Lloyd Jenkins, "Is Safety Knowledge Enough?" *Journal of Health, Physical Education and Recreation,* vol. 308 (April, 1959), 32.

11. Discuss what evidence you have that man has failed so far to adjust to his changing environment.
12. Discuss, plan, and conduct a safety program in your school.
13. Discuss how accidents among adults can be prevented.
14. Discuss, plan, and give a P.T.A. program designed to secure parent cooperation in the prevention of child pedestrian injuries.
15. Discuss the values and problems of bicycle training programs.
16. Talk about ways in which you can help prevent accidents in your own home, at school, and on the playground.
17. Discuss seasonal play activities such as roller skating, kite flying, and sledding from the standpoint of safety.
18. Discuss water and boating safety.
19. Discuss the formation of a safety club in your class, define its purposes, activities, etc.
20. Secure and study any free educational materials available from the National Safety Council in Chicago. Discuss these with the class.
21. Keep a class record of all accidents which happen in the classroom, while going to and from school, or in the playground. Discuss this record periodically.
22. Talk with parents, bus drivers, patrol boys, and others in order to learn if the pupils are becoming more safety conscious when away from their teachers. Discuss transportation safety.
23. Determine through observation if some children have become overcautious or afraid, or if any pupil seems to be accident-prone. Talk individually with such children and help them recognize and overcome these handicaps.
24. Ask the class whether as a group they think that they generally practice good safety habits. Have them give suggestions of how they can still improve. Select one pupil to list these on the board. Refer to this list periodically and have the children again evaluate their progress.

Demonstrations in many areas and activities can add to the effectiveness of knowledge gained in safety education. It has been often said that one of the most effective ways to teach youth the importance of using equipment and facilities safely is the way the instructor herself uses her own tools and body skillfully. Well-conducted demonstrations on the safe use of equipment can and should set an example for the children to copy. Excellent opportunities to teach safety concepts by demonstrations are available in the areas of fire prevention and control, transportation via school bus, private car, or public bus, bicycle safety, common use of home electrical appliances, playground, laboratory, and other types of equipment safety. Pupils must not only see these demonstrations, but be taught through them. Other suggested demonstrations which can be used to teach safety concepts include the safe use of:

Scissors
Crayons, pencils, and pens
Knives
Playground apparatus
Combustible materials
Hard-surface areas
Breakable materials
Ways to use the body skillfully in sports and games
Apparatus in the gymnasium, including ropes, the horizontal bar, traveling rings, and trampoline
Outdoor cooking and camping equipment
Apparatus on the playground, including the monkey bars, jungle gym, chinning and knee-hanging bars

As a cumulative activity, it is suggested that the group plan a school picnic and use this experience to learn about transportation safety, taking a first-aid kit along and what it should contain, how to avoid sunburn, poison ivy, etc. Integrate previously learned materials in nutrition and have pupils plan and cook a simple luncheon in foil.

Field trips interest pupils in the affairs and facilities of their own community, and in turn, stimulate interest among local citizens in what is happening at school. Visits to such places as a traffic court, a modern industrial plant, an airport, fire station, police station, emergency room in a hospital, railroad or bus station, or shipyard can help make safety education a vital and thrilling experience to youth.

Surveys can best be used to teach pupils how to utilize the results of their findings and find ways to improve conditions. Those who come into contact with safety problems in their school or home environment and learn how to solve them correctly are ready to learn next about the larger safety problems which are found in their community, state, and nation. Often the results of surveys made by just one class in the school can improve conditions as well as help other pupils in the entire school become more safety-conscious. Subjects suitable for school surveys include pedestrian problems in the building and in the playground, traffic problems in and around the school, fire-prevention methods and practices, bicycle safety, and field trips safety. A survey of community agencies conducting safety education and accident-prevention programs will give pupils direct contact with these organizations, as well as acquaint both the pupils and teacher with speakers from these agencies who might be brought into the classroom as guests.

Many results can accrue from surveys made by pupils of conditions in their own school. These may include the establishment or enlargement of school safety patrols, the building of bicycle racks and a bicycle safety inspection program, the allocation of safer play areas, the building of a fenced enclosed playground, or even the resurfacing of outdoor play areas.

Guidance, used as a means of reaching those pupils with unique safety problems, can also be brought into the educational program. Those children who are accident prone, too afraid to try new skills, always fearful of getting hurt, and those who play too recklessly without consideration of the well-being of others, all need special help. Often these can best be reached by individual counseling.

THE USE OF INSTRUCTIONAL MATERIALS

Many kinds of instructional materials can be utilized to help children develop good safety practices and safety consciousness. These include:

Equipment which will enable children to touch the "real thing" should be brought into the classroom and used to its fullest educational extent. Such articles as the following can be used for teaching boys and girls how to use play and work equipment safely:

Football shoulder pads, helmets, mouth protectors
Catcher's mask
Scissors, knives
Sewing machines
Saws, hammers
Bicycles, roller and ice skates
Bows and arrows
Sander
Oil and gasoline lamps and engines
Cleaning equipment, including oily rags and mops
Jigsaw
Stoves
Electric fans, lawn mowers
Can openers, razors
Matches
Fishing rods and hooks
Band saw, power drill
Auto engine
Horseback riding equipment
Track and field equipment such as pole vault, shot put, and others

Photographic and Related Materials—Many schools are increasingly utilizing the camera as an instructional device. Often pupils are assigned to photograph school ground and play-area hazards, and then use these pictures in posters. Such photographs help children become cognizant of the location and type of hazards they are likely to encounter. The teacher can also make her own colored slides of a dangerous location, action, or situation to show to her class as she discusses safety problems with them. Still other schools are making their own movies of children at play or at work in the school, with the pupils planning, writing, and producing the film. Their finished product can be used for both classroom and community educational purposes.

The National Safety Council and the state departments of education have many splendid free films available for classroom use. Other visual aids suitable for presenting facts, shaping attitudes, and motivating behavior are cartoons, drawings, water colors, stencils, and crayon and linoleum blocks. Suggested activities using these creative materials are the following:

1. Explore the schoolroom, home, and school playground in order to discover existing hazards. Point these out and list those found in the classroom. Paint those found on the playground, such as rocks or tree trunks, with bright yellow paint. Mark off safety areas, with a line of paint, for waiting one's turn to swing or seesaw.
2. Walk in a class group to the nearest traffic light and discover the safest way to walk to school. Learn the meaning of the various light signals, or those given by the policeman or patrol boy. Make a stop-and-go sign from a milk carton, colored paper, stick supported on a base, and a flashlight. Draw a traffic route in chalk on the floor. Have the class practice operating and responding to the changing signals.
3. Bring or make pictures to show dangerous creatures found in their state, such as the coral snake, a bull, etc. Teach why the pupils should avoid these.
4. Have children bring newspaper or magazine articles for a scrapbook on any phase of the safety education program.
5. Take snapshots of existing school and playground hazards. Elect a committee to plan the removal of these hazards. Write a final report of the project, or have the committee present it orally in a school auditorium program, at a P.T.A. meeting, or over the local radio or television station.
6. Take "before" and "after" snapshots of a playground clean-up cam-

paign. Evaluate the success of this group endeavor and plan another such campaign to be conducted later.

7. Study and make a chart of common poisons, giving suggestions for keeping these away from curious children or animals.

8. Appoint a bulletin-board or display committee to show the best pictures taken and posters made by class members.

9. Have each child make a poster on the safety practices to be carried out during any holiday. Display these in a department-store window.

10. Make an illustrative poster for a fire prevention unit.

Dramatic activities, including role playing, skits, safety plays, puppet shows, and charades can all help pupils express what they have learned in safety education. They can also be used by a creative teacher as a means of having the children "teach" each other. Suggested activities in which dramatic activities can be used are:

1. Play "community" in the sandbox or by moving the chairs in the classroom. Using toy automobiles and trucks, have this traffic respond to hand traffic signals by a pupil "policeman."

2. Act out carrying, passing, and using scissors, knives, saws, hammers, and other tools correctly.

3. Show cans of lye, roach powder, shoe polish, or other products which are dangerous for human beings to swallow.

4. Dramatize the danger of toys left on the floor, medicines or poisons left where babies can get to them, food left cooking on a stove that a child can reach, or other types of common home accidents.

5. Demonstrate safety at the drinking fountain.

6. Bring a pet cat or dog to class and demonstrate petting it correctly, and approaching animals with the hand held out, the back of it toward the floor as though the animal was about to be fed. Warn the class about approaching strange animals. Have the class make a poster on this subject.

7. Have periodic fire or other protective drills and train each child so that he knows what he is to do in case of such an emergency. Have the class make posters on the cause of fires, and write a play about them.

8. Practice getting on and off a stationary school bus, and learn how to ride in it safely.

9. Using chairs for a two- or four-passenger automobile, dramatize the good and bad ways to be a passenger in the family car.

10. Dramatize what to do when injured at school.

11. Demonstrate blanket-wrapping in case clothing catches on fire; how to put out a small grass fire.

12. Have children move folding chairs or other room equipment, demonstrating first incorrectly in an exaggerated fashion, and then showing how to do it correctly. Give a skit on this topic.

Bringing fire equipment to the school improves school-community relations and may provide learning experiences children will value. (Courtesy, Nashville Public Schools.)

13. Play "telephone and emergency," noting carefully if each pupil knows what to do in case of an emergency.

14. Make safety posters, miniature traffic signs. Act out being a policeman, patrol boy, pedestrian, auto driver, etc.

15. Demonstrate safe methods for riding a bicycle. Show the safety devices which should be on every bicycle, such as a horn, reflector light, etc.

16. Have a weekly clean-up contest between squads of playground area. Show dangerous articles found which could cause injury. Act out the wrong and right things to do.

17. Make up and act out walking safely in the rain or when snow or ice is on the ground.

18. Practice safe ways to climb, jump, hang upside down by the knees, or other movement skills.

19. Practice turning electric fans, television sets, irons, and other electrical equipment off and on. Demonstrate how to do these things safely.

20. Ask a safety patrol boy to talk to the class in order to acquaint the children with his job and how they can help him do it better. Give a skit showing the problems he has with some pupils.

Radio and Television—Many schools have real or mock radio and television safety education programs. Short radio dramas, skits, panel discussions, and other types of presentations can be given on a variety of safety topics such as "Safety at Play," "Swimming and Boating Safety," "Our School Safety Patrol," "Bicycle Safety," "Accidents in the Home," and others. Such experiences are often exciting ones in the lives of children, for they like to show adults what they can do, and they should be given many opportunities for them.

DESIRABLE OUTCOMES

A well-taught and directed program in safety education will produce the following desirable outcomes in terms of knowledge, attitudes, and practices:

In the primary grades, the pupils will:

1. Become aware that their own home, school, travel route to school, and playground have hazards, know where these are, and how to cope with them successfully.
2. Know the meaning of traffic signals and the safest way to travel to and from school.
3. Be aware that policemen and firemen are protecting friends and that the school janitor, bus driver, nurse, doctor, and teacher are concerned about their safety too.
4. Know that scissors, knives, saws, or other articles can cause pain or serious injury, and know how to use these tools safely.
5. Know the danger of petting strange animals or picking up queer-looking insects or worms.
6. Be aware that medicine, insect powder, or other similar articles often found in the home can cause death or serious illness if consumed.
7. Know the meaning of school warning signals such as the fire alarm, the air-raid siren, and know what to do when these warnings are sounded.
8. Be safety-conscious while riding in the school bus or family automobile and act accordingly.
9. Be safety-conscious while using the playground apparatus or drinking at the water fountain, and act accordingly.

10. Wear tennis shoes while playing in the gymnasium, and rubbers when it is slick and icy outside.
11. Know what to do when they are hurt at school or at home.
12. Know their complete name, age, address, parents' names and where they can be reached by phone, their family doctor's name, and whom to call in case of an emergency.
13. Know what to do if their clothing catches fire or when a building is burning.
14. Become skilled in using all play equipment, such as the jungle gym, horizontal bars, swings, etc.
15. Know water safety rules and be able to swim.
16. Understand how weather affects safety and precautions which should be taken during adverse conditions.
17. Know how to handle correctly folding chairs or other movable school furniture.
18. Know how to use the telephone in case of an emergency and whom to call.

In the upper elementary grades, the pupils will:

1. Review previously learned safety knowledge and skills.
2. Practice good housekeeping and safety in the playground, at school, in the classroom, and at home.
3. Know the danger of burns, poison ivy, poisonous snakes, and other things which can cause pain or serious injury.
4. Desire to prevent fires, and know what to do in case of a fire.
5. Practice traffic safety while riding a bicycle, in the school bus, or family car.
6. Have favorable attitudes and real concern for the rights and safety of others at work and play.
7. Know how to pass safely from room to room or floor to floor at school, and to use the drinking fountain, dressing-room shower, and other school equipment safely.
8. Play according to game rules, wear protective equipment such as shoulder pads, catcher's mask, or knee guards.
9. Know what to do in case of an emergency at school, home, on the playground, and while traveling.
10. Have earned the Junior Red Cross First Aid Certificate.
11. Use tools and experimental equipment carefully and skillfully in the classroom, manual training room, or science laboratory at school, and in home workshops during leisure time.
12. Recognize fire and accident hazards and remove them.
13. Obey safety patrol and other traffic signals.
14. Be a skilled bicycle rider.

15. Be a skilled swimmer; know how to fish and use a boat safely; be able to handle a gun for hunting safely.
16. Be skilled in body movements and be able to support their own weight while hanging; be able to jump over objects if necessary, swing across space by ropes, and have the strength, confidence, and courage necessary to do so.
17. Know how to care for and repair their own bicycles, skates, and other play equipment.
18. Ride licensed bicycles and have passed a bicycle rider's safety test.
19. Practice safety precautions while traveling on a bus, train, motor scooter, taxi, or airplane, or when using any other method of travel.
20. Understand the hazards of using matches improperly, dynamite caps, firecrackers, guns, etc.
21. Practice safety while on a field trip, camping out, or picnicking.
22. Help members of their own family become more safety-conscious and develop good safety habits.

SUGGESTED READINGS

Learning Aids

Recommended learning aids in safety education include the following:

IN THE PRIMARY GRADES

Pamphlets, posters, and other materials available from the National Safety Council, the local fire department, local and state highway departments, and the Bicycle Institute of America.

Check List for Child Safety, American Red Cross; *Special Days Are Fun,* National Commission on Safety Education.

Play and Radio Scripts, National Safety Council: *Benny, the Matchstick; Mary and the Broken Glass; Tom, the Slow Poke Turtle.*

Story books for children

Dr. Squash, the Doll Doctor, Margaret Brown, Simon and Schuster.

Hercules, the Story of an Old Fashioned Fire Engine, Hardie Gramatsky, Putnam.

Pat and Her Policeman, Frederick Friedman, Morrow.

Safety Can Be Fun, Munro Leaf, Lippincott.

We Went to the Doctor, Carel Menling, McBride.

Color charts and ditto lessons

Elm, Raymond, *Pictures to Color, Safety First Series,* University of Chicago, 1940.

Irwin, Leslie, *Ditto Lessons in Health & Science,* Department of Health and Physical Education, University of Chicago, 1940.

Owen Publishing, *Safety Sets I, II,* and *III,* Chicago.

Films and filmstrips

Safe and Sound at Home, Be a Better Pedal Pusher, Society for Visual Education (filmstrips).

Water, Friend or Enemy, Indiana State Board of Health (film).

Safety on a School Bus, Young American Films (11 minutes).

First Aid, Encyclopedia Britannica Films (11 minutes).

It's Fun to Swim, American Red Cross (11 minutes).

I'm No Fool as a Pedestrian (10 minutes); *The Belt and the Badge* (15 minutes); *Tommy Takes to Traffic* (12 minutes), National Safety Council, Chicago.

I'm No Fool in the Water; I'm No Fool Having Fun; I'm No Fool with Fire; How to Have an Accident in the Home (all 12 minutes). Walt Disney Films, 500 So. Buena Vista St., Burbank, Calif.

Health readers

Ginn, Health For Better Living Series, *Health and Happy Days; Health in Work and Play; Health and Safety for You.*

Macmillan, Science, Health and Safety Series, *Grades I, II, and III.*

Scott, Foresman, Health and Personal Development Series, *Happy Days, with Our Friends; Good Times with Our Friends; Three Friends.*

Winston Health Series, *From Head to Toe; Side by Side; How We Grow.*

IN THE UPPER ELEMENTARY GRADES:

Pamphlets, posters, and other materials available from the National Safety Council, the American Red Cross, Bicycle Institute of America, American Automobile Association, Center for Safety Education of New York University.

Radio scripts

Traffic Safety; Swimming and Water Safety, Bureau of Research in Education, University of Texas.

You Were There—the Tinder Box; You Were There—Water Safety, American Red Cross.

Story books for children

The Safety Club, Catherine Bruce, Nelson.

It's Fun to Be Safe, Herbert Stack, Dallas, Beckley-Cardy Company.

Fireman for a Day, Z. K. McDonald, Messner.

The Firefighter, H. B. Lent, Macmillan.

The Children's Health Bulletin, published for schoolroom use by the National Tuberculosis Association.

The Junior Book of First Aid, Washington, D.C., American Red Cross.

Health readers

Ginn Health Series, *Safety Every Day; Doing Your Best for Health; Building Good Health.*

Lyons and Carnahan Health and Happiness Series, *You; You and Others; You're Growing Up.*

Laidlaw, The Road to Health Series, *Health Trails; Your Health and You; Keeping Healthy.*

Films and filmstrips

Playground Safety, Coronet Films (11 minutes).

Fire Drill Exit, Coronet Films (11 minutes).

Safety in the Winter, Coronet Films (10 minutes).

Safety on the Playground, Encyclopedia Britannica Films (15 minutes).

First Aid, American Red Cross (30 minutes).

How to Have an Accident in the Home; I'm No Fool with a Bicycle (12 minutes each); National Safety Council.

Bicycle Safety Skill, Coronet Films (10 minutes).

Safety in the School Bus, Young America Films (20 minutes).

Look Alert, Stay Unhurt (10 minutes each), National Film Board of Canada.

Teaching Aids

Recommended teaching aids for safety education include the following:

IN THE PRIMARY GRADES:

Free materials from National Safety Council, Texas Department of Public Safety, Socony Mobil Oil Company, American Automobile Association, American Red Cross, Boy Scouts of America, Shell Oil Company, U.S. Department of Interior.

Accident Facts, safety education memos, pamphlets, monthly issues of *Safety Education,* and other materials from the National Safety Council.

Metropolitan Life Insurance Company, Monthly Health Bulletins for Teachers (pamphlets)—*First Steps in Health Education; A Formula for Child Safety; Play It Safe; Stop, Look, and Live; Safety Begins at Home.*

Bicycle Institute of America, *Bicycle Safety Tests; Bike Fun; Bike Regulations in the Community.*

Periodicals

Los Angeles Health Education Journal, Los Angeles Public Schools: *Journal of Health, Physical Education and Recreation; Today's Health; The Grade Teacher; The Instructor; The N.E.A. Journal.*

Reports

AAHPER, *Guide Lines for Health Education; A Suggested Plan of Action,* Health Education Planning Conference Report, 1959.

Unit Grades of Safety in the Primary Grades; Our Schools Plan Safe Living; Preventing Fires in Your School; Fire Safety for Teachers of Primary Grades, National Commission on Safety Education, N.E.A., 1201 16th St. N.W., Washington 6, D.C.

Glen, Harold, *Safe Living,* Peoria, Ill., Charles Bennett, 1958.

Books

Florio, A. E., and G. T. Stafford, *Safety Education,* New York, McGraw-Hill, 1961.

School Health, 5th ed., Washington, D.C., National Education Association and American Medical Association, 1961.

Schneider, Robert, *Methods and Materials of Health Education,* Philadelphia, Saunders, 1958.

Williams, Jesse F., and Ruth Abernathy, *Health Education in Schools,* New York, Ronald, 1959.

IN THE UPPER ELEMENTARY GRADES:

Periodicals

Safety Education (monthly); *Child Safety Program Package* ($3.30 yearly subscription), National Safety Council, Chicago.

"Ideas for Teaching Safety," *The Instructor,* vol. 64 (September, 1954), 17–21.

Current issues of *The Journal of the American Association for Health; Physical Education and Recreation; The Journal of School Health; Today's Health; The N.E.A. Journal.*

Books

Boy Scout Handbook, New York, National Boy Scouts, 1960.

First Aid, American Red Cross, Washington, D.C., 1961.

Florio, A. E., and G. T. Stafford, *Safety Education,* New York, McGraw-Hill, 1961.

National Education Association, *Our Schools Plan Safe Living,* Washington, D.C., 1956.

Virginia State Board of Education, *Health Education, Grades 1–7,* Richmond, Division of Purchasing and Printing, 1958.

Unit Guides for Teaching Safety in the Intermediate Grades; Fire Safety for Teachers of Intermediate Grades; Bicycle Safety in Action; Safety through Elementary Science; Safety in Physical Education for the Classroom Teacher, National Commission on Safety Education, N.E.A., 1201 16th St., N.W., Washington 6, D.C.

14 FAMILY LIFE EDUCATION

Sex education should be an integral part of the health education program on every grade level. However, since the words "sex education" usually bring quick and strong negative reaction from some parents, religious groups, or other adults, schools have increasingly been including materials in this area under the titles of "Family Life Education" or "Developing Wholesome Life Relationships." Regardless of what the material is called, it contains valuable information children should receive. The home, school, church, and community should work closely together in this area, for the education of children is not the sole responsibility of the school. The school must, however, support and provide education which is neglected or inadequate in the home.

Increasingly, educators are becoming aware that sex education possibilities abound in everyday classroom activities, and that since children are receiving some kind of information on their own from their equally uninformed peers or from older youngsters who are misinformed, it is the duty of the school to begin a graded program in the first school year that presents true information and helps young people shape desirable attitudes toward their own and the opposite sex. What children think and feel about themselves and others is far more important than knowing the answers to questions concerning human reproduction.

Young children are curious about themselves and about all aspects of life around them. They need to be given frank but brief answers to their simple questions, such as "Where do babies come from?" or "Why do babies need fathers?" They are not ready for or interested in learning the lengthy facts of reproduction, but do seek the answers to their simple questions. The films they watch, the television programs they both see and hear, the magazines their parents take, the billboard advertisements all about them play up sex and the "sexy." Consequently, an awakening appetite toward "finding out about things" is whetted to the degree that many of their questions are amazingly wise and often show surprised adults that children are far more aware of what is going on around them than they think. Above all, the teacher of elementary school children must be able to answer the many questions youngsters ask about life or to guide them to the needed information with dignity, discretion, and sincerity.[1] Since sex is a normal human function that is the foundation of life itself, education in this area should be treated as just another part of the total school program. Facts concerning the reproductive system should be presented along with those on any of the other systems of the body. Teachers, however, must not only help children find answers to their questions but also shape desirable attitudes, values, and patterns of conduct. Classes should not be separated, although the teacher of sixth grade girls may wish to discuss menstruation with them as a group, or there may be an occasion when she would want to talk to the boys alone. Certainly the school nurse or physician should not be brought in to speak to the class just on sex, for both should visit the classroom often to talk with the children about many aspects of good health.

In reality, sex education begins the very day of birth; it is present in one form or another when the father holds his baby daughter for the first time. Education goes on wherever there is life. It can be positive or negative, and even these contacts in the first few months of life can be of lasting importance to a child. Likewise, teaching geared toward helping pliable youngsters develop wholesome life relationships should start the first day of school. This can begin with taking the children on a tour of the building to show them where the little girls will go to the bathroom, and where the little

[1] James Hymes, *A Pound of Prevention,* New York, National Association for Mental Health, 1954.

boys will go. Throughout the primary grades "teachable moments" in this area should be capitalized upon. Oberteuffer suggests that the following teaching possibilities for sex education in the elementary grades might be used, and recommends that rather than trying to cover everything, the teacher may be wise to leave some areas untouched, while in some communities even more can be included:[2]

PRIMARY YEARS

1. Functions of elimination as they relate to the genitalia, including protection and care.
2. Phenomenon of birth; the coming of the baby; reproduction of plants and animals.
3. Early social friendships, manners, and courtesies between sexes.
4. Early conceptions of sex differences.

INTERMEDIATE YEARS

1. Mental and physiological changes attendant upon growth; continuation of sex differences.
2. Continuation of social and ethical relationships between the sexes, social friendships.
3. Early lessons in hereditary influences.
4. Basic sources of information on sex problems.

Every boy or girl is a member of a family that has representatives of those of the opposite sex. The child will need to know how to work, play, and live successfully in that closely knit group. Consequently, the school must work closely with the home to help prepare the child for his future responsibility as a parent, as well as his present role as a family member. It can do so by providing each youngster with realistic and meaningful girl-boy learning experiences in his formative years.

Guiding principles for the development of a unit or course of study in this area include the following:[3]

1. The home is the major and natural source for information about family life and sex development. The church plays a major role in

[2] Delbert Oberteuffer, *School Health Education,* New York, Harper, 1960, p. 159.

[3] State Superintendent of Public Instruction, *Health Education,* Raleigh, North Carolina Public Schools, 1953, pp. 107–108.

this function in some groups. The school has the responsibility of supplementing what the home has provided.

2. School programs should be planned in cooperation with parents, parent groups, and other community organizations, such as health, welfare, church, and family-life agencies.
3. The school should accept its responsibility for helping parents in the guidance of children in problems of growing up.
4. The school should cooperate in community programs designed to give information about human development and should accept its responsibility for intelligent leadership and direction, when needed, to assure effective results.
5. Sex education should be integrated with the total health program at all grade levels and should be taught by the regular teacher with the usual class groupings.
6. The school should provide individual guidance as well as class instruction to boys and girls in the acquisition of scientific knowledge and the development of wholesome attitudes in regard to growth and development as boys and girls.
7. Opportunities should be provided for school personnel to acquire scientific knowledge; develop wholesome attitudes; acquire the use of a scientific vocabulary; acquaint themselves with questions (and answers) which children are likely to ask; feel secure in beginning and carrying on a program by having knowledge and the support of administrators, other teachers, and the community; understand that certain personal problems of the child should be considered in private conferences.
8. Growth and development including sex education should be treated in a very realistic, normal, and dignified manner.
9. The normal mixed groupings are usually preferable except when, in the judgment of the instructor, it is indicated that topics peculiar to one sex or age group call for separation of the sexes.
10. The teaching approach and the content of the program should give due consideration to the present understanding of the group.

Primary children can best be helped to learn about sex when the teacher answers questions as they arise, or capitalizes upon things happening around the children, such as the appearance of baby chicks at Easter or a new baby sister in the home of a pupil. As pupils advance up the academic ladder, they ask questions which require more detailed answers. Consequently, instruction in family living should become more factual, and be based upon scientific information regarding the human body. As one health education expert has suggested, there are three well-known approaches to classroom instruction: "(1) through animal and plant life (the 'birds, bees, and butterflies approach'); (2) through the anatomy and physiology involved; and (3) through human life situations."[4] Frequently, the wisest approach often is through life situations which arise naturally as boys and girls grow towards maturity.

SUGGESTED GRADED TOPICS

A graded program in family life education might well include the following topics:

GRADE 1

1. The role of the father, mother, and children in a family.
2. Correct terms for the parts of the body having to do with elimination and reproduction.
3. Different toilet procedures for boys and girls.
4. The importance of sharing and being considerate of others.
5. Adult men and women who contribute to the welfare of children, such as the doctor, nurse, school janitor, policemen, etc.

GRADE 2

1. Getting along with others.
2. Good sportsmanship; consideration of other classmates, parents, and family members.
3. What boys and men do at home and at work; what girls and women do.
4. How plants and animals reproduce.
5. The body, its care and function.

GRADE 3

1. Steps toward independence.
2. Assuming one's own sex role in life.
3. The organs and systems of the body.
4. The beginning of life.
5. Desirable conduct patterns.
6. Personal appearance in relationship to personality and growth.
7. Family relationships which influence health.

GRADE 4

1. The role of the father and of the mother in the reproduction of animals and human beings.

[4] Oberteuffer, *op. cit.,* p. 152.

2. How life begins.
3. Growing from an egg into a baby.
4. How we grow up.
5. Work and play with our families at home.
6. How girls and boys differ.
7. Occupations for men and women.

GRADE 5

1. How animals reproduce and care for their young.
2. How the human baby grows inside the mother.
3. How mothers help babies be born.
4. The father's role in reproduction and in the family.
5. Heredity and reproduction.
6. Boy-and-girl relationships.
7. Wholesome life attitudes and values.

GRADE 6

1. Body changes: how boys change, how girls change.
2. Problems of growing up.
3. Relationship between maturity and responsibility.
4. Place of the family in society; social codes and ethics.
5. Family problems and their solution for happy living.
6. Importance of wholesome sex attitudes and behavior.
7. Lives of outstanding persons of each sex.
8. Occupational choices.

CURRICULUM PLACEMENT

Education for family living can and should be correlated with all subjects included in the elementary curriculum. The following are used most often.

Social sciences provide, through study of famous historical families and personalities and their times, such as George Washington and the days of early America; by tracing family customs in relationship to work and recreation; by comparing how ancient peoples reared and disciplined their children with practices of today; by showing the changing role of women throughout history; by contrasting marriage customs among primitive and civilized people, etc., an interesting and informative way of teaching family life education.

The communicative arts can provide pupils with opportunities to write and speak about such things as why women and girls should be protected, what causes families to be unhappy or happy, how to care for babies, what to do when mother and a new baby brother or sister come home from the hospital, how we can help our mothers at mealtime, family fun, what I want to be when I grow up, and other related subjects. The possibilities of topics for use in this area are as great as a teacher's ability to utilize the right moment for doing so. She should listen carefully to what children say about the above-mentioned areas, as well as observe their behavior. Likewise, she should be on the lookout for the "sissy" or "mamma's boy" or the girl who acts and talks like a boy and wishes she were one, for these children need help. Class parties, projects, and other group activities should be initiated as a means of helping both sexes work and play cooperatively together, especially in the fourth and fifth grades, the age when both groups tend to be hypercritical of each other. Among primary children, those who are only children, excessively shy, or aggressive should be aided to contribute to group endeavors. The elementary school *is* the society of children, and each youth therein must learn to become an important, intelligent, and vital contributing member of it.

Science is the foundation upon which sex education rests. It can be utilized in many ways to correlate family life education with needed scientific information about the differences between the sexes and human reproduction. Youth in the upper elementary grades are ready for detailed and more specific factual information, although many of available materials should be modified for them. Such topics as the following might well be included in the materials to be covered in instructional units on this subject:

1. The male and female reproductive organs.
2. Menstruation and nocturnal emissions.
3. Venereal diseases.
4. Pregnancy.
5. The development of the human fetus.
6. Normal and abnormal birth.
7. Heredity.
8. Infant care.

9. Reproduction of plants and animals.
10. The role of sex in mental illness.
11. Your own changing body.

It is not enough, however, merely to teach the facts about reproduction. It could be dangerous to do so, for boys and girls are naturally curious and want to see and try things out for themselves. Unless positive behavior and desirable attitudes are built into each pupil at the same time they learn the facts of life, the program can be harmful rather than beneficial.

Younger children will delight in having a class pet, feeding and caring for it, and watching it change and reproduce its own kind. Rabbits, hamsters, goldfish, chickens, or almost any other kind of small animal can be used. A new "Chick-Chick Egg Incubator" is now on the market which will enable pupils to see the entire hatching process through a plastic dome window. The correct heat and humidity can be maintained in the incubator to hatch ducks, pheasants, and quail.[5] Watching a tiny bird actually breaking out of its egg is a thrilling educational experience for any child. Each should do more than just watch, however, for all should be taught also the magic, miracle, and wonder of life.

Mathematics and family life education can work together in many ways. Suggested activities for doing so include:

1. Preparing a family budget.
2. Determining life and hospital insurance costs and learning which policies give the most benefits for the money spent on them.
3. Discovering the food costs for a baby from birth to the first year.
4. Comparing the amount of money spent on recreation from today's family budget to that spent by one's grandparents.
5. Estimating family food costs over a period of time.
6. Exploring family vacation plans in relation to family income.
7. Studying retirement insurance plans.
8. Determining the relation of take-home pay to salary.
9. Filling out income-tax forms for a married couple.
10. Finding out about loan interest rates.

Dramatic and art activities are especially adaptable for correlation in this area, especially with primary children. They will learn

[5] Write to Insta Sales Corp., Dept. M. 25, 11 E. 47th Street, New York 17, N.Y., for information. This incubator sells for less than $3.00.

many things by making a poster of a happy family from pictures cut out of magazines, as well as provide their teacher with new insights into what they think a happy family would be. Their feelings and emotions, many fears, hatreds, or desires can best be shown by free-hand drawings, cutouts, clay figures, or other creative endeavors. It is of paramount importance that the teacher watch these children "play house," "eat dinner with my family," or other dramatized home and family life experiences, for the children's actions can be most revealing to the trained, sensitive eye.

Suggested creative activities in this area include:

1. Act out going on a family trip.
2. Draw pictures of your family.
3. Act out a story you make up about any child in any kind of a family.
4. Show us how to play the favorite quiet game of your family.
5. Tell us about your favorite relative and why you like him.
6. Have a pet or dog show. Discuss having a pet for a friend, and how to take good care of it.
7. Illustrate a story your parents or grandparents told you about any of their own experiences.
8. Give a short skit showing a typical Saturday or Sunday at your house.
9. Make a poster of what your family does on a holiday.
10. Make clothes for foreign dolls out of cloth, or clothe cardboard figures with costumes made out of colored paper. Tell us about your doll.
11. Dramatize social graces, giving each couple an assigned role to play, such as walking to school with one of the opposite sex, etc.
12. Have an art contest and choose the best painting, water color, or carving which shows human happiness. Talk about what makes people happy or sad.
13. Have each pupil make a poster of snapshots taken of happy people from all ages and walks of life. Choose the best snapshot submitted. Tell about the person shown in the photograph.
14. Conduct a class song- and motto-writing contest. Use both as a means of stressing group solidarity and good conduct.

Physical education can also be correlated in many ways with family life education. It has been said that if you want to know what a child is really like, watch him play, but if you are concerned about what he might become, direct his play. Certainly the child is his real self when he is so completely engrossed in play that he forgets to be the boy his teacher wants him to be, or his mother hopes he is.

Every child in every culture is culturally conditioned by adults. He is taught by adults the games of the clan, tribe, or city block, as well as those favored by his own sex, race, and religion. A boy is taught manly games, little girls are given dolls to play with, in an endeavor to teach them what boys do in contrast with what girls do. Many learn these lessons early and well, but others need extra help and patience before they do so. Even tradition enters the picture of play. Children want to be like grown-ups and thus they engage in activities once favored by adults they admire. Such games as "Run, Sheepie, Run!" or "Red Rover" are "as old as the hills," yet they remain the favorites of children throughout the ages.[6]

Other ways in which physical education can be correlated with family life education are:

1. Participating in many games and sports together, using mixed teams. Relays and other easily organized activities are especially well suited for helping boys see that girls can play skillfully, too.
2. Teaching others the favorite active team game played in your family or block.
3. Having an all-school fun night.
4. Participating in a "Share Your Adult Friends" night by having each pupil bring two admired adult friends outside his own family. Play simple active games in mixed teams with these guests, as planned and conducted by the pupils themselves.
5. Having a class cookout and have campcraft skill contests, such as woodchopping, fire-building, or water-boiling. Evaluate the results by discussing how this experience could have been better planned and conducted so that everyone would have had a better time.
6. Learning several folk dances. Present these in costume to P.T.A. or assembly program. Learn about family groups and foreign customs through class discussions and bulletin board materials.
7. Sharing menstrual hygiene materials with girls who ask for them; answering the direct questions boys ask in the locker room or elsewhere.
8. Discussing the role exercise plays in being physically fit and attractive. Learn several basic conditioning exercises and do them regularly.
9. Playing games according to rules and good conduct; discuss the correlation between the "game of life" and the game of volleyball.
10. Learning games suitable for family backyard fun and sharing them with your own family.

[6] Maryhelen Vannier and Mildred Foster, *Teaching Physical Education in Elementary Schools,* 3rd ed., Philadelphia, Saunders, 1963, p. 13.

The communicative arts. The possibilities for integrated study in this area are many. A fifth grade class in a school in Oregon last year engaged in an intensive study of American Indians in their social science class. Every aspect of the life of various tribes such as the Cherokee, Blackfeet, or Iroquois was studied—their customs, family life, food, form of government, trade, problems, etc. Some pupils made a miniature Indian village, while a group of boys learned and presented the rain dance of the Cherokees, and the girls prepared and served a typical Indian meal. The group became so enthusiastic that they planned and gave an assembly program showing others what they had learned. Such experiences teach children many more things besides the differences between modern customs and ancient ones, for the children learn how to work well with fellow students in a cooperative venture, and how to express themselves. The same kind of an experience can be used with modification on any grade level, and people from any part of the world can be studied. Idealistic youth needs to learn as much about the life of different people as possible. Our future and theirs can depend upon the experiences which boys and girls have today in our schools.

USE OF TEACHING METHODS

The following teaching methods can best be utilized in the instruction of pupils in family life education.

Problem solving. Many aspects of sex education can be used successfully as children explore and find solutions to problems which are important to them. During this school year a group of sixth graders studied the problem of increased juvenile delinquency in a unit on current events in their social studies class. They were amazed to learn that one cause of delinquency was inadequate and faulty home relationships among youth, irrespective of income group. Their next step was to discover what kind of family difficulties were most likely to be at the root of crime. The group spent an entire week tracking down pertinent information which helped them not only to learn much about delinquency but also a great deal about their own personal values and conduct. They were surprised to find out that sex misbehavior and faulty attitudes also played such a major role in delinquency and crime. Finally the group drew up their own code of ethics for youth and made a list of things both children and parents could do in order to become better family members.

In a fourth grade class in a school in Minnesota, the teacher noticed that the boys usually took possession of sports equipment from the storage room, leaving the girls with only broken bats and unsewed, "beat-up" balls. She discussed this problem later in her civics class, and asked the children how it could be solved. The group spent several days discussing the rights of others, why girls should take part in sports and have the use of adequate equipment, and even studied about the lives of famous men and women athletes. Improved behavior and better understanding and respect for each other resulted.

Problem solving should not be merely limited to groups, for almost every child has his own unique set of worries about himself and relationships with others. Concern with children's problems is the duty of their teacher, who sometimes becomes so engrossed teaching subject matter that she forgets that she should also be teaching children *through* it to help them find solutions to their own personal problems. All young people need to think for themselves and control their own behavior. Abraham offers the following suggested ways in which teachers might stimulate independent thinking, and help pupils develop their own ideas and expand their horizons:

1. Let children ask, talk, and converse.
2. Ask each child often, "What do *you* think?" "How do *you* feel about this?"
3. Bring up problems of interest to children, such as "How can we figure out mileage on this map?"
4. Ask questions that dig, such as "Are you *sure?*" or "Are there any other possibilities?"
5. Take them to as many places as your time permits.
6. Involve them in your plans.
7. Encourage the solution that is unusual.[7]

Class discussions can be used in a number of ways in this area, such as:

[7] Willard Abraham, "Helping Children Think," *Today's Health,* vol. 108 (June, 1961).

1. Discuss with the children their mother's and father's place and role in the family; relationships between siblings; how to function successfully in the family.
2. Study about and see vegetables or plants grow from seeds. Discuss what causes things to grow.
3. Read to the class the books *The Wonderful Egg* or *Bambi*. Show and discuss the pictures and story in these books.
4. Bring a bird's nest to class. Show how the nest was built. Discuss the necessity of having a good home.
5. Keep guppies in a bowl in the classroom. Observe them carefully every day. Draw out from the class questions they have about their observations.
6. Discuss the proper way to use bathroom facilities at home or at school.
7. Bring pictures to class of happy families; fathers having fun with their sons; mother-and-daughter activities. Talk about these pictures.
8. Have each pupil tell what he wants to be when he grows up. Decide if this is a wise choice for a girl or boy to make.
9. Have a group discussion on what fathers should do in the home, mothers' responsibilities, etc.
10. Act out and discuss stories and poems about animal families such as "The Three Little Pigs," or "The Night before Christmas." Discuss the role and responsibility of each character.
11. Discuss the film *Human Reproduction* in your sixth grade class.

Special reports might well be assigned in many topics in this field. These may be about famous men and women in various fields such as the arts or politics, family customs among certain religious groups such as the Jewish and Amish, family health problems, the changing role of the mother, family vacations, etc. Such experiences can assist children in gaining skills in speaking before a group, and also help them learn to do library research, which is necessary for the increasing numbers of students who are going on to college.

Demonstrations provide possibilities in teaching and correlating good grooming skills such as how to file fingernails correctly, cut toenails, shampoo the hair, wash the face, the kinds of clothes to wear for certain events such as church or school, etc. Since most boys will be fathers someday, they too can learn many household skills through demonstration and practice, such as cooking, washing dishes, or changing baby diapers. Girls can also learn to do many of the household tasks often done by fathers through this method of teaching, such as learning how to use a hammer, saw, and other tools, how to lay bathroom tile or kitchen linoleum, and how to paint and re-

Children should be given many opportunities to do library research, write reports, and read them aloud in class. (Courtesy, AAHPER.)

pair furniture. Care must be taken, however, lest too much emphasis be placed upon learning to master these skills without teaching the children why both sexes should share and work together. The many "manly" sport skills such as throwing, batting, and catching a baseball, or kicking a football, can also be taught and shared by the boys in the group. The girls, in turn, can help them improve their dance steps. Good partners in work and play tend to become good marriage partners also.

Role playing can be of great value in helping the teacher gain deeper insight into individual behavior and family problems. Children do more than just act out being a father, or having a baby sister, as those expert in the field of play therapy have learned.[8] An observant teacher can always help a child fit into a part that meets

[8] Ruth Hartley, Lawrence Frank, and Robert Goldenson, *Understanding Children's Play,* New York, Teachers College, 1959, p. 337.

his specific needs. Role playing, coupled with music, can help children express feelings of hostility, fear, or anger, as well as make a real contribution to improved mental health. The teacher should keep in the background during these experiences and be a keen observer who focuses her attention on the child more than on what he is doing. Brief notes might be made on filing cards for each child, noting what children choose to engage in, do, and say, as well as what their reactions are. It has been said that to the skilled teacher, dramatic play is a revealing mirror of a child.

Field trips which help children gain understanding of the role of human beings in work and play are many and varied. The group will profit greatly from exploring their community and becoming acquainted with a wide variety of people in it. Trips can be taken to a zoo to observe animal families, to a dog or cat hospital to see new-born puppies and kittens, to a farm to learn how plants and animals are cared for and grow, to a local child day-care center to observe the play activities and care of young children of working mothers, to a church to see a christening or a wedding, to a pediatrician to learn what he does and how he became a baby specialist, to a flower shop to learn how seeds are planted and flowers grow, or to an airplane factory to see what work men do in contrast to that of women working in the same plant. Certainly every community resource should be used to its fullest, and can help children gain an increased understanding and appreciation of their own world.

Surveys can correlate family life education with mathematics. Suggested studies include finding out:

1. How many in the class have brothers and sisters, and how old they are.
2. How many have both parents working, and what kind of work they do.
3. How many have only one parent.
4. How many have fathers who travel and are away from home a great deal.
5. The size of an average family in one block.
6. How many brothers and sisters each parent has.
7. What families do for home fun.
8. The average age of each parent in a family in a block.
9. How many parents are college graduates.
10. Where each member of the family was born.

11. How many times each family in the block had moved to a new house since their first child was born.
12. How many babies live in the block, including those of animals such as puppies, kittens, etc.

USE OF INSTRUCTIONAL MATERIALS

Many kinds of instructional materials can make learning about family life an exciting educational adventure. These include:

Models and specimens of the human body or any of its parts. Children fortunate enough to be near the Dallas or Cleveland Health Museums can there see wonderful models showing the growth of the baby inside the mother's body month by month, and "see" how babies grow and move. Commercial models of the human body can also be used in the classroom to enable children to find answers to their frequent questions such as "Where do babies come from?" or "How does the baby get out?" Likewise, such specimens as a collection of various kinds and sizes of eggs, seeds, plants, wood, etc., can be used by the teacher to "liven up" her materials on instruction about "life."

Bulletin boards and posters can help boys and girls gain a better understanding of this area as well as help them develop creative and communicative skills. Suggested activities include:

1. Have each child make a poster of any aspect of family life. Help each feel secure in the group, and give each many things to do with his own hands so that he will keep them away from his own sex organs.
2. Draw pictures of a happy family spending an evening at home, at the dinner table, or going on a trip.
3. Make posters of ways each can help their families at home.
4. Have a pet show. Draw out the pupils and note their understanding of animals, how they are born, and how to care for them. Record what you learned from this experience on the class bulletin board.
5. Visit a health museum or zoo to gain information about babies or animals. Illustrate what you have seen.
6. Have a child illustrate a visit to a farm. Next, take the class to visit a dairy or other types of farm. See the young ponies, pigs, chickens, or other animals. Observe how their mother helps them.
7. Illustrate a report given on pioneers, Indians, Eskimos, primitive tribes, by making cutout feltboard figures. Compare what is learned with our own American family customs.

8. Raise a class pet. Record its weight, habits, etc., on the bulletin board.
9. Invite a local 4-H club leader to speak to the class and show illustrated materials on animal breeding.

Books, whether used in the classroom and read aloud to the youngest children, or selected and read by older youth, can do much to help pupils gain a clearer understanding of sex, other people, and of themselves. Such books as *The Diary of Anne Frank* appeal to boys as well as girls, as do those written about famous people throughout the world. Oral or written book reports will assist the pupils in expressing themselves as well as in giving them an understanding of what they have read and its relationship to themselves. Written reports are especially valuable in helping their authors gain self-understanding, particularly if the pupils are asked to correlate any incident in the story with their own lives, or express what they feel about the actions of certain characters.

For the younger pupils, having the teacher read aloud to them can be a treat. The instructor should do more than read a story, for she should also draw out the reactions of the children to it. Recently, a young teacher in Dallas read her first graders the book *The Wonderful Egg.* The next day she used their interest in eggs for instruction in her unit on family life education. Note how she asked leading questions in order to learn how much the pupils really knew in this area.

In our health lesson last week we learned that everyone needs to eat a good breakfast. Margaret Rose, do you remember some of the different foods we can eat to have a good breakfast?

That's right! And eggs are a very important part of a healthy breakfast. We have already learned why eggs are good for us to eat. But what else do you know about eggs? Are there any other kinds of eggs besides chicken eggs?

That's right! There are bird, fish, turtle, frog, bee, and snake eggs, just to name a few. So many different kinds of eggs!

Where can we find these different eggs? (Show poster drawings and have children see difference in places eggs are found.)

Do all these eggs look alike? (Poster again, pointing out that there are many kinds.)

Can we eat all these different kinds of eggs?

If we don't eat all of them, what else are they good for?

When we don't eat them, each different kind of egg hatches and then grows into a different kind of animal. (Show pictures.)

Where do these eggs come from?

That's right! They all are laid by their mothers. Then when they are outside their mother's body, they break their shells or coverings.

Did you know that everything else on earth that is alive started as an egg—even the plants and trees? In most plants, though, the eggs grow into seeds. Even though every living thing began from a little egg, each one is different. Each new plant and each new animal grows to be the same kind of living thing as its parents.

Now I know that you are thinking—if everything has eggs, where are they? Trees' eggs are seeds, some animals like a bird lay their eggs and you can see those. But other animals, like my dog, have babies and you never see their eggs at all. Where are they?

You don't see them but they are there just the same. Hidden away inside the mother is a special sac—a warm, safe place where the eggs change into baby animals. They grow and grow inside their mothers until one day they come out into the world through a special tube that stretches to let them out. They are born—just as you were born one day. You grew as a tiny egg inside your mother.

At the beginning of you, you were no bigger than a dot—a tiny dot much smaller than this dot (show picture) or even a single grain of sand. So small that the dot could not be seen at all, except through a strong magnifying glass. That dot that was going to be you was like a tiny little round egg.

Something even more wonderful about this tiny egg—even though it was as tiny as a dot, it had nearly everything that it took to make you! Your eyes, hair, hands, etc. Your being able to grow from something very small and helpless into something pretty big and independent was right there in that tiny egg! Isn't that amazing?

Then the tiny egg that was you grew and grew inside your mother until you were a full-sized baby ready to be born. Then you were born with everything you needed to be a person—and it all came from the wonderful egg.[9]

Radio and television, like the daily newspaper and weekly magazines, have an abundance of materials which can be used by an alert teacher to help children become aware of any aspect of sex education. Cartoons seen on the television such as "The Flintstones," "Captain Kangaroo," or "Donald Duck" are especially appropriate for helping younger boys and girls learn more about families, both

[9] Reported in the class, Teaching Health and Physical Education in Elementary Schools, Southern Methodist University, January 8, 1961.

human and cartoon. Such radio and television programs as "Gunsmoke" or "Stagecoach West" can help children gain a better understanding of how people dressed or what they did during our pioneer days, even though these programs present fictionalized version of the reality. Even encouraging the older pupils to listen to such serials as "One Man's Family" or "Our Gal Sunday" have educational value, but only if they are fully utilized and children are helped to "see through" some of the things they see and hear. Listening to such programs for several days can even become a good introduction to such topics as family problems, the happily married couple, or problems some grown-ups face. The discriminating teacher knows just how much of what exists in the world about her is suitable for classroom use, and uses what she can, wisely and well.

Films can also provide children with learning experiences about family life. *Human Reproduction,* which is perhaps one of the best films available for showing the facts of life, should be used only with older pupils who are ready for such specific information. It might well be seen several times, at well-spaced intervals, in junior and senior high school, for the film contains so much well-presented information that it is impossible to absorb all of it at one time. Almost any health film for any grade can be used for correlating such topics as posture, good grooming, growth, or nutrition with the best ways to grow up to reach maturity.

Sometime during this unit, the teacher should:

1. Talk individually and informally with each pupil. Discover the thoughts, fears, and attitudes toward those of the opposite sex or growing up. Gain the respect, trust, and friendship of each, however, before doing so. Evaluate the results and file summarized notes in the cumulative school record of each child.
2. Have pupils fill out the rest of several sentences similar to these given below, when the occasion best arises:
   1. I like boys because ____________________.
   2. Girls are ____________________.
   3. My parents think that I ____________________.
   4. In my home, we have ____________________.
   5. My greatest worry about growing up is that I ____________________.
   6. I know that I am growing up because I ____________________.
3. Read each answer carefully, keep what has been written confidential, and give assistance where needed.

DESIRABLE OUTCOMES

A well-taught and guided educational experience should produce the following desirable outcomes in terms of knowledge, attitudes, and practices:

In the primary grades, the pupils will:

1. Work and play happily together with members of their own and the opposite sex.
2. Develop interest in nature and in life.
3. Care for their own body needs and know about bodily functions.
4. Be helpful at school and at home and considerate of the rights of others.
5. Be aware of the differences between boys and girls, and know of the role each sex plays in life.
6. Understand that animals and plants reproduce themselves as well as people.
7. Know and appreciate the role each parent plays in the family.
8. Accept and be glad of their own sex.
9. Know how chickens and other animals are born.
10. Have curiosity and questions concerning sex satisfied by truthful information, and not feel ashamed or feel guilty because of their own thoughts.

In the upper elementary grades, the pupils will:

1. Understand and accept changes in their bodies.
2. Appreciate the abilities and differences between boys and girls.
3. Have many friends of both sexes; be respected by their peers and teachers.
4. Accept responsibility and be concerned about group welfare; be sensitive to situations which leave someone out or make someone feel unhappy.
5. Know how the body functions; name correctly the parts of the body.
6. Become increasingly concerned about their own personal appearance; feel secure and confident of their own ability; welcome opportunities to do new things.
7. Enjoy family life activities and share fun and happiness in their own homes.
8. Appreciate the role of the family in society; be aware of the responsibility of each parent and family member.
9. Recognize and accept their own sex role; take pride in being a girl or a boy.
10. Know how boys and girls change in adolescence.

11. Ask frank questions about sex or any aspect of family life without embarrassment or guilty feelings.
12. Belong to a closely knit circle of friends and be well liked by their classmates of both sexes.
13. Desire to have good character; belong to and take an active part in church and youth organizational activities.
14. Develop a deeper appreciation for their families, home, and school.
15. Develop social graces; desire to be popular and well respected in their school and neighborhood.
16. Have several close adult friends outside their family circle.
17. Be able to compete successfully as a member of a mixed team in class contests, physical education activities, and in games played during leisure time in the neighborhood.
18. Enjoy many outings, backyard or other home experiences with their families; take pride in being a member of their own primary group.
19. Increasingly practice good health habits and self-discipline; gain greater self-confidence and independence.
20. Possess strong, skillful bodies, take part in and enjoy a wide variety of vigorous sports, dance well; have many recreational interests.

SUGGESTED READINGS

Learning Aids

There is an abundance of learning aids in this subject. The following materials are recommended:

FOR THE PRIMARY GRADES

Pamphlets

The Story about You, National Education Association.

About Us and Our Friends; Six to Twelve, John Hancock Insurance Company.

Films and Filmstrips

Appreciating Our Parents (11 minutes); *Developing Friendships* (10 minutes).

Friendship Begins at Home (15 minutes), Coronet Films.

When All the People Play (27 minutes), National Film Board of Canada.

He Acts His Age (15 minutes), McGraw-Hill.

Stories and Books for Children

Gruenberg, Sidonie, *The Wonderful Story of How You Were Born,* New York, Doubleday, 1952.

Facts of Life for Children, New York, Child Study Association, 132 W. 74th St., New York 21, N.Y.

Lathrop, Dorothy, *Animals of the Bible,* Philadelphia, Lippincott, 1960.
Jones, Elizabeth, *Prayer for a Child,* New York, Macmillan, 1958.
Schneider, Herman, and Nina Schneider, *How Your Body Works,* New York, W. R. Scott, 1949.
Bibby, Cyril, *How Life Is Handed On,* New York, Emerson, 1947.
Beck, Lester, *Human Growth,* New York, Harcourt, Brace, 1949.
A Story About You, National Education Association and American Medical Association, Washington, D.C., N.E.A., 1957.
Remers, H., and R. H. Bauemfeind, *Your Problems and How to Handle Them,* Chicago, Science Research Associates, 1953.
Neugarten, Bernice, *How You Grow,* Science Research Associates, 1952.
Geirne, M. I., and J. H. Seilgmann, *A Baby is Born,* Simon and Schuster, 1960.
Horowitz, Caroline, *A Children's Treasury of Things to Do,* Hart, 1961.
Leaf, Munro, *Manners Can Be Fun; How to Behave and Why,* Lippincott, 1955.
Gruenberg, J., *The Wonderful Story of How You Were Born,* American Social Hygiene Association, 1956.
Schloot, Warren, *The Wonderful Egg,* New York, Scribner, 1960.
Strain, Frances, *Being Born,* New York, Appleton-Century-Crofts, 1956.

Health Readers
Macmillan Science, Health, and Safety Series, *Books I, II, III.*
Scott, Foresman Health and Personal Development Series, *Happy Days with Our Friends; Good Times with Our Friends, Three Friends.*

FOR THE UPPER ELEMENTARY GRADES

Pamphlets
Understanding Yourself by W. Menninger, Science Research Associates Chicago.
The Story of Life; Sex Education for the Ten Year Old, American Medical Association.
From Boy to Man, Social Hygiene Association.
Very Personally Yours (girls), Kimberly-Clark Corp.
Posture on Parade (poster for girls), National Dairy Council.
Good Grooming Chart, Bristol-Myers.
Health for Man and Boy, American Social Hygiene Association.
Sound Attitudes Toward Sex, American Social Hygiene Association.
Understanding Sex, Science Research Associates.
It's Natural (girls), Tampax, Inc.
Very Personally Yours (girls), International Cellucotton Products Company.
Your Own Story, American Social Hygiene Association.
On Becoming a Woman, Tampax, Inc.

Films and Filmstrips

Confidence Because You Understand Menstruation (record and filmstrip), Personal Products Corporation, Miltown, N.J.

Understanding Your Emotions (15 minutes), Coronet Films.

Human Reproduction (30 minutes), McGraw-Hill.

Good Grooming (30 minutes), McGraw-Hill.

Posters

"Anatomical Chart on Menstruation," Tampax, Inc.

"What Happens During Menstruation," Personal Products Corp.

"Good Grooming," Bristol-Myers.

"Special Days Are Fun," National Commission on Safety Education.

Books, Magazines, and Stories for Children

On Becoming a Woman, Louise Ames, New York, Dell, 1961.

Being Born, Frances Strain, New York, Appleton-Century-Crofts, 1956.

How Life Is Handed On, Lester Beck, New York, Harcourt, Brace, 1960.

The Wonder of Life, Milton Levine and Jean Seiligman, New York, Simon and Schuster, 1961.

Finding Yourself, 1961; *All about You,* 1959; *Facts Are Not Enough,* 1959; Marian Lerrigo and Helen Southard, American Medical Association.

Attaining Manhood; Attaining Womanhood; George Corner, New York, Harper, 1952.

Mei Li, Thomas Handforth, New York, Doubleday, 1959.

They Were Strong and Good, Robert Lawson, New York, Viking, 1960.

Many Moons, Virginia Lee Burton, New York, Viking, 1954.

Calling All Girls, Parents Magazines, Inc., 1960.

Little Women; Blue Willow; Black Beauty; Tom Sawyer; Detective; No Children, No Pets; Just Plain Maggie; Trolley Car Family; Black Spaniel Mystery; Story of John Paul Jones; Silver for General Washington; Horses; Mark Trail's Book of Animals; Odd Pets; Cowdog; Big Red; Gray Wolf; Yellow Eyes; First to Ride. (All of these are pocket books written especially for children. They are available for less than 50¢ per copy from Reader's Choice, 33 W. 42nd St., New York 36, N.Y., a company sponsored by Scholastic Book Services.)

Readers

Scott, Foresman, Health and Personal Development Series, *You; You and Others; You're Growing Up; In the Teens.*

Laidlaw, Road to Health Series, *Health Trails; Your Health and You, Keeping Healthy.*

Bobbs-Merrill, Health for Young America Series, *Health at School; Health Day by Day; Health and Fun; Health and Growth; Health and Living; Health and Happiness.*

Macmillan, Science, Health and Safety Series, Books *III, IV, V.*

Ginn, Safety and Health Living Series, *Helping the Body in Its Work; The Healthy Home and Community.*

Wilcox Health Action Series, *Healthy Days; Stay Healthy; Good for You; Full of Life; Here's Health.*

Ginn, Health for Better Living Series, *Growing Your Way; Keeping Healthy and Strong; Teamwork for Health.*

Teaching Aids

The following materials are recommended teaching aids in family life education:

IN THE PRIMARY GRADES

Sex Education Series, Joint Committee on Health Problems by National Education Association and American Medical Association, available from the American Medical Association, 335 North Dearborn St., Chicago 10, Ill.

Sex Education Series, AAHPER, Washington 6, D.C.

Hayman, H. S., "Basic Issues in School Sex Education," *Journal of School Health,* vol. 23, no. 1 (January, 1953), 15–17.

Kirkendall, Lester, *Sex Education as Human Relations,* New York, Ivor Publications, 1950.

Eckert, Ralph, *Sex Attitudes in the Home,* New York, Associated Press, 1956.

When Children Ask about Sex, Child Study Association, 132 West 74th St., New York 21, N.Y.

How to Tell Your Child about Sex, Public Affairs Pamphlet, 22 East 38th St., New York 16, N.Y.

Some Special Problems of Children, National Association for Mental Health, 1790 Broadway, New York 19, N.Y.

A Healthy Personality for Your Child, Washington, D.C., Children's Bureau, Publications no. 337, 1952, and no. 338, 1958.

Some A-to-Z's of Family Life Education, New York, Y.W.C.A. Publication Service, 600 Lexington Ave., New York 22, N.Y. (An outline with program suggestions, a list of resources including films, filmstrips, recordings, plays and skits, pamphlets, articles, and books.)

McHose, Elizabeth, *Family Life Education in School and Community,* New York, Teachers College, 1952.

A Guide to Teaching Health in the Elementary School, The University of the State of New York, Health Education Series Bulletin no. 2, Albany, 1959.

IN THE UPPER ELEMENTARY GRADES

Menstrual Hygiene Teaching Aid Kit, Tampax, Inc.

A Teaching Guide for Menstrual Hygiene, Personal Products Corporation, Miltown, N.J.

Wolf, Ann, *The Parent's Manual,* New York, Simon and Schuster, 1941.

Bibby, Cyril, *Sex Education* (A Guide for Parents, Teachers, and Youth Leaders), New York, Emerson, 1946.

Jones, Marion, *At What Age Should a Girl Be Told about Menstruation?* (pamphlet), Kimberly-Clark Corporation, Neenah, Wis.

New Patterns in Sex Teaching, New York, Appleton-Century-Crofts, 1934.

Strain, Francis, *Sex Guidance in Family Life Education,* New York, Macmillan, 1942.

Edson, W., "Sex in the Life of a Child," *Childcraft,* vol. 10, Chicago, 1947.

Baruch, Dorothy, *New Ways in Sex Education,* New York, McGraw-Hill, 1959.

Narramore, Clyde, *How to Tell Your Child about Sex,* Detroit, Mich., Zonder-Van Publishing, 1959.

Lerrigo, Marian, and Helen Sutherland, *A Parent's Privilege; The Story about You; Facts Are Not Enough,* Chicago, National Education Association and American Medical Association, 1955.

Hymes, James, *How to Tell Your Child about Sex,* Public Affairs Committee, Inc., 22 East 38th Street, New York 16, N.Y.

Kirkendall, Ralph, *Helping Children Understand Sex,* Science Research Associates, 57 W. Grand Avenue, Chicago 10, Ill.

Ostrovsky, Everett, *Father to the Child,* New York, Putnam, 1960.

Y.W.C.A., *Some A-to-Z's of Family Life Education,* Publication Sources, 600 Lexington Ave., New York 22, N.Y.

Child Study Association of America, *When Your Child Asks about Sex,* 132 East 74th Street, New York 21, N.Y.

Tebbel, John, *The Magic of Balanced Living,* New York, Harper, 1956.

Schweinitz, Karl D., *Growing Up,* New York, Macmillan, 1955.

Issues of *The Journal of School Health; Today's Health; The Journal of the AAHPER.*

Moser, Clarence, *Understanding Boys; Understanding Girls,* New York, Association Press, 1958.

National Association of Mental Health, *What Every Child Needs,* 1790 Broadway, New York 19, N.Y., 1960.

FOUR

IMPROVING THE PROGRAM

A MAN'S MIND STRETCHED BY A NEW IDEA CAN NEVER GO BACK TO ITS ORIGINAL DIMENSIONS.

OLIVER WENDELL HOLMES

15 EVALUATING THE RESULTS

Evaluation is a method used to appraise, measure, and check progress. It is finding out where you are and carefully analyzing how you arrived there in relationship to where you want to go. It is also a process of taking stock or self-discovery so that new and better ways to gain desired goals can be found and used with renewed zest. Or, as Anderson says, it tells what is, what should be, and what should not be, and points out the following values of an evaluation program of the total school health program:

1. Inventories the present status of child health and the health program.
2. Appraises the health of the individual child.
3. Appraises all aspects of the health program.
4. Measures progress.
5. Points out strengths in the program.
6. Reveals places where emphasis is needed.
7. Assists children in understanding their health condition and progress in health education.
8. Helps parents understand the health of their children and the school health program.
9. Gives the school a basis for revising both its health and general programs.
10. Provides a basis for public support and funds for school health work.[1]

PURPOSE AND SCOPE OF EVALUATION

Evaluation in health education should show that the program has had a marked and improved effect upon the health of the pupils.

[1] C. L. Anderson, *School Health Practice,* St. Louis, Mosby, 1960, p. 448.

This is not always easy to measure, for behavior changes occur gradually and their effect may not be fully seen until the pupils reach adulthood. Evaluation should also be a process for determining to what extent the program has reached its stated objectives. The interplay between the objectives of education and health education should be continuous. The total school health program should be judged in terms of its results continuously by the school administrators, school health medical authorities, health supervisors, classroom teachers, school health council, pupils, parents, community health coworkers, and all others included or interested in the program. Such evaluation may range all the way from subjective observation to scientific measurement; it can be done by those with training in health education or methods of educational measurement or by experts in both fields. Many school administrators, pressed by taxpayers who want to get the most from their investment in public education, are including in their annual budget expenses for a scientific evaluation of their total school health program. Although this may be done by a team of experts, this type of evaluation can be an educational experience for those primarily engaged in the health program or those on the school health council. A local survey team guided by a selected health education expert might well take part in such a program. Oberteuffer suggests that any group engaged in such evaluation be first guided by the following principles:

1. Evaluation should be continuous.
2. It should embrace all the important functions of the school health program, including instruction and activities.
3. Evaluation should be cooperative. All those who are affected by the evaluation should participate in it—administrators, teachers, pupils, parents, physician, nurses, dental hygienists, nutritionists and others.
4. It should be concerned both with end products and the means to reach these ends.
5. It should touch upon all health aspects of the school, including curriculum, administration, buildings, grounds, equipment, finances, and community relationships.
6. Evaluation should be focused upon the important values which underlie the health program of the school, and the success or failure of the program should be judged in terms of how well it meets the values held.
7. A long-range evaluation program should be so planned that no one

year would involve the school in a complete study of every aspect of school health education.

8. The collection of data and keeping of records in the school have no value in themselves. Only as the data aid in evaluating the true functions of the school to educate do they attain value.[2]

There are many excellent rating scales and school health standard check lists available for evaluating the school's physical plant, health service, custodial service, health instruction programs, mental, dental, nutrition, and safety education programs.[3] Any such selected tools can assist an evaluation committee engaged in a well-planned, long-range measurement program. The results of the work done by this group should be published and made available to all school personnel and interested citizens in the community.[4] This written report might well contain the findings of the committee, what the school is actually doing in relationship to its declared objectives, and recommendations for the future betterment of the program.

Evaluating the Program

It must be remembered that health instruction is but one of three areas of the total health program and that it must be a part of the work done by those engaged in school health services, and all who are primarily concerned with and responsible for providing a healthful school environment. There must be a direct relationship between what is taught in the classroom and the services provided by the school and the type of school environment in which children are required by law to be 5 to 6 hours daily, 30 weeks a year for 12 or 16 years of their lives.

Evaluation of the health education program should first determine whether it is in accord with sound overall educational objectives and principles, and then measure the degree to which the health education program has reached its established objectives. Such evaluation should lead to curriculum improvement, as well as

[2] Delbert Oberteuffer, *School Health Education,* 3rd ed., New York, Harper, 1960, pp. 525–526.

[3] See the Appendix for suggested sources.

[4] For suggestions of how the report should be written and what they might contain, see *Evaluation of Health Education and Health Services in Los Angeles Public Schools,* 1959. Available from the Los Angeles Public Schools.

the development of better health practices and environmental conditions of the school, home, and community. It should be continuous and include the pupils. Such a study should show the weaknesses as well as the strengths of the school health program, and should be used as a guide for charting needed improvements in all three of its areas.

Measuring instruments. The following instruments can be used successfully in evaluating the school program:

Records. These should include carefully kept records of the school food service department, including food choices made by the pupils, amount of milk sold, and other types of similar information; health service records, including the results of periodic weighing and measuring, physical examinations and tests, records of remedial defects corrected and as yet uncorrected, first-aid treatment given, and other pertinent information; records which show needed changes, or improvements made in the school environment, such as new, fenced-in play areas, additional fire escapes, etc.

Observations. These should include the observations made by all adults connected with the school (as well as those by each teacher of her class) of the health conditions, behavior, and attitudes of the children. The school custodian, nurse, and bus driver should report to those evaluating the school health program what they have seen children do or heard them say in relation to the opportunities provided for them by the school to learn about health.

Surveys. These should include a careful study of the health problems and needs of the school itself, then of the home, and finally of the community. The effectiveness of the school health program should be measured in terms of improvement in relationship to problems and needs in all these places.

Questionnaires and check lists. Such records can show the interests and practices in health among parents and children. Both should be asked to answer such questions as the time children usually go to bed, what they eat for breakfast, etc., and fill out health interest forms. Careful tabulation should be made of these materials; they should be analyzed to determine the amount and degree of changes in behavior, attitudes, and interests which have taken place as a result of the health education program.

Parent conferences. Such experiences are splendid for helping the teacher gain insight into what the child does or does not do at home for his health in relationship to what he has learned in school.

Personal creative work. Diaries, autobiographies, themes, poems, and other samples of personal, creative work done by each child can help adults gain needed insight concerning these pupils, as well as help them discover how effective health education experiences have been to them. Such materials are especially valuable in measuring attitudes.

Written tests. Oral or written tests of knowledge, attitudes, and habits can also be used to evaluate learning results.

EVALUATING PUPIL PROGRESS

Methods of evaluating pupil progress through subjective or objective measurement of the health instruction program include:

Skill tests
Written tests of knowledge, attitudes and habits
Check lists
Rating scales
Interviews
Case studies
Diaries
Parental opinions
Conferences
Self-appraisal
Questionnaires
Group discussion
Posture tests
Attitude tests
Social development tests
Health records
Personality inventories
Progress reports of school health service personnel
School surveys of the use of facilities, such as the lunchroom

These tests may be used for:

1. Motivation
2. Self-evaluation
3. Grading
4. Grouping
5. Diagnosing weakness
6. Guidance

Subjective Tests:

Observation.[5] This is the most frequently used means of evalu-

[5] See Chapter 2, "Teaching through Health Appraisal Activities," for suggestions.

ating behavior in elementary schools. To be of value, such appraisal must be critical, precise, and skilled. Both appearance and behavior can be observed and accurate deductions made by those with trained eyes and ears.

Interviews and Conferences. Interviews and other types of counseling can reveal significant findings as the teacher talks with each child, trying to find out more about him, what he feels, thinks, knows, and does. Conferences should involve the parents, who are more informed about their own child than anyone else. Records should be kept of each conference and used to evaluate progress made by each pupil.

Self appraisal. Check sheets, rating scales, and other such tools used by pupils can do much to stimulate interest in health and motivate the desire to improve health habits. Such methods are superior to direct questions like "What did you have for breakfast?" or "When did you brush your teeth last?", for children soon learn to give back the answers that adults desire or else tell a fib in order to gain recognition or peer status. Any type of self-appraisal record has educational value if checked by each pupil and analyzed carefully by the teacher.

Parental Opinion or Check Lists. Such materials are of value only when the parents feel that they are working partners with the teacher. Those from minority or uneducated groups may use the report as a means of helping their child gain school acceptance or class status and fill out the forms dishonestly. The following type of check list is recommended:

CHECK LIST FOR PARENTS

Does your child:	Yes	No
1. Show improved health habits?		
2. Eat a better balanced diet?		
3. Show more concern for his own safety and health?		
4. Play better with more children?		
5. Seem more concerned about caring for his own body?		
6. Use more of his leisure time in outdoor play?		
7. Go to bed earlier; get more sleep and rest?		
8. Go more willingly to the dentist?		
9. Take better care of his own teeth?		
10. Have improved health, with fewer colds or other types of illness?		

HOW WELL DO I RATE?

	Credits	Possible Daily Score	Mon.	Tues.	Wed.	Thurs.	Fri.	Sat.	Sun.
Milk									
2 glasses	10	20							
4 glasses	20								
Fruit									
1 serving	5								
2 servings	10	10							
Vegetables									
2 vegetables with potatoes	10	10							
if 1 vegetable is raw	5	5							
if vegetable is yellow or leafy green									
1 serving	5								
2 servings	10	10							
if fruits and vegetables include 1 serving of tomatoes, strawberries, melons, or citrus fruits	10	10							
Cereal products									
whole grain enriched									
1 serving	10								
2 servings	15	15							
Eggs, cheese, meat, dried beans, or peas									
1 serving	10								
2 servings	20	20							
Total credits		100							
Deductions									
Any meal omitted		10							
Tea, coffee, soft drink		5							
Sweets between meals		5							
Total deductions		20							
Net Score For Day									

Source: A workshop report, *Techniques of Evaluation in Health Education*, George Peabody College, Nashville, Tenn., 1955, p. 15. Courtesy of George Peabody College.

Case Studies. Each case study should contain:

1. Identification of the pupil
2. Problem faced by the pupil
3. Diagnostic test data
4. Results of interviews of conferences with the pupil, parents, or other adults
5. Pupil's physical condition
6. Pupil's appearance
7. Social and emotional development
8. Mental test results
9. Special interests
10. Home conditions
11. Diagnosis of the case (beginning of the year)
12. Progress made in the case
13. Recommendations

Diaries. A daily diary can be an effective means of self-evaluation and can help the teacher gain insight into each child. In such a report, the pupil should be asked to record everything he did, thought about, or felt keenly during each day for a week. Autobiographies and constructive criticisms written by older children are also revealing and can help both the pupils and their teacher gain better understanding of each learner.

Cumulative Health Records. Such records follow the child throughout his school career and move with him as he goes from school to school. They are invaluable in helping teachers understand the physical handicaps and special needs of each pupil.

Surveys. These can be uesd to survey home or school hazards, check the number of glasses of milk consumed by the school, etc. Surveys may be made by observation, check lists, interviews, reading records, or any other method which will reveal people's behavior.

Skill Tests. These may include testing the ability to read a mouth thermometer correctly, use a microscope, give any aspect of first aid, use equipment safely, or any other type of technical skill.

Picture Tests. Since primary children cannot read or write well, a good way to measure their knowledge or attitude toward health is through pictures. They may either write or check an answer sheet, after seeing a picture, to tell their teacher what they "see" in it. Suggested pictures can be of such things as a toothbrush, wash cloth, microscope, nail file, traffic light showing the color red, etc. Pictures can be used with the whole class, small groups of three or four children, or pupil by pupil.

STANDARDIZED TESTS

Although there are many standardized tests available in the area of health education, there are few good ones which have been devised specifically for elementary children. The following are recommended for measuring health knowledge, habits, interests, and attitudes:

Recommended Standardized Health and Safety Tests for Elementary Schools

Tests of Health Knowledge, New York, Association Press.

Acorn National Achievement Test (Grades 3–6), Rockville Center, N.Y., Acorn Publishing, 1947.

Cincinnati Health Knowledge Test, Cincinnati Public Schools, Cincinnati, Ohio.

Clark, Harrison, *Clark Health Habit Questionnaire,* University of Oregon, Eugene, Ore.

Gates, A. I., and Ruth Strang, *Gates-Strang Health Knowledge Test,* New York, Teachers College, 1945.

Franzen, R. H., M. Derryberry, and W. A. McCall, *Health Awareness Test,* New York, Teachers College, 1946.

Gold, Leah, *Tests in Health Knowledge,* Northfield, Minn., Carleton College, 1954.

Blanchard, B. E., "Character and Personality Rating Scale," *Research Quarterly,* vol. 7 (May, 1936), 78–81.

Health Tests, Bloomington, Ill., Public School Publishing.

Smith, Sara, *Evaluation of the School Health Program,* Department of Health and Physical Education, Florida State University, Tallahassee, Fla., 1960.

Health Tests, National Achievement Tests, 221 East 20th Street, Chicago, Ill., 1959.

A Community Bicycle Program, Association of Casualty and Surety Companies (3 bicycle skill tests), 60 John Street, New York 38, N.Y.

Rugen, Mabel, and Dorothy B. Nyswander, *The Measurement of Understanding in Health Education,* National Society for the Study of Education, Forty-fifth Yearbook, Chicago, University of Chicago Press, 1946.

Trusler, V. T., C. E. Arnett, and H. E. Schrammel, *Trusler-Arnett Health Knowledge Test,* Emporia, Kan., Bureau of Educational Measurement, Kansas State Teachers College, 1940.

Crow, D., and Loretta Ryan, *Health and Safety Education Tests* (Tests for grades 3–6): *I. Good Health and Safety Habits; II. Cause and Effect in Relation to Health and Safety; III. Facts about Health and Safety; IV. Application of Health and Safety Rules,* Rockville Center, N.Y., Acorn Publishing, 1947.

Shaw, John, and Maurice Troyer (Grades 7–12); a test which can be used with some accelerated upper elementary classes, or used as a model for a teacher-devised objective test), *Health Knowledge Test: Knowledge and Application,* Rockville Center, N.Y., Acorn Publishing, 1946.

Health Education Test Forms, American Child Health Association, 1201 Sixteenth Street, N.W., Washington 6, D.C.

Health Information Tests, American Museum of Health, 1790 Broadway, New York 9, N.Y.

Health Tests (Grades 3–8); Benjamin Sanborn, 221 East 20th Street, Chicago, Ill.

Manchester Unit Elementary Tests (Grades 5 through 8), Bureau of Tests and Measurements, Manchester College, North Manchester, Ill.

Brewer, J. W., and H. E. Schrammel, *Brewer-Schrammel Health Knowledge and Attitude Test,* Bureau of Educational Measurement, Kansas State Teachers College, Emporia, Kan.

Johns, Ned, *Johns Health Practice Inventory,* Palo Alto, Calif., Stanford University, 1943.

Southerland, Warren, Jean Latimer, and Claire Turner, "Test of Health Knowledge, Practice, Attitudes, and Interests," *Research Quarterly,* vol. 15 (May, 1934), 47–51.

National Safety Council Tests, National Safety Council, Chicago, Ill., 1959.

Teacher-Devised Tests

Any of the above-mentioned standardized tests might well be studied carefully for suggested patterns by those teachers who devise their own written tests. The characteristics of any good test are that it:

1. Is easy to understand and the directions are simply stated.
2. Is easy to give, grade, and record.
3. Measures what it is supposed to measure (validity).
4. Has measurement consistency (reliability).
5. Is composed of some difficult and some easy items.
6. Challenges all who take it.
7. Is interesting and meaningful.

Written tests include objective questions which require short answers, longer essay answers to general questions, rating scales (those filled in by self or others), and problem situation questions which require short but well thought out answers.

True-and-false Tests. Educators contend that these are the poorest kind of objective test questions to use. Pupils tend to read their own meanings into each statement, it is difficult to tell the difference between a correct or incorrect statement, or the pupil may retain a false concept by not knowing wherein he made an error.

All written statements in such a test should be short and simple. Avoid using the words "never" or "always." Have the pupils use the symbols (+) or (0) instead of (T) or (F) because those unsure of the answer often deliberately make the marks hard to tell apart. Other ways to score the test include encircling T if the statement is entirely true, or the F if it is only partly true, or blocking out X in the first column if the sentence is correct and encircling it if the second one is wrong. In the first grade, the children might draw a face with the mouth turned down if the statement is false, or draw it with the mouth turned up if it is true.

Example: Write + if the statement is true, 0 if it is false.

__0__ 1. Your baby teeth are not important.
__+__ 2. Children should drink a quart of milk a day.
__0__ 3. The red traffic light says "go."
__0__ 4. If you are lost, sit down and cry.
__0__ 5. Pet all dogs, even strange ones.

Multiple Choice. These questions should be short, clearly written, and never copied word for word from the textbook. Care must be taken not to make all possible answers so wrong that it is obvious which one is correct, or set a pattern through which the correct answer can usually be found.

Example: Place the letter of the most correct answer in the blank.

__b__ 1. The gland that gives great strength in time of excitement or anger is the (a) pancreas, (b) adrenal, (c) thyroid, (d) pituitary.
__d__ 2. The part of the eye that sends the message about an image to the brain is the (a) iris, (b) cornea, (c) pupil, (d) retina.
__c__ 3. Calcium makes strong (a) muscles, (b) brain, (c) bones, (d) nerves.
__a__ 4. A disease transmitted by a mad dog is (a) rabies, (b) pellagra, (c) anemia, (d) scurvy.
__b__ 5. Brush the upper teeth (a) up, (b) down, (c) across, (d) around.

Matching. These questions are best for measuring the mastery of "where," "when," "what," and "who" types of information. They do not develop the ability to interpret or express oneself. The responses to the items to be matched should be placed alphabetically or numerically in the right-hand column. Blank spaces should be provided in the left column before each item to be matched. There should be at least two more answers in the right column than in the left.

Example: Match the items in the left column with those in the right. Some answers in the latter may be used twice:

b	Bone	a. Cornea
d	Hair	b. Marrow
a	Eye	c. Dentine
f	Blood	d. Follicle
g	Skin	e. Semicircular canal
		f. White corpuscle
		g. Epidermis
		h. Subconscious
		i. Crown

Fill-in Blanks. The chief drawback to this type of an examination is that pupils have difficulty filling in blanks in the exact words the teacher expects; thus, they often must be given the benefit of the doubt or cause the teacher to become irritated and more exacting as she continues to grade the paper. Also, it is time-consuming to grade such questions. One advantage to using this type of test is that the pupil is not guided to the answer.

Example: Write the correct answer in the blank provided for it below.

1. We should brush our teeth after ____________.
2. ____________ has more calcium than any other food.
3. We should go to the dentist at least ____________ times a year.
4. Our first teeth are called ____________ teeth.
5. Every grown person should have ____________ teeth.

Essay Questions. These questions are valuable in that they provide pupils with opportunities to write and read aloud complete sentences or whole paragraphs using good grammar, and to think problems through carefully. Their drawback is that they are time-consuming to read and difficult to grade objectively.

Example: Answer the following question in not less than one hundred words. Think through your answer carefully.

What seems to you to be the chief value in observing good health habits?

Rating Scales. Pupils enjoy rating and evaluating their work or habits learned in health education. The best scales for doing so are those devised by the class. Teachers can help children benefit from this type of experience by a personal follow-up conference with each child.

EXAMPLE: PUPIL'S PERSONAL EVALUATION SHEET

	Always	Frequently	Seldom	Never
1. I brush my teeth after eating.				
2. I eat fruits and vegetables every day.				
3. I drink a quart of milk daily.				
4. I usually go to bed before 9 P.M.				
5. I worry about my school work.				

Student Evaluation. Students should be given many opportunities to evaluate what progress they have made in relation to the goals set individually and by the class. The teacher should appraise their progress with them, as well as observe their reactions to what they are doing, their attitude toward her, the group, themselves, and life in general. Time should be taken frequently to discuss these reactions and problems which have arisen concerning individual or group behavior, and to formulate future goals and plans.

Deeper insight and a clearer understanding of the class as a whole, as well as the feelings of the group toward the teacher, can be gained by having each pupil write on an unsigned paper answers to the following questions at the end of a semester or a major class project.

1. Did you enjoy this experience? Why?
2. List the new things you have learned in order of importance to you.
3. What activities did you do away from school that you learned here?
4. Which person do you most admire in our class? Why?
5. How could you be like this person, if you wanted to?
6. What did you hope to do or learn that you did not?
7. What pupil do you think improved the most? In what ways?
8. Are the pupils here learning to be good citizens? In what ways?

Much information can also be gained concerning each pupil by having him complete statements which show his inner feelings, fears, or thoughts. Suggested questions include the following:

1. My greatest fear is that I ______________________.
2. At night I usually dream about ______________________.
3. I dislike ______________ because ______________________.
4. I would like to be just like ______________ when I grow up because ______________________.
5. I ______________ school, because here I______________________.

There is educational value in having pupils submit sample objective test questions with their correct answers, and in their grading each other's papers in class as the teacher reads the correct answer. Such practices put children on their honor. They are less likely to be dishonest if they feel secure, if the teacher has a high degree of expectancy for each child, and if the class respects her as a leader. Every real educator will find ways to utilize any time spent in evaluating progress to its utmost. She will make good use of test findings in order to improve her skill as an effective youth leader.

EVALUATING CHANGES IN THE SCHOOL, HOME, AND COMMUNITY

A well-planned, well-conducted, and well-administered school health program should have far-reaching effects in the school, home, and community. Although these improvements are more difficult to measure, they should be included when evaluating the results of the program. Suggestions for doing so include:

The School. An environmental school survey should give evidence of actual improvements made in the school as a result of the total school health program. A list of the things to be checked and discovered from this study should be drawn up by the principal and teachers. Such a survey might well discover the answers to the following questions:

Yes No

__ __ 1. Are the seats arranged so all children can see the chalkboard, and the shades adjusted so the room is well lighted?

__ __ 2. Is the room temperature checked periodically and kept around 70° in the primary grades and around 68° for the upper elementary grades?

__ __ 3. Are the school grounds a safe place for the children to play?

Yes No

— — 4. Do we always have soap, towels, and warm water in the toilet rooms?

— — 5. Is the lunchroom a relaxed, quiet place in which to eat?

— — 6. Are our health services adequate?

— — 7. Are our equipment and facilities checked periodically for hazards?

— — 8. Are we supervising our stairways, corridors, halls, classrooms, and the playground enough; have fewer accidents occurred in these places?

— — 9. Do we have enough fire and air-raid drills for the safety of all the people in our building?

— — 10. Do our swimming pool and shower room facilities meet sanitary standards?

— — 11. Are our toilet facilities clean, well ventilated, properly lighted, and adequate?

— — 12. Is our curriculum well balanced and does it provide opportunities for relaxation and change of pace?

A survey should also be made by the cooperative efforts of the whole staff to evaluate the school health instructional program. The following questions illustrate the type of information which should be sought:[6]

Yes No

— — 1. Is the program based upon an understanding of child growth and development and upon the needs inherent in this development?

— — 2. Does the program deal with significant health problems as revealed through studies of the health status of individuals and health problems found in the school, home, and community?

— — 3. Is the program properly related to other health education efforts within the school, home, and community?

— — 4. Is health instruction a planned part of the total school health program?

— — 5. Are opportunities for health education provided in the control of the school environment?

— — 6. Are opportunities provided for health education in the health appraisal plan and in health counseling?

— — 7. Are the health education and physical education aspects of the program interrelated?

[6] *Health Education,* National Education Association and American Medical Association, 5th ed., Washington, D.C., 1961, p. 356.

Yes No

___ ___ 8. Are sound psychological principles used in the organization and application of health teaching?

___ ___ 9. Is health teaching a definite part of teaching in other subjects?

___ ___ 10. Is there well-balanced health instruction at both elementary and secondary levels with adequate time allotment, suitable teaching materials, and well-prepared teachers?

___ ___ 11. Is there a planned program of adult health education on a community-wide basis?

___ ___ 12. Are all possible sources of help being used?

An evaluation should also be made of the school health service program in order to discover if it is fully meeting the health needs of the pupils. Records of the kinds and number of treatments given, health examination findings, and other types of recorded information should be analyzed.

A realistic measurement of the results of the total school health program should reveal if it is getting its intended job done, and if not, why. Such an evaluation can be of the greatest value when all wasteful conditions and inferior practices are eliminated, and changes made or plans modified when needed.

The Home. Although the far-reaching influences of the school health program cannot be readily seen or measured, behavior changes and new health knowledge gained by the pupils in the school should carry over into the home. Individual conferences with parents, home visits made when possible, or even telephone conversations with parents can help teachers gain needed information regarding the effectiveness of their health teaching. Obtaining such facts is well worth the effort it takes. Increasingly, public schools are conducting night classes for adults in such areas as child growth and development, nutrition, first aid and water safety, and physical fitness. These can help parents reinforce at home what is being taught at the school, as well as give them needed information and desire to increase the health and well-being of their own families. The community-centered school is fast becoming a reality, and Americans no longer feel that only children can or should be educated at the school. In many of our larger cities, such as Milwaukee, Los Angeles, and Flint, Michigan, model adult education programs are being conducted which reach thousands of adults.

The Community. Surveys should be made of conditions and practices related to the well-being and safety of all who live in the community, for if the total school health program has been effective, needed improvement will result. In some cities an intensive educational program sponsored by the school has succeeded in convincing the citizens to adopt water fluoridation, take part in polio vaccination drives, or see to it that needed additional stop signals are installed near playground areas.

The schools should join hands with their local co-workers in health, such as the Red Cross, youth organizations, and the police and fire departments, and help further their efforts to make the community a cleaner, better, healthier, and safer place in which to live for all its citizens, including children.

Although community surveys will not provide teachers with the answers to educational problems, it is imperative that educators know much more than they do about the locality in which they work. The teacher who spent precious time "teaching" her class the chemical properties of water seemingly was unaware that most of her group lived in a slum area where there were no bathrooms and water had to be carried into each home from a public fountain, nor was she too concerned about the fact that many of her group were badly in need of a bath. Such examples of educational waste are unfortunately quite common.

Those who engage in community surveys or capitalize upon the information gained by local community social agencies or a community health council will know more about the area in which they work and the kind of backgrounds and homes from which their pupils come. All teachers should conduct or take part in various surveys of their own school in order to gain valuable information which will enable them to become more productive, understanding, and knowledgeable teachers.

SELF-EVALUATION FOR THE TEACHER

It is not enough, however, to evaluate pupil progress, the total school health program, and changes made in the school, home, and community as a result of a well-conducted school health program. Any teacher who desires to become a productive educator should also fully evaluate her teaching results and her own health. There are many challenges that a teacher faces but perhaps none is more important than an ever-deepening desire to improve herself and her own teaching ability. Preliminary professional education is but one aspect of effective teaching. Each professional worker is obligated to herself to do her best and contribute to the growth and improvement of education and to her specialized field.

Evaluating Teaching Results. Every educator needs to know whether she is getting desired results. Such self-appraisal and evaluation should occur daily as well as periodically. The approach should be "How could I have done this better?" rather than "What did I do that was wrong?" The teacher should always be aware of whether or not her pupils were interested in the daily health lesson, motivated to improve themselves, increase their knowledge of health, or change their attitudes. Such research and "soul-searching" can go a long way toward improving teaching skill as well as the health education program itself. Such appraisal is basic if one wishes to become a skilled educator.

Some teachers are fortunate enough to work in a school system where there is a health education specialist, who serves as a consultant or supervisor. This expert should not only give every kind of assistance to the classroom teacher, but also help her evaluate her teaching results. The following evaluation check list can be filled out by the teacher alone, or by both the teacher and supervisor and used as a basis for a helpful conference:

TEACHER'S EVALUATION SHEET

	Always	Frequently	Seldom	Never
1. Do I motivate pupil interest in learning about health?				
2. Do I talk too much and "preach" about the necessity of developing good health habits?				
3. Do I draw all pupils into class discussion?				
4. Do I use enough audio-visual aids?				
5. Do I make the fullest use of audio-visual aids?				
6. Do I use a variety of teaching methods?				

TEACHER'S EVALUATION SHEET (*Continued*)

	Always	Frequently	Seldom	Never
7. Do I integrate and correlate health enough with other subjects?				
8. Do the things I teach have real carry-over value and reach into the home?				
9. Are the health practices of my pupils improving?				
10. Am I observant enough of what the pupils do and say, and how they look?				
11. Do I underplan my work?				
12. Do I really try to build skill upon skill, and knowledge upon knowledge?				
13. Is every class period a positive, productive, educational one?				
14. Do I utilize community resources enough?				
15. Do I evaluate each daily lesson?				
16. Do I observe children with emotional and physical disturbances?				
17. Do I share in planning and evaluating with pupils?				
18. Do I try to understand boys and girls as individuals?				
19. Do I have a sense of humor?				
20. Do I like to teach?				
21. Do I like to teach health?				
22. Am I improving as a teacher?				

The Teacher's Health. Every teacher must be in top physical and mental condition, but there are far too many who are not. Unfortunately, these are the ones who sometimes attempt to teach children how to be healthy. The teacher's own example, however, is one of the most effective ways to change and improve the health behavior and values of children. Teaching is largely setting an example in the areas of behavior, attitudes, and character. If the teacher is healthy and respected, her pupils will want to be like her, do what she does, and follow her suggestions for their own improvement.

The following check list will enable each teacher to see for herself if she is merely existing, or really living:

Are You

Living?	or	Existing?
Score Yourself:		Rate Yourself:
5–Excellent (always)		170–136–"Living"
4–Good (most of the time)		135–110–"Acceptable"
3–Fair (half and half)		109 and below–"Existing"
2–Poor (seldom)		
1–Very Poor (never)		

Health Rating Scale[7]

DO YOU:

_____ Eat three meals every day?
_____ Include the seven basic foods in your daily diet?
_____ Drink six to eight glasses of liquid every day?
_____ Limit your "between-meal snacks" to fruit and milk?
_____ Sleep at least eight hours every night?
_____ Relax at intervals during the day?
_____ Exercise at least one hour every day (preferably out of doors)?
_____ Keep healthy—free from colds, headaches, sore throats, etc.?
_____ Keep your smoking to a minimum?
_____ See your dentist at least twice a year?
_____ Brush your teeth after every meal?
_____ Wear shoes which fit properly?
_____ Use your feet correctly when standing and walking?
_____ Carry yourself well when standing, sitting, and walking?
_____ Take mild exercise during your menstrual period?
_____ Bathe (or take a sponge bath) at least once a day while menstruating?
_____ Have a menstrual period free from pain?
_____ Have regular bowel movements?
_____ Take a daily shower or bath?
_____ Wear clean underwear and socks each day?
_____ Use a deodorant?
_____ Keep your hands and fingernails clean?
_____ Take care of your complexion?
_____ Dress appropriately for the occasion?
_____ Keep your clothes neat and clean?
_____ Keep yourself well-groomed?

[7] Reproduced by permission from the *Student Handbook for Health Information, Posture, and Body Mechanics,* Department of Physical Education for Women, Austin, University of Texas, 1961, pp. 21–23.

PERSONALITY AND CHARACTER RATING SCALE

ARE YOU:

_____ Enthusiastic?
_____ Cooperative?
_____ Dependable?
_____ Loyal?
_____ Friendly?
_____ Receptive to new ideas?
_____ Total

PROFESSIONAL GROWTH

There are two chief ways to grow professionally: (1) through in-service training, and (2) engaging in further professional pursuits.

In-Service Training

In-service training is an on-the-job self-improvement program. Educators learn how to teach by capitalizing upon their own trial-and-error attempts. "Experience is the best teacher" is only true if one is wise enough to profit from the experience which brought success or failure. For some, the longer one stays in the profession, the greater the temptation becomes to teach in the same old way and stay in the same well-worn groove. Such teachers, who are scornfully called "professional barnacles" by some, should be reminded that the only difference between a groove and a rut is depth. Fortunately, most teachers have high professional goals and are keenly interested in improving their effectiveness as educators and leaders of youth.

Staff Meetings. Democratically led staff meetings with fellow teachers can be a splendid way to grow in understanding and appreciation of the unique and valuable contribution each makes to the school program. Such meetings should be well-planned, and real problems which affect all who attend the school studied carefully. The old saying "two heads are better than one" is not necessarily true, for it depends upon the heads involved. Likewise, merely bringing a group of teachers together after a long school day to discuss unimportant business is a waste of time and effort. In order that staff meetings be beneficial, each participant must feel she has a real contribution to make to the group as well as be aware that her time is being well spent in a pursuit which will help her become a better teacher, a member of an important and successful educational team.

Curriculum Study. Increasingly, schools are providing released time for teachers to work on curriculum improvement, and regard such work as part of their job, rather than compelling them to take part in such projects after school. All schools should periodically evaluate their programs, and be aided in this task by teachers, lay citizens, youth, administrators, supervisors, and from time to time assisted by a small group of experts. The total school program should be revised at frequent intervals and as needed, but nothing requiring immediate revision should be allowed to remain as it is until the time comes for a major "house cleaning" or curriculum change.

Every teacher will profit greatly from engaging in the following pursuits:

1. Continually studying the purposes of education and her objectives for each class in relationship to her classroom teaching and its results.
2. Working closely with administrators, fellow teachers, lay people, and children in order to assure that all educational pursuits have meaning, and value in the daily lives of each learner.
3. Working individually as well as in small committees to prepare resource units and other teaching aids.
4. Taking part in the study and discussion of the purposes of education and the improvement of the quality of American education at her own school.

Research. Many teachers fail to realize that research and experimentation which they do on their own teaching situation and effectiveness can often be far more valuable and meaningful to them and lead to their own professional growth much more than reading about the research findings done by others. Although the majority of teachers have taken courses in "Tests and Measurements" or "Methods of Research," only a few ever use the research techniques they learned in college to conduct their own learning experiments, or use the other research tools to investigate their own teaching situation or educational effort.

Although much is known about how pupils learn and how to

increase the rate and effectiveness of learning, much yet remains a mystery. Educators tend to teach as they have been taught and to travel along well-trodden paths. Few are courageous enough to blaze new educational trails. Far too many are doing traditional teaching in traditional ways in spite of their dim awareness of the need for new methods and great improvements of our old ones if American education is ever to improve. Great teachers are those who have found their own teaching methods, and have dared to be different and creative.

Workshops. Teacher workshops are rich sources of self-improvement. These often provide opportunities to obtain new teaching methods and materials, and help instructors gain a renewed interest in and enthusiasm for their work. Such workshops should be carefully planned by a steering committee who should select problem areas from teachers' responses to questionnaires. Health education specialists will add much to the value of a workshop. The use of films, educational displays of free and inexpensive literature and recommended books, and mimeographed materials will increase interest as well as give teachers something to take away with them.

Although it takes precious free time to attend these weekend meetings, and extra money and energy to travel long distances, teachers can find such trips valuable for gaining new ideas, materials, and friendships. Most educators do want to do a good job. The majority of them welcome opportunities to gain as well as give assistance in the raising of standards in order to obtain excellence in education.

Home Study. Correspondence extension courses are now available in many communities. Although there may be merit in securing materials via the correspondence course method, most teachers will profit more from attending an extension course and gaining inspiration, along with other things, from working with an educational authority and exchanging ideas with other teachers from other schools. Even if only one teacher from each school in the system attends such a course, her fellow instructors can profit from her experience by reading suggested new materials, her class notes, or by having her share with them the new ideas and concepts she has learned in staff meetings and workshops.

Some school systems provide scholarships to selected teachers so that they may gain further training and new materials and ideas to share with other instructors.

Professional Organizations. All teachers should be members of and contribute to professional organizations. Likewise, each should read the official publications of these groups, as well as contribute articles periodically, either individually or as a member of a committee, to them. All should attend as many local, state, regional, and national meetings of their professional organizations as possible. Increasingly, students majoring in education are taking out student memberships and attending the conventions of their professional group. The chief value for such students is that they gain a deeper respect for their chosen field and earlier become more professionally minded. Many of them become active participants on both the local and regional levels early in their careers. Certainly all who attend educational conventions, whether they are experienced teachers or beginners, return to their jobs or school from these meetings as more enthusiastic members of their profession.

Organizations which teachers of health or other classroom subjects can join with profit are the American Association for School Health, the American Association for Health, Physical Education, and Recreation, American Public Health Association, and the National Education Association.

Hobbies which include reading, photography, collecting things from other places including foreign countries, and many other kinds of similar activities are especially recreational and refreshing for teachers. They can also supply them with new materials to bring into their classrooms to stimulate increased pupil interest, knowledge, and understanding. Travel can also help any instructor gain new interests, perspective, and enthusiasm which will, in turn, carry over into the classroom and increase her effectiveness as an educator. There are many ways to motivate learners, but none is as powerful as a skilled, interesting, and enthusiastic teacher.

Further Professional Pursuits

Many large school systems require teachers to take a refresher course in a field of their choice every three years. Although doing so takes time, effort, and money, these teachers usually have a rich educational experience, and return to school with renewed interest in their work. Increasingly those with a bachelor's degree are going on for graduate work to receive a master's degree. This usually takes one year, or 30 hours, of advanced work obtained in summer school or night courses. Some institutions require a written thesis, others require the student to take additional courses and write at least one long research paper.

Those who wish to advance themselves professionally, to teach on the college level, or to become national leaders in their field should seek further study beyond the master's degree. Supervisory and administrative positions increasingly require broad professional experience and a doctorate. If candidates qualify for admission and pass preliminary examinations, they then work toward the Doctor of Philosophy or Doctor of Education degree. Both degrees are similar in admission standards, matriculation procedures, residence and other time requirements. The Ed.D. tends to be more appropriate for those who wish to become education specialists while the Ph.D. comprehends more general, noneducational study. Graduate teaching fellowships, assistantships, scholarships, and loans are available for those qualified to receive them.

Every teacher, regardless of the educational level he works on, must be well selected, highly trained, and deeply desirous of becoming a professional leader who continues to grow in productive skill as an educator. Through the united efforts of every such skilled, capable, and inspired person, a happier, healthier, safer, and better world *can* become a reality. This is the time of our greatest opportunity as educators. It is also the time of our greatest challenge.

SUGGESTED READINGS

A Checklist for Appraising the Elementary and Secondary School Health Program, Texas Education Agency, Austin, 1951.

Bucher, Charles, *Administration of School Health Programs,* 2nd ed., St. Louis, Mosby, 1959.

"Evaluating Your Health Education Program," in *A Handbook for Health Education Teachers,* Ohio Department of Education, Columbus, 1947.

Evaluation of School Health Education, University of the State of New York, Albany, State Department of Education, 1952.

Fast, Charles, *Health Education Evaluation Form,* Portland, Ore., TB and Health Association, March, 1957.

Fraser, Ellen, "Looking Back on a School Health Program," *Journal of Health, Physical Education, and Recreation,* vol. 25, no. 10 (December, 1954), 14–17.

Gold, Leah, *New Tests in Health Knowledge,* Northfield, Minn., Carleton College, 1954.

Jackson, C. O., "Let's Rate Your Health Education Progress," *Journal of Health, Physical Education, and Recreation,* vol. 26 (September, 1955), 49–51.

Kearney, Nolen, *A Teacher's Professional Guide,* Englewood Cliffs, N.J., Prentice-Hall, 1958.

Mayer, Martin, *The School,* New York, Harper, 1961.

Methods of Research in Health and Physical Education, AAHPER, 1949; *Research Methods Applied to Health, Physical Education, and Recreation,* AAHPER, 1952.

Moss, Bernice, "Guideposts for Evaluating Health Classes," *Journal of Health, Physical Education and Recreation,* vol. 23, no. 3 (March, 1952), 31–34.

Prescott, David, *The Child in the Educative Process,* New York, McGraw-Hill, 1957.

Rogers, James, *What Every Teacher Should Know about the Physical Condition of Her Pupils,* Pamphlet no. 68, Washington, D.C., Government Printing Office, 1955.

Scott, Harry, and Ray Snyder, *Professional Preparation in Health, Physical Education, and Recreation,* New York, McGraw-Hill, 1954.

Sharp, Louise, *Why Teach?* New York, Holt, 1958.

Shaw, John, "Evaluation in the School Health Instruction Program," *American Journal of Public Health,* vol. 47, no. 5 (May, 1957), p. 56.

Simpson, Ray, *Improving Teaching-Learning Processes,* New York, Longmans Green, 1953.

Teicher, Joseph, *Your Child and His Problems,* Boston, Little, Brown, 1953.

"The Elementary School Health Program" (entire issue), *The National Elementary Principal,* vol. 39, no. 4 (February, 1960).

Toward Better Teaching, Association for Supervision and Curriculum Development, 1949 Yearbook, Washington, D.C., 1949.

APPENDIXES

SOURCES OF FREE OR INEXPENSIVE HEALTH EDUCATION MATERIALS

Abbott Laboratories
North Chicago, Ill.

Aetna Life Insurance Company
151 Farmington Ave.
Hartford 15, Conn.

Alcoholics Anonymous
General Board
P.O. Box 459
New York 17, N.Y.

Allied Youth, Incorporated
1709 M St., N.W.
Washington 6, D.C.

American Automobile Association
Pennsylvania Avenue at 17th St.
Washington, D.C.

American Association for Health, Physical Education and Recreation
1201 16th St., N.W.
Washington 6, D.C.

American Can Company
230 Park Ave.
New York 17, N.Y.

American Cancer Society
521 West 57th St.
New York 19, N.Y.

American College Health Association
Cornell University
Ithaca, N.Y.

American Dental Association
222 East Superior St.
Chicago, Ill.

American Diabetic Association
1 Nevins St.
Brooklyn 17, N.Y.

American Dietetic Association
620 North Michigan Ave.
Chicago 11, Ill.

American Foundation for the Blind, Inc.
15 West 16th St.
New York 11, N.Y.

American Genetic Association
1507 M St., N.W.
Washington 5, D.C.

American Hearing Society
817 14th St., N.W.
Washington 5, D.C.

American Heart Association, Inc.
1775 Broadway
New York 19, N.Y.

American Home Economics Association
1600 20th St., N.W.
Washington, D.C.

American Hospital Association
18 East Division St.
Chicago 10, Ill.

American Institute of Baking
400 East Ontario St.
Chicago 11, Ill.

American Institute of Family Relations
5287 Sunset Blvd.
Los Angeles 27, Calif.

American Medical Association
535 North Dearborn St.
Chicago 10, Ill.

American Museum of Natural History
Central Park West at 79th St.
New York 24, N.Y.

American National Red Cross
529 South Wabash Ave.
Chicago, Ill.

American Nurses Association
2 Park Ave.
New York, N.Y.

American Occupational Therapy Association
33 West 42nd St.
New York 18, N.Y.

American Physical Therapy Association
1790 Broadway
New York 19, N.Y.

American Rheumatism Association
44 East 23rd St.
New York, N.Y.

American School Health Association
228 North LaSalle St.
Chicago, Ill.

American Seating Company
Grand Rapids, Mich.

Association of American Soap and Glycerine Producers
295 Madison Ave.
New York, N.Y.

Association of Casualty and Surety Companies
60 John St.
New York 30, N.Y.

Association for Childhood Education International
1201 15th St., N.W.
Washington, D.C.

Association for Family Living
28 East Jackson Blvd.
Chicago 4, Ill.

Association for Physical and Mental Rehabilitation
1472 Broadway
New York, N.Y.

Association Press
347 Madison Ave.
New York, N.Y.

Better Vision Institute, Inc.
Suite 3157
630 Fifth Ave.
New York 20, N.Y.

Bicycle Institute of America, Inc.
122 East 42nd St.
New York 17, N.Y.

Bristol-Myers Company
Educational Service Department
630 Fifth Ave.
New York 20, N.Y.

Bureau of Human Nutrition and Home Economics
U.S. Department of Agriculture
Washington, D.C.

California Fruit Growers Exchange
Educational Division
Box 5030, Metropolitan Station
Los Angeles, Calif.

The Cancer Bulletin
1603 Oakdale St.
Houston 4, Tex.
Carnation Company
Box 2035
Los Angeles 36, Calif.
Center for Mass Communication
Columbia University Press
1125 Amsterdam Ave.
New York 25, N.Y.
Cereal Institute
135 South LaSalle St.
Chicago 3, Ill.
Chicago Heart Association, Inc.
Suite 1608
203 North Wabash Ave.
Chicago 1, Ill.
Child Study Association of America
132 East 74th St.
New York 21, N.Y.
Child Welfare League of America, Inc.
130 East 22nd St.
New York 10, N.Y.
Children's Bureau
Washington 25, D.C.
Cleveland Health Museum
8911 Euclid Ave.
Cleveland, Ohio
Committee on Mental Health State Charities Aid Association
105 East 22nd St.
New York, N.Y.
Common Cold Foundation
370 Lexington Ave.
New York, N.Y.
Commonwealth Fund
41 East 57th St.
New York 22, N.Y.
Communications Material Center
Journalism Building
2960 Broadway
New York 27, N.Y.
Connecticut Mutual Life Insurance Company
Hartford, Conn.
Consumer Services, Borden Company
350 Madison Ave.
New York 17, N.Y.
Cream of Wheat Corporation
Minneapolis 13, Minn.

Denoyer-Geppert Company
5235–59 Ravenswood Ave.
Chicago 40, Ill.

E. C. Brown Trust
220 Southwest Alder St.
Portland 4, Ore.
Employers Mutual Liability Insurance Company
407 Grant St.
Wausau, Wis.
Equitable Life Assurance Society of the United States
393 Seventh Ave.
New York, N.Y.
Evaporated Milk Association
307 North Michigan Ave.
Chicago 1, Ill.

Family Life Publications, Inc.
Box 6725, College Station
Durham, N.C.
Fawcett Publications, Inc.
67 West 44th St.
New York 18, N.Y.
Federal Civil Defense Administration
Washington, D.C.
Florida Citrus Commission
Lakeland, Fla.

General Mills, Inc.
Minneapolis, Minn.
Good Teeth Council for Children
17th Floor, Wrigley Building
400 North Michigan Ave.
Chicago 11, Ill.

Harvard School of Public Health
Cambridge, Mass.
Health Education Council
10 Downing St.
New York, N.Y.
Health Information Foundation
420 Lexington Ave.
New York 17, N.Y.
Health Publications, Inc.
216 North Dawson St.
Raleigh, N.C.
Hogg Foundation for Mental Health
University of Texas
Austin, Tex.

International Cellucotton Products Company
919 North Michigan Ave.
Chicago 11, Ill.
Iowa Child Welfare Research Station
State University of Iowa
Department of Publications
Iowa City, Iowa

John Hancock Mutual Life Insurance Company
Box 111
Boston, Mass.
Johnson and Johnson Baby Products
New Brunswick, N.J.

Kellogg Company
Battle Creek, Mich.
Kimberly-Clark Corporation
Cellucotton Division
Education Department
919 North Michigan Ave.
Chicago, Ill.
Kraft Cheese Company
500 Peshtigo Court
Chicago, Ill.

Ladies' Home Journal
The Curtis Publishing Company
Philadelphia 5, Pa.
Lever Brothers Company
50 Memorial Drive
Cambridge 39, Mass.

The Massachusetts Society for Social Hygiene, Inc.
1145 Little Building
Boston 16, Mass.
Maternity Center Association
654 Madison Ave.
New York, N.Y.
Mental Health Materials Center
1790 Broadway
New York, N.Y.
Meredith Publishing Company
Des Moines 3, Iowa
Metropolitan Life Insurance Company
1 Madison Ave.
New York 10, N.Y.
Muscular Dystrophy Associations of America
39 Broadway
New York, N.Y.

National Association for Mental Health, Inc.
1790 Broadway
New York 19, N.Y.
National Board of Fire Underwriters
85 John St.
New York, N.Y.
National Canners Association
Home Economics Division
1739 H St., N.W.
Washington, D.C.
National Commission on Safety Education
National Education Association
1201 16th St., N.W.
Washington 6, D.C.

National Committee on Alcoholism
2 East 103rd St.
New York, N.Y.

National Congress of Parents and Teachers
700 North Rush St.
Chicago, Ill.

National Dairy Council
111 North Canal St.
Chicago 6, Ill.

National Dental Hygiene Association
934 Shoreham Building
Washington, D.C.

National Education Association
1201 16th St., N.W.
Washington 6, D.C.

National Epilepsy League
130 North Wells St.
Chicago, Ill.

National Fire Protection Association
60 Batterymarch St.
Boston, Mass.

National Foot Health Council
The Phoenix Building
Rockland, Mass.

The National Foundation
301 East 42nd St.
New York 17, N.Y.

National Foundation for Infantile Paralysis
120 Broadway
New York, N.Y.

National Health Council
1790 Broadway
New York 19, N.Y.

National League for Nursing
2 Park Ave.
New York, N.Y.

National Livestock and Meat Board
Department of Nutrition, Room 825
407 South Dearborn St.
Chicago, Ill.

National Multiple Sclerosis Society
270 Park Ave.
New York, N.Y.

National Research Council
Food and Nutrition Board
Washington, D.C.

National Rifle Association
1600 Rhode Island Ave.
Washington 6, D.C.

National Safety Council
425 North Michigan Ave.
Chicago 11, Ill.

National Society for Crippled Children and Adults, Inc.
11 South LaSalle St.
Chicago 3, Ill.

National Society for the Prevention of Blindness
1790 Broadway
New York 19, N.Y.

National Tuberculosis Association
1790 Broadway
New York 19, N.Y.

National Women's Christian Temperance Union
1730 Chicago Ave.
Evanston, Ill.

New York State Charities Aid Association
105 East 22nd St.
New York 10, N.Y.

New York State Society for Mental Health
105 East 22nd St.
New York 10, N.Y.

A. J. Nystrom and Company
3333 Elston Ave.
Chicago 18, Ill.

Ohio State Medical Association
79 East State St.
Columbus 15, Ohio

Paper Cup and Container Institute
250 Park Ave.
New York, N.Y.

Pepsodent Division
Lever Brothers Company
141 West Jackson Blvd.
Chicago 4, Ill.
Personal Products Corporation
Miltown, N.J.
Planned Parenthood Federation of America
501 Madison Ave.
New York, N.Y.
Pocket Books, Inc.
Rockefeller Center
New York, N.Y.
Procter & Gamble
Cincinnati, Ohio
Prudential Life Insurance Company
Newark, N.J.
Public Affairs Committee, Inc.
22 East 38th St.
New York 16, N.Y.
Public Health Nursing
1790 Broadway
New York 19, N.Y.

Quarterly Journal of Studies on Alcohol
Box 2161, Yale Station
New Haven, Conn.

Ralston Purina Company
Checkerboard Square
St. Louis 2, Mo.

School and College Service
Station B
Columbus, Ohio
Science Research Associates, Inc.
259 East Erie St.
Chicago 11, Ill.
Smith, Kline & French Laboratories
1530 Spring Garden St.
Philadelphia 1, Pa.
Society for Visual Education, Inc.
100 East Ohio St.
Chicago 11, Ill.

Superintendent of Documents
Government Printing Office
Washington 25, D.C.

Tampax
161 East 42nd St.
New York, N.Y.
Travelers Insurance Company
Hartford 15, Conn.

United Cerebral Palsy Associations
369 Lexington Ave.
New York, N.Y.
United Fruit Company
Education Department
Pier 3, North River
New York 6, N.Y.
United Nations
Department of Public Information
New York, N.Y.
U.S. Department of Agriculture
Washington 25, D.C.
U.S. Department of Health, Education, and Welfare
Washington 25, D.C.
Government Printing Office
Washington 25, D.C.
University of Minnesota Press
Minneapolis, Minn.

VD Education Institute
North Dawson St.
Raleigh, N.C.
Volta Bureau
1537 35th St., N.W.
Washington, D.C.

Wheat Flour Institute
309 West Jackson Blvd.
Chicago 6, Ill.
World Health Organization
Columbia University Press
International Documents Service
2960 Broadway
New York 27, N.Y.

Yale Center of Alcohol Studies
Yale University
New Haven, Conn.

Young Women's Christian Association
600 Lexington Ave.
New York, N.Y.

FILM AND FILMSTRIP SOURCES

American Dental Association
222 East Superior St.
Chicago 11, Ill.

American Film Center
Post Office Box 363
San Jose 3, Calif.

American Film Company
24 East 8th St.
Chicago, Ill.

American Foot Care Institute
1775 Broadway
New York 19, N.Y.

American Medical Association
535 North Dearborn St.
Chicago 10, Ill.

American Petroleum Institute
50 West 50th St.
New York, N.Y.

American Social Hygiene Association
1790 Broadway
New York 19, N.Y.

American Society of Bakery Engineers
Department of Visual Education
208 Third Ave., Southeast
Minneapolis, Minn.

Association Films, Inc.
351 Turk St.
San Francisco, Calif.

Bailey Films, Inc.
6509 DeLonpre Ave.
Hollywood 28, Calif.

Brandon Films, Inc.
200 West 57th St.
New York, N.Y.

Brandon Films, Inc.
Western Cinema Guild
290 Seventh Ave.
San Francisco 18, Calif.

British Information Service
30 Rockefeller Plaza
New York, N.Y.

Castle
7356 Melrose Ave.
Hollywood 46, Calif.

Columbia University Press
Center for Mass Communication
1125 Amsterdam Ave.
New York 27, N.Y.

Contemporary Films
Alvin J. Gordon
1859 Powell St.
San Francisco 11, Calif.

Cornet Films
Coronet Building
Chicago, Ill.

Eastman Films: Eastman Kodak Company
Informational Films Division
343 State St.
Rochester 4, N.Y.

Eli Lilly
Public Relations Department
Indianapolis, Ind.

Encyclopaedia Britannica Films, Inc.
Wilmette, Ill.

Film Publishers
25 Broad St.
New York 4, N.Y.

Gateway Productions, Inc.
1859 Powell St.
San Francisco 11, Calif.
General Mills, Inc.
400 2nd Avenue, South
Minneapolis, Minn.
General Motors Corporation
3044 West Grand Blvd.
Detroit 2, Mich.
General Picture Production
621 6th Ave.
Des Moines 9, Iowa

Institute of Inter-American Affairs
499 Pennsylvania Ave., N.W.
Washington 25, D.C.
International Film Bureau
Suite 308-316
57 East Jackson Boulevard
Chicago 4, Ill.

Johnson & Johnson
Promotion Department
New Brunswick, N.J.

Kimberly-Clark Corporation
Neenah, Wis.
Knowledge Builders
Visual Education Center Building
Lowell and Cherry Lane
Floral Park, N.Y.

March of Time
369 Lexington Ave.
New York 17, N.Y.
McGeary-Smith Laboratories
1905 Fairview Ave., N.E.
Washington 2, D.C.
McGraw-Hill Book Company, Inc.
Text Film Department
330 West 42nd St.
New York 18, N.Y.
Medical Motion Pictures
Committee on Medical Motion Pictures, A.M.A.
535 North Dearborn St.
Chicago 10, Ill.
Modern Talking Picture Service, Inc.
45 Rockefeller Plaza
New York 20, N.Y.
Museum of Modern Art Film Library
11 West 53rd St.
New York, N.Y.

National Dairy Council
111 North Canal St.
Chicago 6, Ill.
National Film Board of Canada
1270 Avenue of the Americas
New York 20, N.Y.
The National Foundation
301 East 42nd St.
New York 17, N.Y.
National Foundation for Infantile Paralysis
120 Broadway
New York 5, N.Y.
National Society for the Prevention of Blindness
1790 Broadway
New York 19, N.Y.
North Carolina Board of Health
Film Section
Raleigh, N.C.

Perry-Mansfield
15 West 67th St.
New York, N.Y.

Social Science Films
4030 Chouteau Ave.
St. Louis 10, Mo.
State University of Iowa
Iowa City, Iowa

Teaching Film Custodians, Inc.
25 West 43rd St.
New York 18, N.Y.

U.S. Department of Agriculture
Motion Picture Service
Office of Information
Washington 25, D.C.

U.S. Department of Health, Education, and Welfare
Washington 25, D.C.

U.S. Public Health Service
Communicable Disease Center
605 Volunteer Building
Atlanta 3, Ga.

United World Films, Inc.
Educational Film Department
7356 Melrose Ave.
Hollywood 46, Calif.

University of Michigan
Ann Arbor, Mich.

Visual Training Institute
40 East 49th St.
New York, N.Y.

Young America Films, Inc.
18 East 41st St.
New York 17, N.Y.

SUGGESTED PERIODICALS

American Journal of Hygiene
American Journal of Public Health
American Medical Association NEWS

Camping Magazine
Child Development
Childhood Education
Chronicle of the World Health Organization

Journal of the American Dental Association
Journal of American Dietetic Association
Journal of the American Medical Association
Journal of Health, Physical Education and Recreation
Journal of Nutrition
Journal of Social Hygiene
Journal of School Health

Mental Hygiene
Motive

National Education Association Journal

Panorama (Teaching throughout the World)
Progressive Education

Recreation
Research Quarterly (AAHPER)

Safety Education
Science Digest

The Crippled Child
The Elementary School Journal
The Exceptional Child
The Instructor
The Journal of Abnormal and Social Psychology
The Nervous Child
Today's Health

Understanding the Child

What's New?
World Health

HEALTH EDUCATION TEXTBOOK SERIES

A. *Health and Personal Development Series:* Dorothy Baruch, Gladys G. Jenkins, Helen Shacter, Elizabeth R. Montgomery, W. W. Bauer, and W. S. Gray, Chicago, Scott, Foresman & Co., 1954.

Grade	
1	*Happy Days with Our Friends*
1	*Good Times with Our Friends*
2	*Three Friends*
3	*Five in the Family*
4	*The Girl Next Door*
5	*You*
6	*You and Others*
7	*You're Growing Up*
8	*In Your Teens*

B. *The Health, Happiness, Success Series:* L. W. Irwin, W. W. Tuttle, and Caroline DeKelver, Chicago, Lyons & Carnahan, 1958.

Grade	
1	*Awake and Away*
2	*Growing Day by Day*
3	*Keeping Fit for Fun*
4	*All Aboard for Health*
5	*Better Health for You*
6	*Safeguards for Your Health*

C. *The Road to Health Series:* O. E. Byrd, Edwina Jones, Edna Morga, and P. E. Ladis, River Forest, Ill., Laidlaw Brothers, 1960.

Grade

1 *My First Health Book*
2 *My Second Health Book*
3 *Easy Steps to Health*
4 *Health Trails*
5 *Your Health and You*
6 *Keeping Healthy*

D. *Science, Health, and Safety Series:* Barnard, M. R., *et al.,* Books I, II, III, IV, V, and VI, New York, The Macmillan Co., 1958.

E. *The American Health Series:* C. C. Wilson, J. C. Almack, C. B. Baker, P. J. Abbott, and H. B. Pryor, Indianapolis, Bobbs-Merrill Co., 1948.

Grade

1 *Our Good Health*
2 *Healthy and Happy*
3 *Everyday Health*
4 *Health at Home and School*
5 *Health at Work and Play*
6 *Growing Healthful*

F. *American Book Company Health Series:* C. L. Brownell, R Evans, and L. B. Hobson, New York, American Book Co., 1959.

Grade

1 *All Day, Every Day*
2 *Blue Skies*
3 *Come Rain, Come Shine*
4 *Among Friends*
5 *Broad Streets*
6 *Cross Roads*

G. *Winston Health Series:* Pattric Ruth O'Keefe, Cyrus Maxwell, and Mary Sue White, Philadelphia, John C. Winston Co., 1954.

Grade

1 *From Head to Toe*
2 *Side by Side*
3 *How We Grow*
4 *Bigger and Better*
5 *Getting Acquainted*
6 *Knowing Yourself*

H. *Health for Better Living Series:* Grace T. Hallock, R. L. Allen, and Eleanor Thomas, Boston, Ginn & Co., 1958.

Grade

1 *Health and Happy Days*
2 *Health in Work and Play*
3 *Health and Safety for You*
4 *Growing Your Way*
5 *Keeping Healthy and Strong*
6 *Teamwork for Health*

I. *Safe and Healthy Living Series:* J. M. Andress, I. H. Goldberger, M. P. Dolch, and G. T. Hallock, Boston, Ginn & Co., 1955.

Grade

1 *Spick and Span*
2 *The Health Parade*
3 *Growing Big and Strong*
4 *Safety Every Day*
5 *Doing Your Best for Health*
6 *Building Good Health*

J. *Health Action Series:* C. G. Wilcox, et al., Chicago, Benefic Press, 1956.

Grade

1 *Come On*
2 *Here We Go*
3 *Step Lively*
4 *Good for You*
5 *Full of Life*
6 *Here's Health*

K. *Health for Young America Series:* Indianapolis, Bobbs-Merrill Co., 1961.

Grade

1 *Health at School*
2 *Health Day by Day*
3 *Health and Fun*
4 *Health and Growth*
5 *Health and Living*
6 *Health and Happiness*
7 *Men, Science, and Health*
8 *Health, Fitness, and Safety*

L. *Basic Health and Safety Program:* Chicago, Scott, Foresman and Co., 1958.

Grade	
1	*Being Six*
2	*Seven or So*
3	*From Eight to Nine*
4	*Going on Ten*
5	*About Yourself*
6	*You*
7	*Just Like Me* (picture primer)

SUGGESTED GENERAL INFORMATION SHEET FOR PARENTS TO FILl OUT AND RETURN TO THE SCHOOL*

Date..

Dear Parent:

In planning a school health program which meets the individual needs of your child, it is necessary for the school to secure from you certain information about your child. Please fill in and return to the school the information requested on this sheet.

....School

General Information

Name of Pupil.................................... Date of Birth: Year.... Month.... Day....
School.. Race................ Sex..............
Name of Parent – Guardian..
Residence Address.. Phone................
Business Address.. Phone................
Family Physician.................................... Dentist..........................
In case of accident phone { Father / Mother } at..
Family Physician at..
In case the child requires emergency care while at school, phone..................
or take to Dr..
Diseases that child has had: (If year unknown, write **yes**).

Disease	Year	Disease	Year	Disease	Year
Measles		Infantile Paralysis		Running Ear	
German Measles		Sore Throat (Frequent)		Worms (Type)	
Mumps		Rheumatic Fever		Rupture	
Chickenpox		Heart Disease		Typhoid Fever	
Whooping Cough		Headache (Frequent)		Convulsions	
Diphtheria		Asthma and Hay Fever			

Other Diseases, Injuries, or Operations (Explain):

....

....

Inoculations child has had: (If year unknown, write **yes**).

	Basic Series	**Booster**
Diphtheria	....	....
Whooping Cough	....	....
Tetanus	....	....
Smallpox	....	....
Typhoid Fever	....	....

Request for Health Services

....School, through its approved facilities, is given authority and hereby requested to serve my child when clinics are held for any of the following:

(**Note to School Personnel:** List here all the health services rendered through your school such as smallpox vaccination, typhoid inoculations, etc.)

Signed..
(Parent or guardian)

* (Courtesy, South Carolina State Department of Education.)

LETTER TO PARENTS WITH FORM REQUESTING HEALTH EXAMINATION AT SCHOOL*

Date:

To the Parents of :

Some time ago you were asked to arrange with your private or family physician for the health examination of your child. To date we have not received a report from your physician on the health status of your child. If you plan to have your child examined by your physician, please do so as soon as possible.

If you prefer to have the health examination provided through the School, please fill in the attached request form.

Request Form

I hereby request that ______________________________ be given a health
(name of child)
examination at school. My family physician is ______________________________

(name of physician) ____________________ (address) ______________

Date: ______________ Parent's Signature: ______________________________

FORM FOR INVITING PARENTS TO HEALTH EXAMINATION

The ____________________ School
advises periodic health examinations for all children. You are invited to be present at

on ____________________ at __________o'clock

A physician will examine your child at this time and discuss health problems with you.

* (Courtesy, State Medical Society of Wisconsin.)

Form 3J.6—6-59—20M

LOS ANGELES CITY SCHOOL DISTRICTS
Auxiliary Services Division — Health Education and Health Services Branch

PHYSICIAN'S REPORT*

School ______________________________ Date ____________

GENERAL DATA

		Totals
1. Routine physical examinations (complete)	______	
2. Physical examinations of children specially referred by school personnel	______	
Total Physical Examinations		______
3. Health inspections for contagion, cafeteria work, readmissions, etc.	______	
4. Routine athletic inspections	______	
Total Inspections		______
5. Consultations with school personnel	______	
6. Consultations with parents **at school or by telephone**	______	
7. Consultations with private physicians, dentists, or others	______	
Total Consultations		______
8. Home notices sent		______
9. First aid given		______
10. Sanitary inspections of school plant		______
11. Lectures to faculty	______	
to parent-teacher associations	______	
to pupils	______	
Total lectures		______

CONDITIONS FOUND

CHECK ONLY ONE COLUMN

	Needing Correction †	Under School Physician's Observation ††	Under Care *	Irremediable **
1. Malnutrition				
2. Obesity				
3. Defective vision				
4. Diseases of the eyes				
5. Defective hearing				
6. Diseases of the ears				
7. Diseases of the nose and throat				
8. Tonsils (greatly enlarged or diseased)				
9. Dental defect (a) caries				
(b) malocclusion				
10. Heart defects (organic)				
11. Heart defects (functional or questionable)				
12. Chest diseases				
13. Chest deformities				
14. Orthopedic defects (a) posture				
(b) foot				
(c) miscellaneous				
15. Neurological diseases				
16. Nervous and emotional disorders				
17. Speech defects				
18. Skin diseases (communicable)				
19. Skin diseases (non communicable)				
20. Endocrine disorders				
21. Miscellaneous				
TOTALS				

†Definite recommendation is being made to parents
††For recheck or health counseling at school only
*Under care of private physician or clinic. No recommendation to be made at this time
**A congenital or acquired defect where medical or surgical treatment is not indicated.

Remarks ____

____

______________________________ M.D.
Examining Physician

* (Courtesy, Los Angeles Public Schools.)

orm 33.364 (6-55)

LOS ANGELES CITY SCHOOL DISTRICTS

Auxiliary Services Division – Health Education and Health Services Branch

ear Parent: Your answers to the following questions will help the school to meet your child's needs in planning his school program nd provide valuable information for our school records. Please fill out the answers and bring them with you or send them with your child.

HEALTH HISTORY FORM*

Date __________

School __________ Room __________

ame __________ Address __________ Phone __________

irth Place __________ Birth Date __________ Grade __________

amily Doctor __________ Address __________ __________ Date of last visit

amily Dentist __________ Address __________ __________ Date of last visit

lease check any of the following conditions that your child has had:

sthma		Chickenpox		Tires Easily	
ayfever		Measles		Fainting	
czema		German Measles		When?	
iabetis		Whooping Cough		Recent Bed Wetting	
eart Disorder		Mumps		Nose Bleeds	
oliomyelitis		Hernia		Growing Pains	
neumonia		Frequent Colds		Operations – what?	
heumatic Fever		Frequent Sore Throats			
carlet Fever		Frequent Coughs		Accidents	
uberculosis: Child		Frequent Headaches		Other Serious Illness	
uberculosis: Family		Wears Glasses		What?	

las the child been immunized against the following:	No	Yes	If Yes, give date or dates
mallpox			
iphtheria			
hooping Cough			
etanus (Lockjaw)			
oliomyelitis			
thers			

amily History:

ho lives in the home?	Yes?	No?	Health Condition
ather			
lother			
rothers – Ages			
isters – Ages			
thers			

lealth Habits

ppetite __________ How much milk daily? __________

ny food allergies? __________ What? __________

hat does child eat for breakfast? __________

hat time does child go to bed? __________

hat time does child get up? __________

ive any other health or behavior information you feel we should have: __________

____

Signature of Parent

* (Courtesy, Los Angeles Public Schools.)

CUMULATIVE SCHOOL HEALTH RECORD*

SCHOOL:

Child's name: Birth date:
Address: Location:
Father's name: Occupation: Business phone:
Mother's name: Occupation: Home phone:

Emergency Care Plan

Physician's name: Phone:
Address:
Dentist's name: Phone:
Address:
Hospital: Phone:

Health History

	Kind	Date
Measles		
Poliomyelitis		
Rheumatic Fever		
Tonsilitis		
Tuberculosis Contact		
Operations		
Accidents		
Other		

Immunization History

	Date	Date	Date	Comment
Diphtheria				
Booster diphtheria				
Whooping cough				
Tetanus				
D.P.T.				
Booster D.P.T.				
Poliomyelitis				

	Date	Result	Date	Result
Smallpox				
Tuberculin test				

Dental Health

Grade											
Date											
Needs attention											
Care received											
Decayed perm. teeth											
Missing perm. teeth											
Filled perm. teeth											

Health Appraisal by Physician Code: O–satisfactory X–needs attention

Grade						
Date						
Height (inches)						
Weight (pounds)						
Nutrition						
Skin & hair						
Eyes						
Vision						
Ears						
Hearing						
Nose & throat						
Teeth & gums						
Thyroid gland						
Lymph nodes						
Heart						
Lungs						
Abdomen						
Genitalia						
Nervous system						
Bones & joints						
Muscle tone						
Posture						
Any restrictions on physical activity						
Parent present						
Examining physician						

* (Courtesy of Bureau of Public Health Education, Indiana State Board of Health.)

ACCIDENT REPORT FORM*

PART A. Information on All Accidents

1. Name: Home address:
2. School: Sex: M ☐ F ☐ Age: Grade or classification
3. Time accident occurred: Hour A.M.; P.M. Date:
4. Place of accident: School building ☐ School grounds ☐ To or from school ☐ Home ☐ Elsewhere ☐

5\.

Nature of injury		
	Abrasion	Fracture
	Amputation	Laceration
	Asphyxiation	Poisoning
	Bite	Puncture
	Bruise	Scalds
	Burn	Scratches
	Concussion	Shock (el.)
	Cut	Sprain
	Dislocation	
	Other (specify)	

Part of body injured		
	Abdomen	Foot
	Ankle	Hand
	Arm	Head
	Back	Knee
	Chest	Leg
	Ear	Mouth
	Elbow	Nose
	Eye	Scalp
	Face	Tooth
	Finger	Wrist
	Other (specify)	

Description of the accident
How did accident happen? What was student doing? Where was student? List specifically unsafe acts and unsafe conditions existing. Specify any tool, machine or equipment involved.

6. Degree of injury: Death ☐ Permanent impairment ☐ Temporary disability ☐ Nondisabling ☐
7. Total number of days lost from school: (To be filled in when student returns to school)

PART B. Additional Information on School Jurisdiction Accidents

8. Teacher in charge when accident occurred (Enter name):
   Present at scene of accident: No: Yes:

9\.

Immediate action taken		
	First-aid treatment	By (Name):
	Sent to school nurse	By (Name):
	Sent home	By (Name):
	Sent to physician	By (Name):
	Sent to hospital	Physician's Name:
		By (Name):
		Name of hospital:

10. Was a parent or other individual notified? No: Yes: When: How:
    Name of individual notified:
    By whom? (Enter name):
11. Witnesses: 1. Name: Address:
    2\. Name: Address:

12\.

Location	Specify activity	Specify activity
	Athletic field	Locker
	Auditorium	Pool
	Cafeteria	Sch. grounds
	Classroom	Shop
	Corridor	Showers
	Dressing room	Stairs
	Gymnasium	Toilets and washrooms
	Home econ.	Other (specify)
	Laboratories	

What recommendations do you have for preventing other accidents of this type?

Teacher: Signed: Principal:

* Courtesy of the National Safety Council, Chicago, Illinois.

SUGGESTED LETTERS TO PARENTS CONCERNING NUTRITION*

(Duplicate on school letterhead)

1 BEFORE FOOD SURVEY

SCHOOL LETTERHEAD

Date__________

Dear__________:

__________brought home a sheet for keeping a record of the food he eats for three days. All our pupils are keeping this record in connection with our class study of "Food for Health."

We hope you will check the list to see that it is filled in as accurately as possible.

Thank you so much for your help. We will tell you the results of the class survey and the progress of our "Food for Health" program.

Sincerely yours,

Mary Smith
Teacher

2 AFTER FOOD SURVEY

SCHOOL LETTERHEAD

Date__________

Dear__________:

You already know something of our "Food for Health" project in__________ class in school. We thought you would be especially interested in knowing the results of our eating habits survey.

The class studied the "Basic 7" food guide and decided we would like to measure our own eating habits by it. The "Basic 7" is a plan developed by the Food and Nutrition Board of the National Research Council. Home economists and nutritionists assure us that if we eat a selected variety of foods from the "Basic 7," we can be pretty sure we are getting the foods needed to promote proper growth and development and help us stay in good health.

__________checked his diet for a three-day period and scored it against the "Basic 7." He found that he was getting the recommended amount of foods in Groups __________; but he found that he was not eating quite enough foods in Groups __________.

The "Basic 7" is an easy checklist. You may find it helpful in planning the meals for your family. Here are the 7 groups and the recommended needed amounts.

GROUP 1 — Green and Yellow Vegetables — 1 or more servings daily.

GROUP 2 — Citrus Fruit, Tomatoes, Raw Cabbage, Salad Greens and Similar Foods — 1 or more servings daily.

GROUP 3 — Potatoes and Other Vegetables and Fruit — 2 or more servings daily.

GROUP 4 — Milk, Cheese, Ice Cream — Children through teen-age need about 3 to 4 cups of milk daily. Adults need 2 or more cups of milk daily. (1 oz. Cheddar-type cheese or 2 to 3 large dips of ice cream may be considered the same as 1 cup milk.)

GROUP 5 — Meat, Poultry, Fish, Eggs, Dried Beans and Peas, Nuts — 1 serving of meat, poultry or fish daily if possible; 4 or more eggs per week; 2 or more servings a week of dried peas or beans or nuts and peanut butter.

GROUP 6 — Bread, Flour and Cereals — Whole-grain or enriched or restored — 1 serving at each meal.

GROUP 7 — Butter and Fortified Margarine — some daily.

We thought you would like to have this information. We need your help in guiding children into good habits of food selection. Children, for one reason or another, often reject foods which are set before them. We can't always do anything about it at the time. But perhaps the check which the children themselves made of their eating habits will help create an interest and desire to eat the kinds of foods they need.

We would like very much to discuss our program with you and will look forward to visiting with you about it during the next parents' meeting or at another time to suit your convenience.

Sincerely yours,

Mary Smith
Teacher

* (Courtesy, Wheat Flour Institute).

TEACHER OBSERVATION REPORT FORM*

Directions: 1. Put an X after the item when there *seems to be* deviation from normal or a defect.
2. Circle the X (X) when the defect has been corrected and/or the pupil is under medical care.

	YEAR IN SCHOOL	1	2	3	4	5	6	7	8	9	10	11	12	13	14
General	Does not look well (physically)														
	Very fat														
	Very thin														
	Tires easily														
	Posture seems poor in general														
	Lacks appetite														
	Frequent headache														
	Other														
Behavior	Very withdrawing—seems afraid or shy														
	Cries easily														
	Usually gives in (submissive)														
	Fails to play most of the time														
	Often very restless														
	Daydreams excessively														
	Very inattentive														
	Very hostile and/or destructive														
	Excessive bragging														
	Irritable—most of the time														
	Excessive use of the toilet														
	Bites nails or chews objects														
	Usually does not get along with others														
	Has many accidents														
	Stutters or other speech defect														
	Other														
Eyes	Styes or crusted lids														
	Crossed														
	Squints or frowns														
	Holds book very close—or very far														
	Other														
Ears	Discharge														
	Earache														
	Turns head to side														
	Other														
Mouth Teeth	Obvious cavities														
	Obviously irregular														
	Need cleaning														
	Inflamed gums														
	Other														
Nose Throat	Persistent mouth breathing														
	Frequent sore throat														
	Frequent colds														
	Persistent cough														
	Constant clearing the throat														
	Other														
Skin Scalp	Rashes or sores														
	Extremely rough and dry														
	Other														
Orthopedic	Chronic limp														
	Toes pointed in or pointed out														
	Stiff or swollen joints														
	One shoulder higher than the other														
	Holds head to side habitually														
	Other														
	Number of days absent due to illness (record at end of year)														

* (Courtesy, North Carolina State Department of Education.)

RECOMMENDED FORMS FOR EVALUATING THE SCHOOL HEALTH PROGRAM

A Checklist Appraising the Elementary and Secondary Health Program, Texas Education Agency, Bulletin 519, Austin, April, 1951.

Administrator's Outline for Study of the School Health Program, Wisconsin Cooperative School Health Program, Madison, State Department of Public Instruction.

"Appraisal Form for Evaluating School Health Services," rev. 1947, *Journal of School Health,* vol. 28, no. 1 (January, 1948).

A Yardstick for School Lunches, Nutrition Education Series, Pamphlet no. 4, Washington, D.C., Government Printing Office, 1958.

Checklist for Healthful and Safe School Environment, California State Joint Committee on School Health, San Francisco, State Department of Public Health, March, 1949.

Checklist of Safety and Safety Education, National Education Association, Washington, D.C., 1939.

Dental Health Program for Elementary and Secondary Schools, American Dental Association, Chicago, 1947.

Evaluate Your School Health Program, American Public Health Association, School Health Section, Committee on Evaluation of School Health Programs, 1955.

"Evaluate Your School Health Program," American School Health Association, Report of the Joint Committee on Evaluation of School Health Programs, *Journal of School Health,* June, 1956, p. 167.

Evaluation in Mental Health, U.S. Department of Health, Education, and Welfare, Washington, D.C., 1955.

Fast, Charles, and Sara Williams, *Health Education Evaluation Form,* Portland, Oregon Tuberculosis and Health Association, March 14, 1957.

Health in Schools, National Education Association, Twentieth Yearbook of the American Association of School Administrators, Washington, D.C., 1951.

Jackson, Chester O., "Let's Rate Your Health Education Program," *Journal of Health, Physical Education and Recreation,* September, 1955.

Linn, H. H., and L. C. Helm, *Checklist Forms for Rating School Custodial Service,* New York, Teachers College, 1940.

Price, Bronson, *School Health Services,* Washington, D.C., U.S. Department of Health, Education, and Welfare, Social Security Administration, Children's Bureau, 1957.

Suggested Standards for Health Services in Secondary Schools, American Journal of Public Health Yearbook, vol. 42 (May 5, 1952), 41–45.

Survey on School Lunch Operation, Parts I and II, New York, Public Health Committee of the Paper Cup and Container Institute, 1961.

INDEX

INDEX